THE LONDON CIGARETT

CIGAR CAR CATALOGUE

2014 edition

FIRST CATALOGUE PRODUCED IN 1929

ISBN 978-1-906397-14-2

Compiled by

IAN A. LAKER and Y. BERKTAY

Published by

THE LONDON CIGARETTE CARD COMPANY LTD
Sutton Road, Somerton, Somerset, England TA11 6QP

Telephone: 01458-273452
Fax: 01458-273515
International Calls: Telephone: ++44 1458-273452
Fax: ++44 1458-273515
E-Mail: cards@londoncigcard.co.uk

www.londoncigcard.co.uk

Cards illustrated on the front cover are from the series:
Gallaher Ltd. Trains of the World 1937
Gallaher Ltd. Wild Animals 1937
Ardath Tobacco Co. Ltd. Proverbs c1936
John Player & Sons. Hints on Association Football 1934
John Player & Sons. Uniforms of the Territorial Army 1939

Back cover:
John Player & Sons. Motor Cars 2nd Series 1937
W.D. & H.O. Wills. British Aviation 1994
Gallaher Ltd. Butterflies and Moths 1938

CARD COLLECTING

Wills
Garden Flowers
(1939)

When you mention cigarette cards, most people think of cricketers, footballers and film stars of the 1930s. This was the heyday of cigarette card issues when virtually every packet contained a little picture and the major companies like Wills and Players had their own studios and artists devoted entirely to the production of cigarette cards. It was big business, and massive print-runs often ran into hundreds of millions for each series. That's why there are still lots of them around today — sets can still be bought for around £20 upwards in very good condition, which is a major reason for their popularity for those of us wishing to indulge in nostalgia for Hollywood legends, sporting heroes, military hardware, famous trains and graceful ocean liners from a golden age.

Players
Uniforms of the
Territorial Army
(1939)

In The Beginning

In fact the hobby goes back to the 1890s, to a time when cigarettes were wrapped in paper packets. Manufacturers began inserting pieces of card to protect the contents, quickly realising that these would be useful for advertising their products. Soon these were followed by pictorial sequences, which would build up into sets. The object was to encourage repeat purchases and establish brand loyalty, and the subjects chosen were those most likely to appeal to the predominantly male customer base. Beautiful young women, sportsmen and soldiers dominated the earliest series, followed by ever more diverse topics in the early 20th century as companies competed for trade by offering something new.

Wills
Ships (1902)

Remember this was before the days of cinema, radio or TV, let alone the modern technological wonders we now take for granted. Newspapers carried few illustrations, and living standards were much lower. For most smokers, therefore, the cards they collected from their packets were their window on the world, serving to educate, excite or amuse — they were colourful, informative and free!

Many of these early cards were from firms whose names would mean nothing to a non-collector, little companies which went out of business or were swallowed up by the big boys before World War I. And it is these cards, few of which have survived, which are often the most valuable.

The 1920s and 1930s

Wills
Railway Engines (1936)

The 1920s and 1930s are generally regarded as the golden age of cards. Competition was fierce and rival firms were constantly looking for something different to stand out from the crowd. Players and Wills went in for adhesive-backed cards and offered special albums to stick them in. So many were produced that there are still loads around today, and they fetch only a few pounds. Another idea was cards that made up into a sectional picture of a work of art, a map or an historic event like the 1937 Coronation Procession. Some makers developed cards with push-out sections which could be made into models, whilst others came out with sequences of silk embroidered flowers, cards in miniature frames, bronze plaques, metal charms to hang on a bracelet — even little gramophone records which could actually be played!

A New Dawn

Paper shortages halted card production in 1940. Cigarette cards would never be issued on the same scale as before the war, but even so there have been quite a few over the years, starting with the blue and white pictures of film stars and footballers printed in the sliding trays in Turf Cigarettes, and progressing to many series of popular cards in packets of Tom Thumb, Doncella and Grandee Cigars. Recent anti-smoking legislation has ended any hope of new cards with tobacco products, but we will continue to welcome new trade card issues.

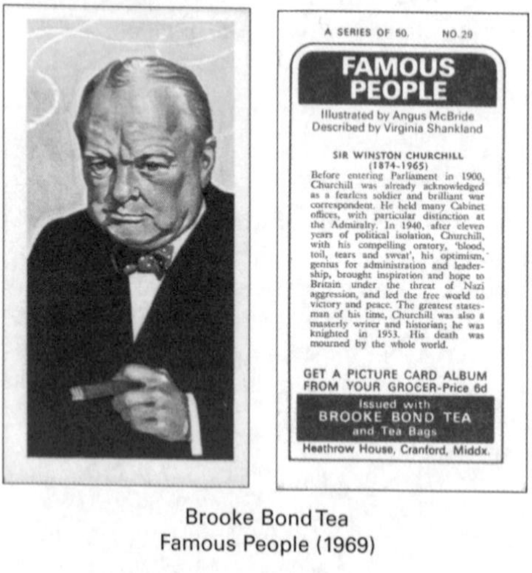

Brooke Bond Tea
Famous People (1969)

Trade cards, or 'trading cards' as they are often called, are picture cards issued with non-tobacco products and they have a distinguished history which pre-dates even the earliest cigarette cards. On the continent of Europe, one of the first to recognise the sales potential of cards was the Liebig Meat Extract Company, which over a period of 120 years from 1872 onwards issued no fewer than 1,800 different series. In the 1920s and '30s firms like chocolate makers Frys and Cadburys, tea companies such as Typhoo, periodical publishers etc. mimicked their tobacco counterparts by producing a regular flow of picture cards. But it was in the post-war environment that trade cards really came into their own, filling the gap left by the demise of cigarette cards.

From the 1950s onwards came a flood of 'trade' cards issued with tea, confectionery, biscuits, cereals, ice cream and so on. Among them were companies such as A & BC Gum, Bassetts and Brooke Bond, who regularly released one set after another year after year. I expect many of you will remember collecting them — and really there has been a notable trend for this age group to begin collecting them again, which can be satisfyingly inexpensive with some Brooke Bond cards from the 1960s and '70s priced at around £4 or £5 for a mint set.

Cards at War

Wills
Military Motors (1916)

During World War I many patriotic collections were issued — 'Recruiting Posters', 'Infantry Training', 'Modern War Weapons', 'Military Motors', 'Allied Army Leaders', 'Britain's Part in The War' and so on. All were subject to Government scrutiny to ensure no secrets reached the enemy, and 'passed for publication by the Press Bureau' is printed on many of these cards. In the run-up to World War II, out came cards demonstrating the nation's apparent military strength and preparedness for action — 'Britain's Defences', the 'R.A.F. at Work' and 'Life in the Royal Navy' to name a few. 'Aircraft of the R.A.F.' cards showed our latest fighters, the Spitfire and Hurricane ('the performance of this machine is an official secret' we are warned). It is rumoured that German agents were buying up Player's 1939 'British Naval Craft' in London to send back to U-Boat crews. Meanwhile the authorities sponsored a series of 'Air Raid Precautions', 'cigarette cards of national importance', endorsed by Home Secretary Samuel Hoare, with useful hints on how to put on a gas-mask or extinguish an incendiary bomb. How effective or otherwise these proved in the blitz we shall never know, but they raised public awareness.

The Cards That Never Were

Wills
Waterloo (c1916)

The Wagner cards were not the only ones never to see the light of day. Britain's biggest maker, W.D. & H.O. Wills of Bristol prepared a series of 50 cards to celebrate Wellington's victory over Napoleon at the Battle of Waterloo, but when the date for issue came up in 1915 their release was cancelled so as not to offend the French who were our allies fighting the Germans. And in a series of 'Musical Celebrities' all the German subjects were withdrawn and substituted by lesser-known individuals from other nationalities. Another Wills casualty was a series of 50 cards prepared to mark the coronation of King Edward VIII. Edward's abdication in 1936 put paid to this and the cards were destroyed — all except, that is, for a handful of sets presented to the firm's directors and top management.

A World Record

Early in 2007, a world record price was paid in America for a single card — $2,350,000, roughly equivalent to £1,200,000. This card was sold later on in the year for another world record price, $2,800,000 (approximately £1,500,000). The card in question featured Honus Wagner, one of the great names in U.S. baseball at the turn of the 20th century. Wagner was a dedicated non-smoker and objected when America's biggest tobacco corporation planned to picture him on a cigarette card without his permission. Threats of legal action prevented its release, but a few slipped out, and it was one of these that stunned the collecting world when it was auctioned.

Today's Hobby

Remember *The Saint*, *The Avengers*, *The Prisoner*, *Thunderbirds*, *Captain Scarlet* and *Doctor Who*? They all have huge followings and collectors are snapping up new sets as they come onto the market. The same goes for *Star Trek*, Buffy, Disney, Harry Potter and *The Lord of the*

Strictly Ink
Doctor Who 3rd Series (2002)

Rings. Cult TV series and blockbuster movies are sure to be pictured on cards. That goes for football too. There are hundreds of different sets to chose from, some going back to the days of Matthews, Finney and Lofthouse, others bringing us right up to date with the latest Premiership players and stars like Lampard and Rooney.

The thing is, card collecting is a living hobby with many new series being produced each year attracting a new generation of collectors. Whatever your age or interests, you're going to be pleasantly surprised by what cards can offer. Collecting cards has come a long way since its pre-war image and people from all walks of life are now keen collectors.

Topps UK
Star Wars (1978)

The London Cigarette Card Company

In 2014 the London Cigarette Card Company will be celebrating its 87th anniversary. The firm's remarkable history as the world's first company devoted solely to the needs of card collectors began in 1927 when Colonel C.L. Bagnall D.S.O, M.C., set up business at 47 Lionel Road, Brentford with a capital of just £500. The enterprise proved popular with collectors, and card stocks quickly grew to the point where an extension had to be built to house them, and the first catalogue was published in 1929. Four years later came another momentous event — the launch of the monthly magazine *Cigarette Card News* now renamed ***Card Collectors News*** and still being published today. By 1933, the business had expanded to such a degree that larger premises were essential and, in October of that year, the L.C.C.C. moved to Wellesley Road, Chiswick, their address until 1977 when they moved again, this time to Somerset. Today, the company's headquarters in Sutton Road, Somerton houses one of the world's largest stocks of cigarette cards and trade cards — **MORE THAN 50 MILLION** — and serves collectors around the world. In September 1999 they set up their website (**www.londoncigcard.co.uk**) which now offers over 6,000 different series, all with sample colour illustrations.

They publish the hobby's essential reference catalogues with prices for over 13,000 different series on every subject imaginable. The 2014 editions — The ***Cigarette Card Catalogue*** at £7.50 and the ***Trade Card Catalogue*** at £7.00, are widely regarded as the definitive guides to collecting. They also publish a monthly magazine called ***Card Collectors News*** (available by post, at £2.20 each or £26 for a year's subscription) which keeps everyone up to date with news about the latest card issues, stories and features. Cards can be ordered by post, telephone, fax or e-mail and through this website.

For further information contact The London Cigarette Card Company Ltd, Sutton Road, Somerton, Somerset TA11 6QP, telephone 01458-273452, e-mail cards@londoncigcard.co.uk.

HOW TO USE THE CATALOGUE

This catalogue is published in three sections. Section 1 covers the cigarette card issues of British Tobacco Manufacturers for the home market together with overseas series. Section 2 deals with cards issued by foreign tobacco manufacturers. Section 3 covers reprinted series.

In each section manufacturers are featured in alphabetical order, and the issues of each firm are catalogued alphabetically within suitable sub-divisions, such as, in Section 1, Silks, Overseas Series etc. and, in Section 2, 'With Brand Name', 'Without Brand Name', 'Silks', etc. Where a brand name but no maker's name is shown on the card, reference should be made to the appropriate Index of Brands. Anonymous series, that is those with printed backs but no brand or maker's name, are listed under the firms to which the issue has been attributed. Anonymous British issues are also listed at the end of Section 1.

Information is given in the columns from left to right as follows:

Size

(a) British issuers and reprints series: the code letter refers to the size of the card as indicated in the chart on page xvi. A number 1 or 2 after the letter means that the card is slightly larger or smaller than shown.

(b) Foreign issuers: the absence of a code letter indicates that the series is of standard size. A code letter 'L' defines the card as being large (about 80 × 62 mm). Other codes are 'K' = smaller than standard, 'M' = between standard and large, and 'EL' = larger than large.

Printing

(a) British issues and reprint series: the code indicates the printing on the front of the card. 'BW' = black-and-white; 'C' = coloured; 'CP' = colour photograph; 'P' = photograph; 'U' = uncoloured (monochrome).

(b) Foreign issues: the letter 'P' is used to show that a series consists of photographs.

Number in Set

This figure gives the number of cards in the series. A question mark alongside shows the exact number is unknown.

Title and Date

Where a series title is printed on the cards, this is used in the catalogue. For cards which do not exhibit a series title, an 'adopted' title is shown (indicated by an asterisk in the British section). Where a firm issued more than one series with the same title, these are distinguished by the addition of 'Set 1', 'Set 2', etc. or a code letter. The date of issue, where known, is shown in brackets, otherwise an approximate date is shown prefixed by 'C'.

Reference Code

(a) British issues: un-numbered series, series issued by more than one manufacturer, and different series of the same title issued by a single firm, have been given an 'H', 'OG', 'GP' or 'W' number cross-referencing them to provide further information.
H refers to *The British Tobacco Issues Handbook* 2003 Edition.
OG refers to *The Ogdens Reference Book* 2005 Edition.
GP refers to *The Godfrey Phillips & Associated Companies Reference Book* 2008 Edition.
W refers to *The W.D. & H.O. Wills Reference Book* 2011 Edition.

(b) Foreign issues: 'RB.118' or 'RB.21' followed by a number refers to the Tobacco War reference book or the British American Tobacco reference book respectively. 'WI' or 'RB.23'and 'WII' refer to World Tobacco Index Part I and Part II respectively. (Details of these publications will be found on page viii.)

Code Letters Used After the Set Title

In Some Early series a code word has been created. This is to help identify the various manufactures that printed the same set, i.e. Actresses, Beauties, Boer War Celebrities etc. For example: Beauties 'PAC' was issued by **P**ritchard & Burton, **A**dkin and **C**ope. Some series may not include all manufactures within the coded word, therefore for full listing please use the appropriate reference number in the catalogue with their respective reference books. For Example: Beauties 'PAC' – see H.2 in the *British Tobacco Issues Handbook*.

The Definition of Multi-Backed & Vari-Backed

Where each number in the set can be collected in each advertisement back these are listed in the catalogue.

Multi-Backed

If only certain cards can be collected within a set with the same advertisement these are referred to as multi-backed. For instance in Wills Sports of All Nations numbers 1 to 9 can be collected with a Three Castles or Traveller back but not a complete set in these advertisement backs.

Vari-Backed

The term vari-backed means you can only collect one advertisement back of each card for instance numbers 1 to 9 of a set would only be available in one advertisement back and number 10 to 19 in another back and so on.

Prices

The last two columns show the London Cigarette Card Company's selling prices for odd cards and complete sets in very good condition. Where cno price is shown, this does not necessarily mean that the Company are permanently unable to supply, and if you require items in this category please request a quotation.

HOW TO ORDER

Availability

We have one of the world's largest stocks of cigarette cards and the chances are that we will be able to supply your requirements for most series at the prices shown in the catalogue. However, certain odd cards, particularly from rarer series, may not be available in top condition and in such cases it is helpful if you indicate whether cards of a lower standard are acceptable at reduced prices. If a complete set is not in stock, we may be able to offer a part set, with one or two cards missing, at the appropriate fraction of full catalogue price. In some instances we can supply sets on request in fair to good condition at half catalogue price. If in doubt, please write for a quotation, enclosing a stamped, self-addressed envelope.

End Numbers

When ordering 'end' numbers, for example Nos. 1 and 50 of a set of fifty, please note that the following applies. For series catalogued up to £1 per card, end cards are charged at treble price. For series catalogued from £1 to £3 per card, end cards are charged at £3 per card. And for series catalogued at more than £3 per card there is no additional charge for end numbers.

Postage and Handling Fee

Orders are sent post free to UK addresses, but **please note** orders under £20.00 will incur a handling fee of £2.00. Overseas postage is charged at cost and there is no handling fee.

Ordering and Payment

Please ensure that your name and full address are clearly shown. State the maker's name and the set title required (with 'first series', 'second series', date of issue, etc. as appropriate). For odds, please list each individual number wanted. Make your crossed cheque or postal order payable to The London Cigarette Card Company Limited and enclose with order. Notes and coins should be registered. Overseas payments can only be accepted by Sterling cheque drawn on a British bank or by credit/debit card. We accept Mastercard, Visa, Visa Delta, Electron, JCB, American Express and Maestro credit/debit cards. Quote your card number and the card security code (which is the last three numbers in the signature strip), expiry date (and, for Maestro cards, the issue number if one is shown, or start date). Please allow 14 days for delivery. Send your order to:

The London Cigarette Card Co. Ltd, Sutton Road, Somerton, Somerset TA11 6QP, England

Please note: *Orders sent to addresses outside the European Community will have 15% (UK tax) deducted off card and album prices.*

24-Hour Telephone Order Line (01458-273452)

For the convenience of customers, an answering machine is in operation to receive orders when the office is closed. Just leave your order, name and address with credit or debit card number, expiry date, and the card security code, which is the last three numbers on the signature strip (and, for Maestro cards, the issue number, if one is shown, or start date). Your order will be dealt with as soon as possible. Please note that we can only deal with general enquiries in office hours. Telephone number: **01458-273452** (international ++44 1458-273452).

Fax Machine (01458-273515)

Our fax machine is on 24 hours a day to receive orders. Just place your order stating your name, address, credit or debit card number, expiry date and the card security code, which is the last three numbers on the signature strip (and, for Maestro cards, the issue number, if one is shown, or start date). The fax number is **01458-273515** (international ++44 1458-273515).

E-Mail (cards@londoncigcards.co.uk) & Website (www.londoncigcards.co.uk)

Our e-mail address is **cards@londoncigcard.co.uk** . Orders can also be placed using our secure website through the special requests page (**www.londoncigcard.co.uk**).

Remember that your cards will look their best when displayed in one of our albums: please see pages xiv and xv. Value Added Tax where applicable is included in all prices shown, at the current rate of 20%.

Guarantee

In the unlikely event that you, the collector, are not satisfied with the cards supplied, we guarantee to replace them or refund your money, provided the goods are returned within 14 days of receipt. This guarantee does not affect your statutory rights.

OPENING TIMES AT SUTTON ROAD

Collectors are welcome to call at our offices in Sutton Road, Somerton, where you will be able to purchase your requirements direct from the massive stocks held at the premises – sets, albums, books and accessories plus odd cards. We do not have items on display, but we are more than happy to get things out for you to view.

**Our offices are open to customers Monday to Friday
9.30am-12.30pm and 2.30pm-4.30pm**

NEW ISSUES

We usually have between 5 and 20 new issues (mostly trade card issues) added to stock each month, and if you wish to keep up-to-date why not subscribe to ***Card Collectors News* magazine** (see page ix), in which Frank Doggett, the magazine editior, gives a description of all new additions and includes sample illustrations of most of them. A sample of the back and front of each new issues can also be found on our website each month (www.londoncigcard.co.uk).

Our Website

www.londoncigcard.co.uk

Quite Possibly the best Website for collecting both Cigarette and Trade Cards in the UK with huge stocks!!

What's on our website

- An impressive list of over 6000 series available to purchase with images to complement them.
- Subject lists (Thematic lists) covering interesting matter such as

— Sci-fi
— Films
— Animals
— Sport (Football, Rugby, Tennis, Speedway)
— Military
— Music (Pop Stars and Singers)
— General Interests etc.

<u>And so much more...</u>

<u>Why don't you look for yourself?</u>

The website also includes

— Information about our company
— History of Collecting Cards
— New card issues into stock every month from various Manufacturers
— Availability of Albums, Reference books, Magazines and Catalogues
— Information on how to Value and sell your collection

Why not try our Monthly Auctions?

We have auctions every month, with at least 400 lots in each. Lots starting from as low as £2. Just pop onto our website to view the list (hard copies are available on request)

Discounts Discounts Discounts!!!!

Our website offers discounts every month on various different sets and you can get up to 33% off selected sets so why wait log on now!

Come on in you might be surprised!!!!!!!!

www.londoncigcard.co.uk

CARTOPHILIC REFERENCE BOOKS

British Tobacco Issues Handbook (updated 2003 edition). Updates the original Handbooks Parts I & II, but excludes Ogden, Wills and The Godfrey Phillips Group of Companies. 369 pages **£24.00**

Handbook Part II (1920 to 1940) British Tobacco Issues. Updated by the above book, but includes Godfrey Phillips Silks listings. 164 pages, illustrated. Published at £12.00 . . . . **Special Offer Price £6.00**

The Card Issues of Abdulla/Adkin/Anstie (reprint, originally published 1943). 20 pages **£4.50**

The Card Issues of Ardath Tobacco (reprint, originally published 1943). 28 pages **£4.50**

The Card Issues of W.A. & A.C. Churchman (reprint, originally published 1948). 36 pages . . . **£4.50**

The Card Issues of W. & F. Faulkner (reprint, originally published 1942). 12 pages **£4.50**

The Card Issues of Gallaher (reprint, originally published 1944). 40 pages **£4.50**

The Card Issues of R. & J. Hill (reprint, originally published 1942). 28 pages **£4.50**

The Card Issues of Lambert & Butler (reprint, originally published 1948). 32 pages **£4.50**

The Card Issues of Ogdens (updated 2005 edition). 330 pages **£27.00**

The Card Issues of Godfrey Phillips (reprint, originally published 1949). 40 pages **£4.50**

The Card Issues of Godfrey Phillips & Associated Companies (updated 2008 edition). Includes Cavanders, Drapkin, Millhoff and Muratti. 256 pages **£28.00**

The Card Issues of John Player & Sons (reprint, originally published 1948). 44 pages **£4.50**

Guide Book No. 2, F. & J. Smith Cards (published 1980). 36 pages **£4.50**

The Card Issues of Taddy (reprint, originally published 1948). 32 pages **£4.50**

The Card Issues of W.D. & H.O. Wills (updated 2011 Edition). 214 pages **£25.00**

The Card Issues of Wills and B.A.T. combined (published 1942-1952, reprinted as one volume in 1998). 402 pages **£20.50**

Directory of British Tobacco Issuers (reprint, originally published 1946). 36 pages **£4.50**

World Tobacco Card Index & Handbook Part I & Part II . . . . . . **Out of Print**

World Tobacco Card Index & Handbook Part III. Supplement to Index I & II. 504 pages . . . **£25.50**

World Tobacco Card Index & Handbook Part IV. Supplement to Index I, II & III. 688 pages **£19.00**

World Tobacco Card Index & Handbook Part V. Supplement to Index I, II, III & IV (published 1990). 552 pages **£19.00**

World Tobacco Issues Part 1. Issuers A to K. 344 pages **£23.00**

World Tobacco Issues Part 2. Issuers L to Z, plus Anonymous. 344 pages **£23.00**

The above two books, updated to August 2000, are a revision of the World Tobacco Indexes Parts I to V combined (but not the Handbooks) with many additions & amendments. They do not contain the Handbook and therefore do not have subject listings.

Handbook of Worldwide Tobacco and Trade Silk Issues. 342 pages, some colour illustrations **£50.50**

Australian and New Zealand Card Issues Part 1 . . . . . . **Out of Print**

Australian and New Zealand Card Issues Part 2 (published 1993). 257 pages **£16.00**

The New 'Tobacco War' Reference Book (updated 1999 edition). 236 pages **£20.50**

Glossary of Cartophilic Terms (reprint, originally published 1948). 40 pages **£4.50**

British Trade Card Index Part I, Part II & Part III . . . . . . **Out of Print**

British Trade Card Index Part IV (1986-1994 issues). 412 pages **£20.50**

British Trade Card Index Issues up to 1970 (2006 edition). 516 pages **£25.50**

British Trade Card Handbook Issues up to 1970 (2006 edition). 542 pages **£25.50**

Guide Book No. 1, Typhoo Tea Cards (published 1976). 36 pages **£4.50**

Guide Book No. 3, A. & B.C. Gum Cards (updated 2004 edition). 52 pages **£4.50**

BOOKS FOR THE COLLECTOR

Trade Card Catalogue, 2014 edition with **colour illustrations**. This is the only major catalogue devoted to trade cards. It gives details of a magnificent selection of over 6,000 different series issued by non-tobacco companies, with prices for sets, odd cards and makers' albums. The new 39th edition features the issues of Brooke Bond, Bassett, Topps, Typhoo, Inkworks, Rittenhouse, Comic Images and hundreds of other firms, with prices from £2.50 a set. Contains eight-page section with new colour illustrations. **£7.00**

Liebig Card Catalogue, 2009 edition. This price guide (not illustrated) lists over 1500 of these fascinating sets issued in different European languages (all except the earliest) by this manufacturer. It includes a brief history of the company, an English translation of each set title, together with Fada reference, the number in each set and date of issue from 1891 to 1973. The prices in the 2009 catalogue will remain valid until further notice. **£4.50**

Brooke Bond Tea Cards Reference Book. The definitive reference book with 319 colour illustrations of cards and albums including overseas issues and the story of the company's first hundred years from one shop to market leader. Published 2007. . . . . **£12.50**

Brooke Bond Picture Cards 'The First Forty Years'. This invaluable 72-page reference book detailing all the issues of Brooke Bond Tea from 1954 to 1994. It includes British issues as well as overseas issues with illustrations. . . **£7.00**

Classic Brooke Bond Picture Card Collections. Mark Knowler's 320-page hardback book should appeal to all collectors, not just those specialising in Brooke Bond, because it is a wonderful advert for the hobby. Impeccably presented and with superb colour illustrations throughout, it is the kind of book you can dip into for a few minutes or browse through for hours.

As described by the publisher, 'this beautifully produced nostalgic book comprises the best 12 original albums, presented slightly larger than they were 40 to 50 years ago, to bring out the best in the wonderfully detailed illustrations. Every card is printed in its correct position, making every page an enormously colourful feast for the eyes.'

The albums that have been included are Out Into Space, British Wild Life, Wild Flowers Series 2, Freshwater Fish, African Wild Life, Asian Wild Life, British Butterflies, Wild Birds in Britain, Transport Through The Ages, Trees in Britain, Flags and Emblems of the World and History of The Motor Car, although other UK issues from Frances Pitt British Birds through to the 1999 Thank You Card are covered in the introduction.

. . . . **£25.00**

BOOKS FOR THE COLLECTOR

Collecting Cigarette & Trade Cards by Gordon Howsden. Traces the history and development of cards from their beginning to the present day and includes the background of the issuing firms, thematic collecting, printing and production, grading, pricing and so on. Authoritatively written in an easy-to-read style and beautifully illustrated in colour, the book approaches the subject from a fresh angle which will appeal to seasoned collectors and newcomers alike. Cigarette & Trade Cards is not only an indispensable reference work but also a joy to read or just browse through. 152 large-format pages with 220 colour illustrations featuring 750 cards and related ephemera. **£17.50**

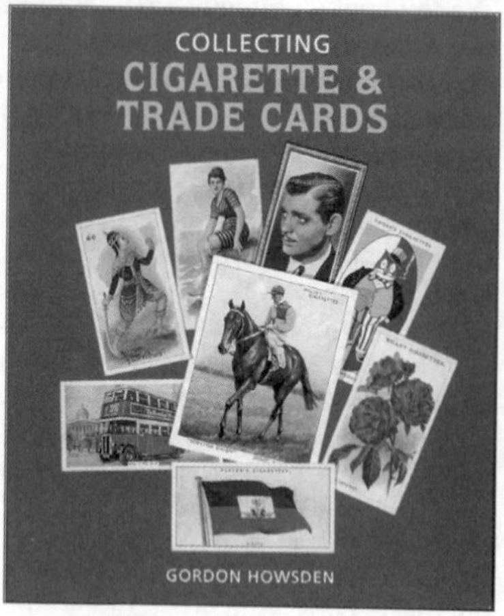

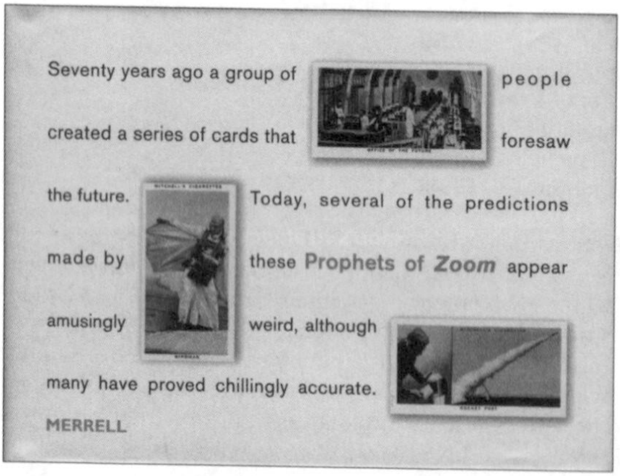

'Prophets of Zoom'. An unusual but fascinating book, 'Prophets of Zoom', with 112 pages, reproduces the front and back of each card in Mitchell's 1936 series of 50 The World of Tomorrow, opposite which is pictured a modern equivalent – and it's surprising how many of the predictions have become true!

From author Alfredo Marcantonio's introduction, we learn that the card set was inspired by a book called *The World of Tomorrow* and drew upon images from contemporary films, in particular Alexanda Korda's *Things to Come*, as well as inventions then at the cutting edge of technology. The individual predictions range from the amazing to the amusing, and together they paint a unique picture of the world we live in now, as pre-war Britain imagined it would be.

To take just one example. The very first card informs us that 'coal-mines and oil-wells will not last forever. We shall have to gain the energy we need, not from fuel, but from the inexhaustible forces of nature', and the set forecasts wind turbines, atomic energy and solar motors as being the power sources of the future.

From space travel and giant television screens, robots and bullet trains, to London's skyscraper skyline, this is highly entertaining stuff, and excellent value. **£7.95**

Orders are sent post free to UK addresses, but PLEASE NOTE orders under £20.00 will incur a handling fee of £2.00. Overseas postage is charged at cost and there is no handling fee.

REGIMENTAL BOOKS

The following series of books featuring the different Regiments and Corps of the British Army illustrated on Cigarette and Trade cards, contain History, Uniforms, Badges, Regimental Colours, Victoria Cross Winners and Personalities. Approximately 200 illustrations in each book, 56 pages with 16 in full colour, all produced by David J. Hunter.

The Coldstream Guards **£8.50**
The Gordon Highlanders **£8.50**
Queen's Own Highlanders (Seaforth & Camerons) **£8.50**
The Queen's Royal Lancers **£8.50**
The Regiments of Wales
(The Welsh Guards, The Royal Welsh Fusiliers & The Royal Regiment of Wales) **£8.50**
The Royal Army Medical Corps **£8.50**
The Royal Marines **£8.50**
The Royal Regiment of Fusiliers — Part 1
(The Royal Northumberland Fusiliers & The Royal Warwickshire Regiment) **£8.50**
The Royal Regiment of Fusiliers — Part 2
(The Royal Fusiliers (City of London Regiment) & The Lancashire Fusiliers) **£8.50**
The Scotts Guards **£8.50**
The Worcestershire & Sherwood Foresters Regiment **£8.50**

Orders are sent post free to UK addresses, but PLEASE NOTE orders under £20.00 will incur a handling fee of £2.00. Overseas postage is charged at cost and there is no handling fee.

LUXURY ALBUMS

LUXURY BINDER WITH 30 LEAVES £13.00

MATCHING SLIP-CASE £6.00 (only supplied with binder) • EXTRA LEAVES 17p EACH

☆ GREY CARD INTERLEAVES — 30 FOR £4.00 ☆

Orders are sent post free to UK addresses, but PLEASE NOTE orders under £20.00 will incur a handling fee of £2.00. Overseas postage is charged at cost and there is no handling fee.

Full display, front and back, is given to your cards in top quality transparent leaves held in a luxurious binder. The leaves are made from a tough, clear optical film. Binders are available in a choice of blue or maroon covers (with matching slip-cases as an optional extra) and each is supplied complete with 30 leaves, of which various sizes are available as listed below.

Page Ref.	**Suitable for**	**Pockets Per Page**	**Pocket size (mm) wide × deep**
A	Standard size cards	10	43 × 83
M	Medium size cards	8	55 × 83
D	Doncella/Grandee/Typhoo size cards	6	111 × 55
L	Large size cards	6	73 × 83
X	Extra large cards	4	111 × 83
P	Postcards	2	111 × 170
C	Cabinet size cards, booklets etc.	1	224 × 170
K	Miniature size cards	15	43 × 55

Remember to state which colour (blue or maroon) and which page reference/s you require.

Order by telephone (01458-273452), fax (01458-273515), e-mail (cards@londoncigcard.co.uk) or through our website (www.londoncigcard.co.uk) 24 hours a day, 7 days a week using your credit or debit cards, or you can order by post.

ALBUMS FOR LARGE TRADE CARDS

- ☆ An album designed specifically for modern trade cards like Skybox, Comic Images, Rittenhouse, Inkworks, Topps etc
- ☆ The ideal way to display your large modern trade cards to their best advantage
- ☆ 3-ring luxury padded binders in a choice of maroon or blue
- ☆ There are two types of leaves:

9 pockets per sheet size 91 × 68mm, reference LT

6 pockets per sheet size 138 × 66mm, reference WV

Orders are sent post free to UK addresses, but PLEASE NOTE orders under £20.00 will incur a handling fee of £2.00. Overseas postage is charged at cost and there is no handling fee.

COMPLETE ALBUM WITH 30 LEAVES
IN A CHOICE OF 'LT' OR 'WV' LEAVES £16.50 • EXTRA LEAVES 22p EACH

☆ COLLECTORS' ACCESSORIES ☆

A neat and tidy way for you to deal with incomplete sets is to use our
numbered, printed 'wants' lists

30 adhesive lists numbered 1 to 50 . . . . **75p**

The professional way to wrap sets with our translucent
glascine wrapping strips

200 strips size 123 × 68 mm for standard size cards **£5.00**
200 strips size 175 × 83mm for large cards **£5.50**
200 strips size 228 × 83mm for extra-large cards **£6.00**

2014 AUCTIONS

We have been auctioning for over 75 years cards to suit every collector

Monthly 400-lot postal auctions of cigarette and trade cards and associated items with estimated values from as little as £1 up to many hundreds. Lots to interest every collector and suit their pocket.

Postal Auctions for 2014 are as follows:

Thursday,	**2nd January**	**Saturday, 28th June**
Saturday,	**25th January**	**Saturday, 26th July**
Saturday,	**22nd February**	**Saturday, 30th August**
Saturday,	**29th March**	**Saturday, 27th September**
Saturday,	**26th April**	**Saturday, 25th October**
Saturday,	**31st May**	**Saturday, 29th November**

Each postal auction finishes at midnight on the above dates.

A guide to how we assess condition and how to bid can be found on our bidding sheet which comes with the free auction catalogue, so it couldn't be easier if you are an 'auction beginner'.

There are no additional charges to bidders for buyer's premium, so bidding is straightforward, with no 'hidden extras'.

Each lot is described with an estimate of its value reflecting the condition of the cards, ranging from poor right through to mint condition, and for over 75 years collectors have bid with complete confidence, knowing that every effort is made to describe the lots accurately.

Each auction contains a selection of rare sets, rare and scarce individual cards, pre-1918 issues, 1920-40 series, old and modern trade issues including Brooke Bond, errors and varieties, silks, albums, books, Liebigs, cigarette packets etc – in fact plenty to interest everyone.

Auction catalogues are available ***FREE OF CHARGE***, 4 weeks before the date of sale from The London Cigarette Card Company Limited, Sutton Road, Somerton, Somerset TA11 6QP
Telephone: 01458-273452 Fax: 01458-273515
E-mail: auctions@londoncigcard.co.uk

The Auction Catalogue can also be found on our website, which contains a preview of each auction as well as facilities for on-line bidding – visit www.londoncigcard.co.uk for further details.

Also a copy of the auction catalogue is automatically sent each month to subscribers to our magazine *Card Collectors News*
(subscription details on page ix of this catalogue)

CARD SIZES (only applies to Section 1). **Please note: (card size) *album leaf size***

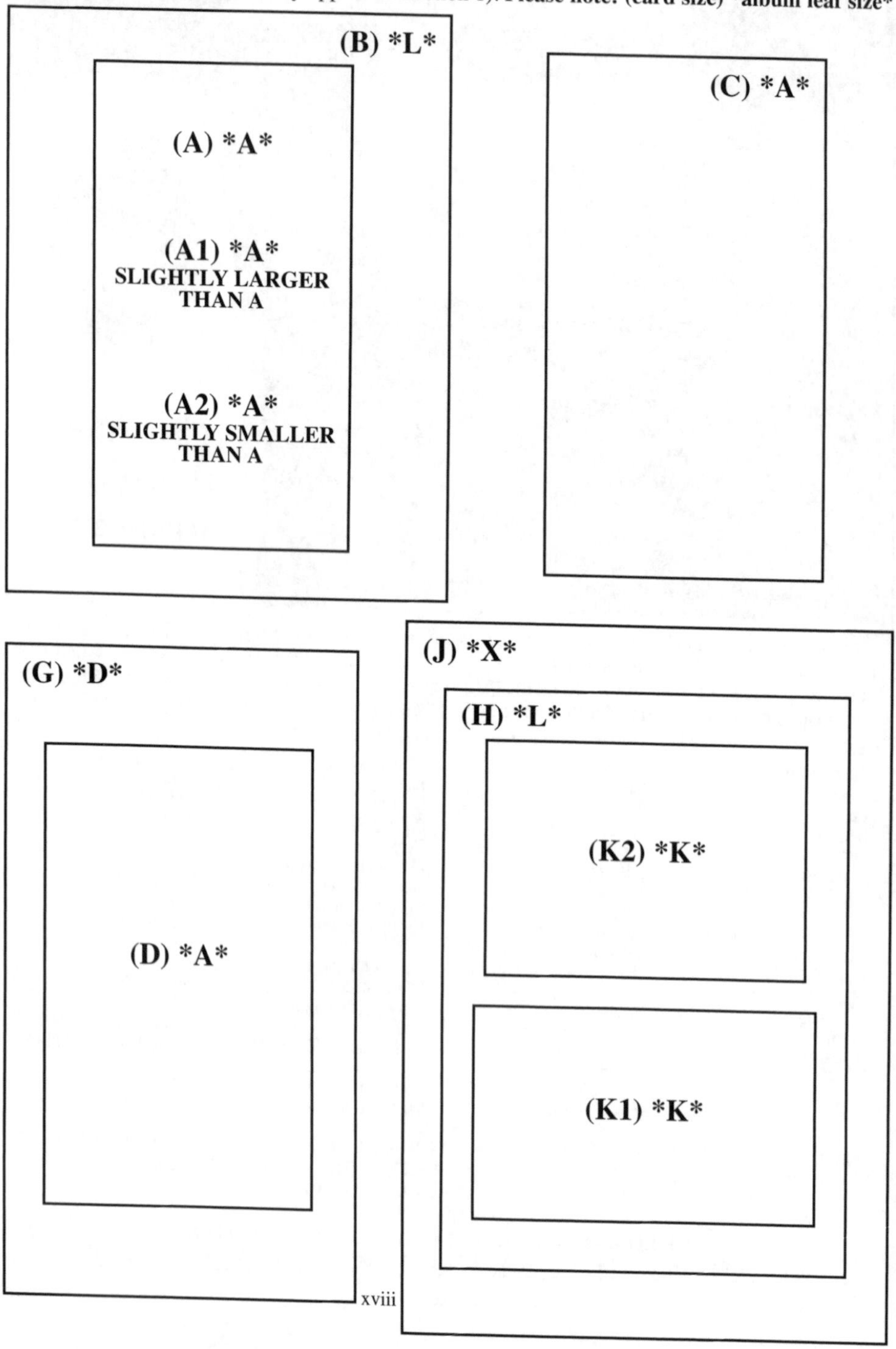

INDEX OF BRANDS

The following is a list of the cases so far known where cards appear without the name of issuer, but inscribed with a brand name or other indication which is the collector's only clue to the identity of the issuer. (1) or (2) indicates in which section of the catalogue the manufacturer appears

GENERAL NOTE: Where no brand name appears on the cards in a lot of cases they were issued by British American Tobacco Co., Imperial Tobacco Company of Canada Ltd or United Tobacco Companies (South) Ltd which all appear in Section 2. As regards to plain back cards, in a lot of cases they will be listed under Anonymous Series (in Section 1) or British American Tobacco Co. section 'F' Plain Backs (in Section 2).

Admiral Cigarettes — see National Cigarette & Tobacco Co. (2)
Airmail Cigarettes — see Hill (1)
Albert Cigarettes — see British American Tobacco Co. (2)
All Arms Cigarettes — see Ray & Co. (1)
S. Anargyros — see American Tobacco Co. (2)

BDV Cigarettes — see Godfrey Phillips (1)
THE B.I. Co. — see Burnstein Isaacs (1)
BEA — see Benson & Hedges (1)
Bandmaster Cigarettes — see Cohen, Weenen & Drapkin (1)
Between the Acts — see American Tobacco Co. (2)
Big Gun Cigarettes — see Sandorides (1)
Big Run Cigarettes — see American Tobacco Co. (2)
Black Cat Cigarettes — see Carreras (1)
Black Spot Cigarettes — see Scerri (2)
Blush of Day Cigarettes — see Robinson & Barnsdale (1)
Borneo Queen Cigars — see B. Morris (1)
British Consuls — see Macdonald (2)
Broadleaf Cigarettes — see American Tobacco Co. (2)
Broadway Novelties — see Teofani (1)
The Buffs — see Drapkin (1)
Bulldog Cigars — see Elliot (1)

C.T. Ltd — see United States Tobacco Co. (2)
Cairo Monopol Cigarettes — see American Tobacco Co. (2)
Cake Walk Cigarettes — see Pezaro (1)
Caps The Lot — see Bewlay (1)
Carolina Brights — see American Tobacco Co. (2)
Casket and Critic Cigarettes — see Pattreiouex (1)
Castella Cigars — see W.D. & H.O. Wills (1)
Chairman Cigarettes — see R.J. Lea (1)
The Challenge Flat Brilliantes — see Gloag (1)
Chantler & Co., Bury — see Lea (1)
Citamora Cigarettes — see Gloag (1)
Club Member Cigarettes — see Pattreiouex (1)
Club Mixture Tobaccos — see Continental Cigarette Factory (1)
Colin Campbell Cigars — see Robinson & Barnsdale (1)
Copain Cigarettes — see British American Tobacco Co. (2)
Coronet Cigarettes — see Sniders & Abrahams (2)
Crowfoot Cigarettes — see Hill (1)
Cycle Cigarettes — see American Tobacco Co. (2)
Cymax Cigarettes — see Coudens (1)

Derby Little Cigars — see American Tobacco Co. (2)
Domino Cigarettes — see British American Tobacco Co. (2)
Double Ace Cigarettes — see Ardath (1)

'Eagle, Cork' — see Lambkin (1)
Egyptienne Luxury — see American Tobacco Co. (2)
Eldona Cigars — see Drapkin & Millhoff (1)
Emblem Cigarettes — see American Tobacco Co. (2)
Erinmore Cigarettes — see Murray (1)
Explorer Cigars — see Drapkin & Millhoff (1)

The Favourite Magnums Cigarettes — see Teofani (1)
Fez Cigarettes — see American Tobacco Co. (2)
The Flor de Dindigul Cigar — see Bewlay (1)
Forecasta — see B. Morris (1)
Four Square — see Dobie (1)
Fresher Cigarettes — see Challis (1)
Fume Emblem — see Westminster Tobacco Co. (2)

GP — see Godfrey Phillips (1)
Gainsborough Cigarettes — see Cohen Weenen (1)
General Favourite Onyx — see E. Robinson (1)
Gibson Girl Virginia, Madrali Turkish and Hungarian — see Golds (1)
Gold Coin Tobacco — see Buchner (2)
Gold Flake Cigarettes — see Hill (1)
Gold Flake, Honeydew and Navy Cut Medium Cigarettes — see Hill (1)
The Greys Cigarettes — see United Kingdom Tobacco Co. (1)
Guards Cigarettes — see Carreras (1)

Hassan Cigarettes — see American Tobacco Co. (2)
Havelock Cigarettes — see Wills (Overseas) (2)
Hawser, Epaulet and Honey Flake Cigarettes — see Wholesale Tobacco Supply Syndicate (1)
Heart's Delight Cigarettes — see Pritchard & Burton (1)
Helmar Cigarettes — see American Tobacco Co. (2)
Herbert Tareyton Cigarettes — see American Tobacco Co. (2)
Hindu Cigarettes — see American Tobacco Co. (2)
Hoffman House Magnums — see American Tobacco Co. (2)
Honest Long Cut — see Duke or American Tobacco Co. (2)
Hustler Little Cigars — see American Tobacco Co. (2)

Imperial Tobacco Limited (Castella) — see W.D. & H.O. Wills (1)
Islander, Fags, Specials, Cubs — see Bucktrout (2)

Jack Rose Little Cigars — see American Tobacco Co. (2)
Jersey Lily Cigarettes — see Wm. Bradford (1)
Cigarette Job — see Societe Job (1)
Junior Member Cigarettes — see Pattreiouex (1)
Just Suits Cut Plug — see American Tobacco Co. (2)

Kensitas Cigarettes — see J. Wix (1)
King Edward VII Cigarettes — see Cabana (1)
Kopec Cigarettes — see American Tobacco Co. (2)

L. & Y. Tobacco Co. -— see Lancs. and Yorks. Tobacco Manufacturing Co. (1)
Lennox Cigarettes — see American Tobacco Co. (2)
Leon de Cuba Cigars — see Eldons (1)
Le Roy Cigars — see Miller (2)
Levant Favourites — see B. Morris (1)
Life Ray Cigarettes — see Ray & Co. (1)
Lifeboat Cigarettes — see United Tobacco Co. (2)
Lotus Cigarettes — see United Tobacco Co. (2)
Lucana Cigarettes — see Sandorides (1)
Lucky Strike Cigarettes — see American Tobacco Co. (2)
Luxury Cigarettes — see American Tobacco Co. (2)

Magpie Cigarettes — see Schuh (2)
Manikin Cigars — see Freeman (1)
Mascot Cigarettes — see British American Tobacco Co. (2)
Matossian's Cigarettes — see Henley & Watkins (1)
Max Cigarettes — see A. & M. Wix (1)
Mayblossom Cigarettes — see Lambert & Butler (1)
Mecca Cigarettes — see American Tobacco Co. (2)
Mills — see Amalgamated (1)
Milo Cigarettes — see Sniders & Abrahams (2)
Miners Extra Smoking Tobacco — see American Tobacco Co. (2)
Mogul Cigarettes — see American Tobacco Co. (2)
Murad Cigarettes — see American Tobacco Co. (2)

Natural American Spirit — see Santa Fe Natural Tob. Co. (2)
Nebo Cigarettes — see American Tobacco Co. (2)
New Orleans Tobacco — see J. & T. Hodge (1)

OK Cigarettes — see African Tobacco Mfrs. (2)
Obak Cigarettes — see American Tobacco Co. (2)
Officers Mess Cigarettes — see African Tobacco Mfrs. (2)
Old Gold Cigarettes — see American Tobacco Co. (2)
Old Judge Cigarettes — see Goodwin (2)
Old Mills Cigarettes — see American Tobacco Co. (2)
1a, 27 & 33 Leigh Road, Eastleigh — see Ingram's (1)
One of the Finest — see Buchner (2)
Oracle Cigarettes — see Tetley (1)
Orient Line Steamships — see Singleton & Cole (1)
Our Little Beauties — see Allen & Ginter (2)
Oxford Cigarettes — see American Tobacco Co. (2)

Pan Handle — see American Tobacco Co. (2)
Park Drive — see Gallaher (1)
Perfection Cigarettes — see American Tobacco Co. (2)
Peter Pan Cigarettes — see Sniders & Abrahams (2)
Pibroch Virginia — see Fryer (1)
Piccadilly — see Carreras (1)
Picadilly Little Cigars — see American Tobacco Co. (2)
Pick-Me-Up Cigarettes — see Drapkin & Millhoff (1)
Piedmont Cigarettes — see American Tobacco Co. (2)
Pinhead Cigarettes — see British American Tobacco Co. (2)
Pinnace — see Godfrey Phillips (1)
Pioneer Cigarettes — see Richmond Cavendish (1)
Pirate Cigarettes — see Wills (Overseas) (2)
PO Box 5764, Johannesburg — see A. & M. Wix (1)
Polo Bear Cigarettes — see American Tobacco Co. (2)
Polo Mild Cigarettes — see Murray (1)
Private Seal Tobacco — see Godfrey Phillips (1)
Pure Virginia Cigarettes — see Thomson & Porteous (1)
Puritan Little Cigars — see American Tobacco Co. (2)
Purple Mountain Cigarettes — see Wills (Overseas) (2)

QV Cigars — see Webster (1)

RS — see Robert Sinclair (1)
Recruit Little Cigars — see American Tobacco Co. (2)
Red Cross — see Lorillard or American Tobacco Co. (2)
Reina Regenta Cigars — see B. Morris (1)
De Reszke Cigarettes — see Millhoff and Godfrey Phillips (1)
Richmond Gem Cigarettes — see Allen & Ginter (2)
Richmond Straight Cut Cigarettes — see American Tobacco Co. (2)
Ringers Cigarettes — see Edwards, Ringer & Bigg (1)
Rock City Tobacco — see Carreras (1)
Roseland Cigarettes — see Glass (1)
Royal Bengal Little Cigars — see American Tobacco Co. (2)

St Dunstan's — see Carreras (1)
St. Leger Little Cigars — see American Tobacco Co. (2)
Scots Cigarettes — see African Tobacco Mfrs (2)
Scrap Iron Scrap — see American Tobacco Co. (2)
Senator Cigarettes — see Scerri (2)
Senior Service Cigarettes — see Pattreiouex (1)
Sensation Cut Plug — see Lorillard (2)
Silko Cigarettes — see American Tobacco Co. (2)
Sovereign Cigarettes — see American Tobacco Co. (2)
Spinet Cigarettes or The Spinet House — see Hill (1)
Sportsman — see Carreras (Overseas) (2)
The Spotlight Tobaccos — see Hill (1)

Springbok Cigarettes — see United Tobacco Co. (2)
Standard Cigarettes — see Carreras or Sniders & Abrahams (2)
Star of the World Cigarettes — see JLS (1)
State Express Cigarettes — see Ardath (1)
Sub Rosa Cigarros — see American Tobacco Co. (2)
Sultan Cigarettes — see American Tobacco Co. (2)
Summit — see International Tobacco Co. (1)
Sunripe Cigarettes — see Hill (1)
Sunspot Cigarettes — see Theman (1)
Sweet Alva Cigarettes — see Drapkin (1)
Sweet Caporal — see Kinney or American Tobacco Co. or ITC Canada (2)
Sweet Lavender — see Kimball (2)

TSS — see Tobacco Supply Syndicate (1)
Tatley's Cigarettes — see Walker's Tobacco Co. (1)
Teal Cigarettes — see British American Tobacco Co. (2)
Three Bells Cigarettes — see J. & F. Bell (1)
Tiger Cigarettes — see British American Tobacco Co. (2)
Tipsy Loo Cigarettes — see H.C. Lloyd (1)
Tokio Cigarettes — see American Tobacco Co. (2)
Tolstoy Cigarettes — see American Tobacco Co. (2)
Tom Thumb — see Players (1)
Topsy Cigarettes — see Richards & Ward (1)
Trawler, Critic and King Lud Cigarettes — see Pattreiouex (1)
Trumps Long Cut — see Moore & Calvi (2)
Turf Cigarettes — see Carreras (1)
Turkey Red Cigarettes — see American Tobacco Co. (2)
Turkish Trophy Cigarettes — see American Tobacco Co. (2)
Twelfth Night Cigarettes — see American Tobacco Co. (2)

U.S. Marine — see American Tobacco Co. (2)
Uzit Cigarettes — see American Tobacco Co. (2)

Vanity Fair Cigarettes — see Kimball (2)
Vice Regal Cigarettes — see Wills (Overseas) (2)
Virginia Brights Cigarettes — see Allen & Ginter (2)

WTC — see Walker's Tobacco Co. (1)
Wings Cigarettes — see Brown & Williamson (2)

INDEX OF INSCRIPTIONS found on British issues of cards

'The Cigarettes with which these Picture Cards are issued are manufactured in England and are Guaranteed Pure' — see Hill
'England expects that Every Man will do his duty — By Purchasing these Cigarettes you are supporting British labour' — issuers unknown, see Anonymous
'Issued with these Famous Cigarettes' — see Teofani
'Issued with these Fine Cigarettes' — see Teofani
'Issued with these High Grade Cigarettes' — see Teofani
'Issued with these Well-known Cigarettes' — see Teofani
'Issued with these World Famous Cigarettes' — see Teofani
'Presented with these well-known choice cigarettes' — see Teofani
'Smoke these cigarettes always' — see Teofani
'These Cigarettes are Guaranteed Best British Manufacture' — see Hill.

SECTION 1

BRITISH TOBACCO ISSUERS

ABDULLA & CO. LTD, London

20 page reference book (combined with Adkin & Anstie) — £4.50

Size	*Print-ing*	*Number in set*		*Handbook reference*	*Price per card*	*Complete set*
A	BW	50	Beauties of To-Day (1938)	GP.20	£3.60	—
		? 4	Bridge Rule Cards (various sizes) (c1935)	GP.311	£16.00	—
A	C	25	British Butterflies (1935)	GP.42	£1.20	£30.00
A	P	52	Cinema Stars Set 1 (c1933)	GP.306	£4.00	—
A2	U	30	Cinema Stars Set 2 (c1933)	GP.51	£5.00	—
A2	U	30	Cinema Stars Set 3 (c1933)	GP.52	£4.00	—
A2	U	32	Cinema Stars Set 4 (c1933)	GP.53	£2.50	£80.00
A2	C	32	Cinema Stars Set 5 (c1933)	GP.54	£2.50	£80.00
A2	C	30	Cinema Stars Set 6 (c1933)	GP.55	£3.60	—
—	C	2	Commanders of the Allies (127 × 67mm) (c1915)	GP.313	£80.00	—
D	C	25	Feathered Friends (1935)	GP.70	£1.20	£30.00
A2	C	50	Film Favourites (1934)	GP.71	£4.00	—
A	C	50	Film Stars (1934)	GP.73	£8.00	—
—	C	24	*Film Stars (128 × 89mm) (c1934)	GP.76	£8.00	—
—	BW	3	Great War Gift Packings Cards (78 × 48mm) (1916)	GP.314	£80.00	—
A	U	18	Message Cards (letters of the alphabet) (c1936):	GP.315		
			A Back in blue		£14.00	—
			B Back in green		£14.00	—
			C Back in orange		£14.00	—
K2	U	18	Message Cards (letters of the alphabet) (c1936):	GP.315		
			A Last line 'may be used'		£15.00	—
			B Last line 'of Jokers may be...'		£15.00	—
A	C	25	Old Favourites (1936) (Flowers)	GP.106	80p	£20.00
—	C	1	Princess Mary Gift Card (67 × 49mm) (1914)	GP.317	—	£30.00
A	C	40	Screen Stars (1939):	GP.307		
			A Normal Abdulla back		£1.25	£50.00
			B 'Issued by the Successors to ...' back		£2.50	—
A2	C	50	Stage and Cinema Beauties (1935)	GP.135	£4.00	—
A	—	30	Stars of the Stage and Screen (c1934):	GP.308	£4.00	—
			A Black and White		£4.00	—
			B Coloured		£6.00	—

ADCOCK & SON, Norwich

A1	U	12	Ancient Norwich (1928)		—	£140.00
			11/12 Ancient Norwich (No. 6 missing)		£3.00	£33.00

ADKIN & SONS, London

20 page reference book (combined with Abdulla & Anstie) — £4.50

D	BW	25	*Actresses — French. Nd. 126-150 (c1898)	H.1	£200.00	—
A	C	15	*Beauties 'PAC', multi-backed (c1898)	H.2	£325.00	—

ADKIN & SONS, London *(continued)*

Size	*Print-ing*	*Number in set*		*Handbook reference*	*Price per card*	*Complete set*
A	C	50	Butterflies and Moths (1924)	H.80	£1.90	£95.00
		12	Character Sketches:	H.3		
A2	C		A Black printing on back (1901)		£7.50	£90.00
A2	C		B Green printing on back (1902)		£7.50	£90.00
—	C		C Premium issue (145 × 103mm) (1901)		£100.00	—
—	C	4	*Games — by Tom Browne, postcard back (135 × 85mm) (c1900)	H.4	£300.00	—
		12	A Living Picture (c1901):	H.5		
A2	C		A 'Adkin & Sons' at top back			
			(i) crimson		£7.50	£90.00
			(ii) scarlet		£7.50	£90.00
A2	C		B 'These cards are ...' at top back		£7.50	£90.00
—	C		C Premium issue (145 × 103mm)		£100.00	—
A	BW	25	Notabilities (1915)		£5.00	£125.00
A1	C	12	Pretty Girl Series (Actresses) (c1897)	H.7	£60.00	—
A2	C	12	*Pretty Girl Series 'RASH' (1897):	H.8		
			A Calendar back		£60.00	—
			B Advertisements back		£38.00	—
			C Figure and verse back		£38.00	—
D	C	12	A Royal Favourite (1900)	H.9	£12.00	£145.00
A	BW		Soldiers of the Queen (1899-1900):	H.10		
			A Series of 50:			
		24	(a) Nos. 1-24 '... and exclusively with'		£27.00	—
		50	(b) Nos. 1-50 and variety '... and issued with ...'		£5.00	£250.00
		59	B Series of 60, plus No. 61 (Nos 28, 33 not issued)		£4.50	—
A	BW	31	*Soldiers of the Queen and Portraits (1901)	H.11	£6.00	£185.00
A	C	30	Sporting Cups and Trophies (1914)		£17.00	—
A	BW	25	War Trophies (1917)		£5.00	£125.00
A	C	50	Wild Animals of the World (1922)	H.77	£1.70	£85.00

AIKMAN'S, Montrose

D	C	30	*Army Pictures, Cartoons, etc. (c1916)	H.12	£120.00	—

H.J. AINSWORTH, Harrogate

D	C	30	*Army Pictures, Cartoons, etc (1916)	H.12	£120.00	—

ALBERGE & BROMET, London

A	C		*Boer War and General Interest (c1900):	H.13		
		? 11	A 'Bridal Bouquet' and 'El Benecio' wording on green leaf design back		£110.00	—
		? 2	B 'La Optima' and 'Federation' wording on green leaf design back		£180.00	—
		? 8	C 'Bridal Bouquet' and 'El Benecio' wording on brown leaf design back		£110.00	—
		? 1	D 'La Optima' and 'Federation' wording on brown leaf design back		£200.00	—
Dl	C	40	*Naval and Military Phrases (c1904):	H.14		
			A 'Bridal Bouquet' and 'El Benecio'		£100.00	—
			B 'La Optima' and 'Federation'		£100.00	—
Dl	C	30	*Proverbs (c1903)	H.15	£100.00	—

PHILLIP ALLMAN & CO. LTD, London

A	C	50	Coronation Series (1953)		90p	£45.00

Size	Printing	Number in set		Handbook reference	Price per card	Complete set

PHILLIP ALLMAN & CO. LTD, London *(continued)*

Size	Printing	Number in set		Handbook reference	Price per card	Complete set
			Pin-up Girls (1953):	H.851		
A1	C		A First 12 subjects:			
		12	Ai Unnumbered, 'For men only'		£5.00	£60.00
		12	Aii Numbered, 'Ask for Allman always'		£4.00	£50.00
		12	Aiii Unnumbered, 'Ask for Allman always'		£4.00	£50.00
A1	C	12	B Second 12 subjects		£5.00	—
A1	C	24	C Inscribed '1st series of 24'		£8.00	—
—	C	24	D Large size (75 × 68mm)		£4.00	—

AMALGAMATED TOBACCO CORPORATION LTD ('Mills' Cigarettes)——

Size	Printing	Number in set		Handbook reference	Price per card	Complete set
—	C	25	Famous British Ships 'Series No. 1' (75 × 48mm) (1952)		20p	£3.50
—	C	25	Famous British Ships 'Series No. 2' (75 × 48mm) (1952)		20p	£4.00
—	C	50	History of Aviation (75 × 48mm) (1952):			
			A Nos. 1 to 16, 18 to 25 and 27		£2.00	—
			B Nos. 17, 26 and 28 to 50		24p	£6.00
A	C	25	Kings of England (1954)		£1.60	£40.00
A	C	25	Propelled Weapons (1953)		20p	£4.00

OVERSEAS ISSUES

Size	Printing	Number in set		Handbook reference	Price per card	Complete set
A	C	25	Aircraft of the World (1958)	H.852	80p	£20.00
A	C	25	Animals of the Countryside (1957)	H.853	30p	£7.50
A	C	25	Aquarium Fish (1960)	H.854	20p	£5.00
A	C	25	Army Badges — Past and Present (1960)		90p	£22.50
A	C	25	British Coins and Costumes (1958)	H.855	40p	£10.00
A	C	25	British Locomotives (1961)	H.856	60p	£15.00
A	C	25	British Uniforms of the 19th Century (1957)	H.857	90p	£22.50
A	C	25	Butterflies and Moths (1957)	H.858	36p	£9.00
A	C	25	Cacti (1960)	H.859	50p	£12.50
A	C	25	Castles of Britain (1961)	H.860	£1.20	£30.00
A	C	25	Coins of the World (1960)	H.861	20p	£4.00
A	C	25	Communications (1961)	H.862	£1.00	£25.00
A	C	25	Dogs (1958)	H.863	70p	£17.50
A	C	25	Evolution of the Royal Navy (1957)	H.864	60p	£15.00
A	C	25	Football Clubs and Badges (1961)	H.865	£1.60	—
A	C	25	Freshwater Fish (1958)	H.866	24p	£6.00
A	C	25	Guerriers à Travers les Ages (French text) (1961)	H.882	80p	£20.00
A	C	25	Historical Buildings (1959)	H.867	80p	£20.00
A	C	25	Histoire de l'Aviation, 1st series (French text) (1961)	H.868	24p	£6.00
A	C	25	Histoire de l'Aviation, 2nd series (French text) (1962)	H.868	£1.00	£25.00
A	C	25	Holiday Resorts (1957)	H.869	20p	£3.00
A	C	25	Interesting Hobbies (1959)	H.870	60p	£15.00
A	C	25	Into Space (1958)	H.871	28p	£7.00
A	C	25	Les Autos Moderns (French text) (1961)	H.875	50p	£12.50
A	C	25	Medals of the World (1959)	H.872	24p	£6.00
A	C	25	Merchant Ships of the World (1961)	H.873	70p	£17.50
A	C	25	Merveilles Modernes (French text) (1961)	H.876	40p	£10.00
A	C	25	Miniature Cars and Scooters (1959)	H.874	£1.20	£30.00
A	C	25	Nature (1958)	H.877	20p	£3.00
A	C	25	Naval Battles (1959)	H.878	40p	£10.00
A	C	25	Ports of the World (1957)	H.869	20p	£3.00
A	C	25	Ships of the Royal Navy (1961)	H.879	50p	£12.50
A	C	25	Sports and Games (1958)	H.880	£1.20	£30.00
A	C	25	Tropical Birds (1959)	H.881	£1.20	—
A	C	25	Weapons of Defence (1961)	H.883	£1.00	£25.00
A	C	25	Wild Animals (1958)	H.884	20p	£5.00
A	C	25	The Wild West (1960)	H.885	90p	£22.50
A	C	25	World Locomotives (1959)	H.886	£1.20	£30.00

Size	Printing	Number in set		Handbook reference	Price per card	Complete set

THE ANGLO-AMERICAN CIGARETTE MAKING CO. LTD, London

A	C	20	Russo-Japanese War Series (1906)	H.100	£400.00	—

THE ANGLO CIGARETTE MANUFACTURING CO., London

A	C	36	Tariff Reform Series (1909)	H.16	£30.00	—

E. & W. ANSTIE, Devizes

20 page reference book (combined with Abdulla & Adkin) — £4.50

A2	C	25	Aesop's Fables (1934)	H.518	£3.00	£75.00
A	C	16	*British Empire Series (1904)	H.17	£12.50	£200.00
A	BW	40	Nature Notes (1939)		£10.00	—
A	U	50	People of Africa (1926)		£3.50	£175.00
A	U	50	People of Asia (1926)		£3.50	£175.00
A	U	50	People of Europe (1925)		£3.50	£175.00
A2	BW	40	Places of Interest (1939):			
			A Varnished front		90p	£36.00
			B Unvarnished front		£3.00	—
—	C	8	Puzzles (26 × 70mm) (1902)	H.18	£200.00	—
A	C	50	*Racing Series (1922):			
			1-25 — Racing Colours		£5.00	—
			26-50 — Horses, Jockeys, Race-courses, etc		£6.50	—
—	C	5	Royal Mail (70 × 50mm) (1899)	H.19	£300.00	—
A	C	50	Scout Series (1923)		£3.50	£175.00
A2	C		Sectional Series:			
		10	Clifton Suspension Bridge (1938)	H.519-1	£2.50	£25.00
		10	Stonehenge (1936)	H.519-2	£2.50	£25.00
		10	The Victory (1936)	H.519-3	£4.00	—
		20	Wells Cathedral (1935)	H.519-4	£2.50	£50.00
		20	Wiltshire Downs (1935)	H.519-6	£2.50	£50.00
		10	Windsor Castle (1937)	H.519-5	£2.50	£25.00
A2	BW	40	Wessex (1938)		£1.50	£60.00
A	U	50	The World's Wonders (1924)		£1.60	£80.00

SILKS. Anonymous unbacked woven silks. Width sizes only are quoted as the silks were prepared in ribbon form and length sizes are thus arbitrary.

—	C	10	**Flags, large (width 95mm) (c1915)*	H.495-1	£11.00	—
—	C	36	**Flags, small (width 42mm) (c1915)*	H.495-1	£1.80	—
—	C	85	**Regimental Badges (width 32mm) (c1915)*	H.495-3	From £2.00	—
—	C		**Royal Standard and Portraits (c1915):*	H.495-2		
		1	*Royal Standard (width 95mm)*		—	£15.00
		1	*King George V:*			
			(a) Large (width 71 mm), black frame		—	£70.00
			(b) Large (width 71mm), gold frame		—	£60.00
			(c) Small (width 32mm)		—	£70.00
		1	*Queen Mary:*			
			(a) Large (width 71 mm)		—	£60.00
			(b) Small (width 32mm)		—	£75.00
		1	*Lord French (width 71mm)*		—	£85.00
		1	*Lord Kitchener (width 71mm)*		—	£20.00

H. ARCHER & CO., London

C	C		*Actresses — Selection from 'FROGA A and B' (c1900):	H.20		
		? 20	A 'Golden Returns' back		£70.00	—
		? 13	B 'M.F.H.' back		£70.00	—

Size	Print-ing	Number in set		Handbook reference	Price per card	Complete set

H. ARCHER & CO., London *(continued)*

Size	Print-ing	Number in set		Handbook reference	Price per card	Complete set
C			*Beauties — 'CHOAB' (c1900):	H.21		
	U	50	A 'Bound to Win' front		£30.00	—
	C	? 4	B 'Golden Returns' back		£75.00	—
	C	? 5	C 'M.F.H.' back		£75.00	—
C	C	20	*Prince of Wales Series (c1912)	H.22	£30.00	—

ARDATH TOBACCO CO. LTD, London

28 page reference book — £4.50

Size	Print-ing	Number in set		Handbook reference	Price per card	Complete set
A1	C	50	*Animals at the Zoo (export) (c1924):	H.520		
			A Back with descriptive text		£2.50	—
			B Back without description, 'Double Ace' issue		£20.00	—
A	C	96	Ardath Modern School Atlas (export) (c1935)		£1.60	—
A2	P	54	Beautiful English Women (1928) (export)		£3.50	—
A	C	25	Big Game Hunting (export) (c1930):			
			A Back in blue		£4.00	—
			B Back in black		£15.00	—
—	U	30	Boucher Series (77 × 62mm) (c1915)		£3.00	—
A	U	50	Britain's Defenders (1936)		80p	£40.00
	U	50	British Born Film Stars (export) (1934):			
A2			A Small size, back white semi-glossy		£1.60	—
A2			B Small size, back cream matt		£1.60	—
—			C Medium size (67 × 53mm)		£2.70	—
	U		Camera Studies (c1939):	H.644		
—		36	A Small size (70 × 44mm)		£1.25	£45.00
—		45	B Large size (79 × 57mm)		£1.20	£55.00
—	C	25	Champion Dogs (95 × 67mm) (1934)		£1.80	£45.00
A	C	50	Cricket, Tennis and Golf Celebrities (1935):			
			A Home issue, grey back		£1.40	£70.00
			B Export issue, brownish-grey back, text revised		£2.50	£125.00
—	U	25	Dog Studies (95 × 68mm) (1938)		£5.00	£125.00
A	C	25	Eastern Proverbs (export) (c1930)	H.521	£1.80	£45.00
A	C	48	Empire Flying-Boat (sectional) (1938)		£1.60	£80.00
A	C	50	Empire Personalities (1937)		80p	£40.00
A	C	50	Famous Film Stars (1934)		£1.20	£60.00
A	C	50	Famous Footballers (1934)		£1.60	£80.00
A	C	25	Famous Scots (1935)		£1.60	£40.00
—	C	25	Fighting and Civil Aircraft (96 × 68mm) (1936)		£2.60	£65.00
A	C	50	Figures of Speech (1936)		£1.40	£70.00
A	C	50	Film, Stage and Radio Stars (1935)		£1.10	£55.00
—	C	25	Film, Stage and Radio Stars (96 × 68mm) (1935)		£1.20	£30.00
—	BW	? 22	Film Stars (postcard size) (c1935)	H.645	£30.00	—
—	U	40	Franz Hals Series, Dutch back (70 × 60mm) (c1916):			
			A Without overprint		£15.00	—
			B With overprint		£25.00	—
—	C	50	From Screen and Stage (96 × 65mm) (1936)		£1.20	£60.00
—	U	30	Gainsborough Series (77 × 62mm) (c1915)	H.714	£3.00	—
—	C	30	Girls of All Nations (78 × 66mm) (c1916)		£17.00	—
A1	U	50	Great War Series (c1916)		£6.00	—
A1	U	50	Great War Series 'B' (c1916)		£6.00	—
A1	U	50	Great War Series 'C' (c1916)		£6.00	—
A2	P	35	Hand Shadows (c1930) (export)		£32.00	—
—	BW	25	Historic Grand Slams (folders) (101 × 70mm) (c1935)		£30.00	—
			Hollandsche Oude Meesters, Dutch back (70 × 60mm) (c1916):			
—	U	25	A First 25 subjects		£15.00	—
—	U	25	B Second 25 subjects		£15.00	—

Size	*Print-ing*	*Number in set*		*Handbook reference*	*Price per card*	*Complete set*

ARDATH TOBACCO CO. LTD, London *(continued)*

J2	U	48	How to Recognise the Service Ranks (holed for binding) (c1939)	H.642	£5.00	—
			Industrial Propaganda Cards (c1942):	H.914		
H1	C	2	A Black background		£7.50	£15.00
H1	C	4	B Coloured fronts		£7.50	£30.00
J2	BW	11	C White fronts		£4.00	£45.00
J2	U	? 171	Information Slips (holed for binding) (1938)	H.643	£3.50	—
A	U	50	Life in the Services (1938):			
			A Home issue, adhesive		70p	£35.00
			B Export issue, non-adhesive		£1.20	£60.00
			Ministry of Information Cards (1941-3):			
J2	U	5	A Calendar — 'It all depends on me'		£4.00	£20.00
J2	U	1	B Greeting Card — 'It all depends on me'		—	£10.00
—	C	24	C 'It all depends on me' (80 × 63mm)	H.913	£1.25	£30.00
—	C	1	D Union Jack Folder (60 × 46mm)		—	£10.00
—	C	1	E 'On the Cotton Front' (80 × 63mm)	H.913	—	£2.50
—	BW	1	F 'On the Kitchen Front' (70 × 55mm)	H.913	—	£2.50
A	C	50	National Fitness (1938):			
			A Home issue, adhesive		60p	£30.00
			B Export issue, non-adhesive		£1.00	£50.00
A2	CP	50	New Zealand Views (1928) (export)		£2.50	—
A	U	50	Our Empire (export) (c1937)	H.522	£1.40	£70.00
A	C		Proverbs (c1936):			
		25	A Home issue Nos 1-25		£1.40	£35.00
		25	B Export issue Nos 26-50		£3.00	—
—	U	30	Raphael Series (77 × 62mm) (c1915)		£3.00	—
—	U		Rembrandt Series (1914):			
		30	A Large size (77 × 62 mm), English back		£4.00	—
		40	B Large size (77 × 62mm), Dutch back		£16.00	—
		30	C Extra-large size (101 × 62mm)		£6.00	—
—	U	30	Rubens Series (77 × 61 mm) (c1915):			
			A English 'State Express' back		£3.00	—
			B English 'Winfred' back		£17.00	—
			C Dutch back		£17.00	—
			D New Zealand 'State Express' back		£17.00	—
	U	100	Scenes from Big Films (export) (1935):			
A			A Small size, white back		£2.00	—
A			B Small size, cream back		£4.00	—
—			C Medium Size (67 × 52mm)		£4.00	—
—	BW	20	Ships of The Royal Navy (Double Ace Cigarettes Slides) (c1955)	H.887	£18.00	—
A	C	50	Silver Jubilee (1935)		70p	£35.00
A	C	50	Speed — Land, Sea and Air (1935):			
			A Home issue, 'Issued with State Express'		£1.50	£75.00
			B Export issue, Ardath name at base		£2.00	—
—	C	25	Speed — Land, Sea and Air (95 × 68mm) (1938)		£1.80	£45.00
A	C	50	Sports Champions (1935):			
			A Home issue, 'State Express' at base		£1.10	£55.00
			B Export issue, 'Ardath' at base		£2.00	£100.00
A	C	50	Stamps — Rare and Interesting (1939)		£1.50	£75.00
A	C	50	Swimming, Diving and Life-Saving (1937) (export)	H.523	£2.00	—
A	C	50	Tennis (1937) (export)	H.524	£2.00	—
A	C	48	Trooping the Colour (sectional) (1939)		£2.00	£100.00
—	C	12	Types of Smokers (c1910):	H.716		
			A Size 77 × 64mm		£80.00	—
			B Size 102 × 64mm		£80.00	—

ARDATH TOBACCO CO. LTD, London *(continued)*

Size	*Print-ing*	*Number in set*		*Handbook reference*	*Price per card*	*Complete set*
—	U	30	Valasquez Series (c1915):			
			A Large size (77 × 62mm)		£3.50	—
			B Extra-large size (101 × 62mm)		£6.00	—
A	C	50	Who is This? (1936) (Film Stars)		£1.80	£90.00
J2	U	? 5	Wonderful Handicraft (c1935)	H.717	£45.00	—
—	BW	24	World Views (No. 13 not issued) (95 × 68mm) (1937)		50p	£12.00
A	C	50	Your Birthday Tells Your Fortune (1937)		70p	£35.00

PHOTOGRAPHIC ISSUES

H	P		Photocards — Numbered Series (1936)*:			
		110	'A' — Football Clubs of North West Counties		£2.00	£220.00
		110	'B' — Football Clubs of North East Counties		£2.20	—
		110	'C' — Football Clubs of Yorkshire		£1.70	£190.00
		165	'D' — Football Clubs of Scotland		£1.40	£230.00
		110	'E' — Football Clubs of Midlands		£2.00	£220.00
		110	'F' — Football Clubs of London and Southern Counties		£1.70	£190.00
		99	'Z' — General Interest (Sports):			
			Nos. 111-165		70p	£38.00
			Nos. 166-209 (Cricket etc)		70p	£32.00
		11	'A.s' (1), 'C.s' (2-3), 'E.s' (4-10), 'F.s' (11) — Football Clubs (supplementary)		£5.00	£55.00
		?	Selected cards from the above 8 series:			
			A With red overprint		£7.00	—
			B Thin paper attached to back covering front of card advertising Ardath 'Kings'		£7.00	—
	P		Photocards — 'A Continuous Series of Topical Interest' (1937):	H.525		
		22	Group A — Racehorses and Sports		£1.25	£27.50
		22	Group B — Coronation and Sports		—	£35.00
			21 Different (minus Walter Neusel)		80p	£16.00
		22	Group C — Lancashire Personalities		—	£45.00
			21 Different (minus Gracie Fields)		£1.25	£25.00
		22	Group D — Sports and Miscellaneous		£1.50	£33.00
		22	Group E — Film Stars and Sports		£1.25	£27.00
		22	Group F — Film Stars and Sportsmen		£1.50	£33.00
		66	'G.S.' — Miscellaneous subjects (export)		£2.50	—
H	P		Photocards — 'A Continuous Series of General interest', with Album offer (1938):	H.526		
		11	Group G — Australian Cricketers		£20.00	—
		22	Group H — Film, Radio and Sporting Stars		£1.25	£27.00
		22	Group I — Film Stars and Miscellaneous		£1.25	£27.00
	P		Photocards — 'A Continuous Series of General Interest', without Album offer — uncoloured (1938):	H.527		
H		22	Group J — Film Stars and General Interest		£1.10	£24.00
H		22	Group K — Film, Radio and Sporting Stars:			
			1 With 'Kings' Clause		£1.25	£27.00
			2 Without 'Kings' Clause (export)		£1.60	—
H		44	Group L — Film Stars and Miscellaneous		70p	£30.00
		45	Group M — Film Stars and Miscellaneous:			
C			1 Small size		90p	£40.00
—			2 Large size (80 × 69 mm), with 'Kings' Clause		90p	£40.00
—			3 Large size (80 × 69mm), without 'Kings' Clause		90p	£40.00
	P	45	Group N — Film, Stage and Radio Stars:			
C			1 Small size		90p	£40.00
—			2 Large size (80 × 69mm)		90p	£40.00

Size	*Print-ing*	*Number in set*		*Handbook reference*	*Price per card*	*Complete set*

ARDATH TOBACCO CO. LTD, London *(continued)*

H	CP		Photocards — 'A Continuous Series of General Interest', without Album offer — Hand coloured (export) (1938):	H.528		
		22	Group 1 — Views of the World		90p	£20.00
		22	Group 2 — Views of the World		90p	£20.00
		22	Group 3 — Views of the World		80p	£17.50
			Real Photographs:			
	P	45	Group O — 'A Continuous Series of General Interest' — Films, Stage and Radio Stars (1939)	H.529	70p	£32.00
C	P	45	'1st Series of 45' — Film and Stage Stars (1939)		£1.00	—
C	P	54	'2nd Series of 54' — Film and Stage Stars (1939)		£1.00	—
J2	P	18	'First Series' — Views (1937)		£2.50	—
J2	P	18	'Second Series' — Film and Stage Stars (1937)		£2.50	—
J2	P	18	'Third Series' — Views (1937)		£2.50	—
J2	P	18	'Fourth Series' — Film and Stage Stars (1937)		£2.50	—
J2	P	18	'Fifth Series' — Views (1938)		£2.50	—
J2	P	18	'Sixth Series' — Film and Stage Stars (1938)		£2.50	—
H	P	44	'Series One' 'G.P.1' — Film Stars (export) (1939)		90p	£40.00
H	P	44	'Series Two' 'G.P.2' — Film Stars (export) (1939)		45p	£20.00
H	P	44	'Series Three' 'G.P.3' — Film Stars (export) (1939)		£3.00	—
H	CP	44	'Series Three' 'C.V.3' — Views (export) (1939)		80p	£35.00
H	CP	44	'Series Four' 'C.V.4' — Views (export) (1939)		35p	£15.00
J2	P	36	'Series Seven' — Film and Stage Stars (1938)		£1.00	—
J2	P	54	'Series Eight' — Film and Stage Stars (1938)		80p	£45.00
	P	54	'Series Nine' — Film and Stage Stars (1938):			
H			A Medium size		80p	£45.00
J2			B Extra-large size		80p	£45.00
	P	54	'Series Ten' — Film and Stage Stars (1939):			
—			A Large size (80 × 69mm)		80p	£45.00
J2			B Extra-large size		£1.00	£55.00
	P	54	'Series Eleven' — Film and Stage Stars (1939):			
—			A Large size (80 × 69mm)		80p	£45.00
J2			B Extra-large size		£1.20	—
—	P	54	'Series Twelve' — Film and Stage Stars (80 × 69mm) (1939)		80p	£45.00
—	P	54	'Series Thirteen' — Film and Stage Stars (80 × 69mm) (1939)		80p	£45.00
	P	36	'Of Famous Landmarks' (1939):			
—			A Large size (80 × 69 mm), titled 'Real Photographs'		£3.50	—
	J2		B Extra-large size, titled 'Real Photographs of Famous Landmarks'		£1.70	£60.00
	P	36	'Of Modern Aircraft' (1939):			
—			A Large size (80 × 69mm)		£4.25	—
J2			B Extra-large size		£3.25	—
SILKS						
—	C	1	Calendar for 1937 (silk) (138 × 102mm)	H.508	—	£120.00
—	C	1	Calender for 1938 (silk) (160 × 102mm)	H.508	—	£120.00

THE ASSOCIATED TOBACCO MANUFACTURERS LTD

C2	C	25	Cinema Stars (export) (c1926):	H.530		
			A 'Issued with Bond Street Turkish Cigarettes'		£32.00	—
			B 'Issued with John Bull Virginia Cigarettes'		£32.00	—
			C 'Issued with Club Virginia Cigarettes'		£32.00	—
			D 'Issued with Heliopolis Turkish Cigarettes'		£32.00	—
			E 'Issued with Sports Turkish Cigarettes'		£32.00	—

Size	*Print-ing*	*Number in set*		*Handbook reference*	*Price per card*	*Complete set*

A. ATKINSON, London

D	C	30	*Army Pictures, Cartoons, etc (c1916)	H.12	£120.00	—

AVISS BROTHERS LTD, London

D1	C	40	*Naval and Military Phrases (c1904)	H.14	£200.00	—

J.A. BAILEY, Swansea

D1	C	40	*Naval and Military Phrases (c1904)	H.14	£250.00	—

A. BAKER & CO. LTD, London

A	BW	20	*Actresses — 'BLARM'(c1900):	H.23		
			A Long design back (64mm)		£30.00	—
			B Design altered and shortened (58mm)		£30.00	—
A	BW	10	*Actresses — 'HAGGA' (c1900)	H.24	£30.00	£300.00
	BW		*Actresses 'Baker's 3-sizes' (c1900):	H.25		
A		25	A Small cards		£32.00	—
—		25	B Extra large cards (67 × 127mm)		£225.00	—
—	BW	25	Actresses 'Baker's 3 sizes' (56 × 75mm) (c1900)	H.25	£50.00	—
C	BW	? 41	*Baker's Tobacconists' Shops (c1901):	H.26		
			A 'Try our 3½d Tobaccos' back		£250.00	—
			B 'Cigar, Cigarette, etc. Manufacturers' back		£140.00	—
C	C	25	Beauties of All Nations (c1900):	H.27		
			A 'Albert Baker & Co. (1898) ...' back		£22.00	£550.00
			B 'A. Baker & Co. ...' back		£16.00	£400.00
C	BW	16	*British Royal Family (c1902)	H.28	£50.00	—
A1	BW	20	Cricketers Series (1901)	H.29	£325.00	—
A1	C	25	*Star Girls (c1898)	H.30	£225.00	—

BAYLEY & HOLDSWORTH

A	C	26	*International Signalling Code (c1910)		£180.00	—

E.C. BEESTON, Wales

D	C	30	*Army Pictures, Cartoons etc (c1916)	H.12	£120.00	—

BELFAST SHIPS STORES CO. LTD, Belfast

	C	1	*Dickens' Characters (79 × 40mm) (c1895)	H.31	£950.00	—

J. & F. BELL LTD, Glasgow

A	BW	10	*Actresses — 'HAGGA' ('Three Bells Cigarettes) (c1900)	H.24	£80.00	—
C	C	25	*Beauties — Tobacco Leaf Back (c1898):	H.32		
			A 'Bell's Scotia Cigarettes' back		£120.00	—
			B 'Three Bells Cigarettes' back		£120.00	—
A	C	25	Colonial Series (c1901)		£45.00	—
A	BW	30	*Footballers (c1902)		£70.00	—
A	C	25	Scottish Clan Series No. 1 (c1903)	H.33	£16.00	£400.00

OVERSEAS ISSUES

A	C	60	Rigsvaabner (Arms of Countries) (c1925)		£30.00	—
A	C	60	Women of Nations (1924)		£30.00	—

B. BELLWOOD, BRADFORD

C	C	18	Motor Cycle Series (c1912)	H.469	£120.00	—

Size	Print-ing	Number in set		Handbook reference	Price per card	Complete set

RICHARD BENSON LTD, Bristol

Size	Print-ing	Number in set		Handbook reference	Price per card	Complete set
	U	24	Old Bristol Series:			
—			A Original issue (80 × 70mm) (c1925):			
			i 23 different, minus No. 8		£3.00	£70.00
			ii Number 8		—	£30.00
—			B Reprint (88 × 78-83mm) (1946)		£2.00	£50.00

BENSON & HEDGES, London

Size	Print-ing	Number in set		Handbook reference	Price per card	Complete set
A2	C	1	Advertisement Card, The Original Shop (1973)		—	£2.00
B	C	10	B.E.A. Aircraft (1958)	H.888	£11.00	—
—	C	50	Friendly Games (75 × 45mm) (c1970)		£1.50	—
OVERSEAS ISSUES (CANADA)						
A2	C	48	Ancient and Modern Fire Fighting Equipment (1947)		£6.00	—
—	BW	12	Oxford University Series (90 × 50mm) (c1912)		£40.00	—

FELIX BERLYN, Manchester

Size	Print-ing	Number in set		Handbook reference	Price per card	Complete set
	C	25	Golfing Series (Humorous) (c1910):			
A1			A Small size		£400.00	—
—			B Post card size (139 × 87mm)		£550.00	—

BERRY, London

Size	Print-ing	Number in set		Handbook reference	Price per card	Complete set
D	U	20	London Views (c1905)	H.34	£250.00	—

BEWLAY & CO. LTD, London

Size	Print-ing	Number in set		Handbook reference	Price per card	Complete set
D1	U		Bewlay's War Series (Generals, etc) (c1915):	H.477		
		12	A 'Caps the Lot' Smoking Mixture		£12.00	—
		6	B Try Bewlay's 'Caps the Lot' Mixture		£12.00	—
		6	C Try Bewlay's 'Modern Man' Mixture		£12.00	—
D1	U	25	Bewlay's War Series (Photogravure War Pictures) (c1915):	H.35		
			A 'Modern Man' Mixtures etc		£12.00	—
			B 'Modern Man' Cigarettes		£12.00	—
			C 'Two Great Favourites'		£12.00	—
A	C	6	*Comic Advertisement Cards (1909)	H.36	£200.00	—
—	C	6	*Comic Advertisement Cards (140 × 88mm) (c1909)	H.36	£100.00	—

W.O. BIGG & CO., Bristol

Size	Print-ing	Number in set		Handbook reference	Price per card	Complete set
A	C	37	*Flags of All Nations (c1904):	H.37		
			A 'Statue of Liberty' back, 4d oz		£9.00	—
			B As A:— (a) altered to 4½d by hand		£9.00	—
			(b) 4½d red seal over 4d		£9.00	—
			C Panel design 'New York' Mixture		£9.00	—
A	C	50	Life on Board a Man of War (c1905)	H.38	£10.00	£500.00

JAS. BIGGS & SONS, London

Size	Print-ing	Number in set		Handbook reference	Price per card	Complete set
C	C	26	*Actresses — 'FROGA A' 'Two Roses' in white (c1900)	H.20	£40.00	—
C	C	52	*Actresses — 'FROGA A & B' 'Two Roses' in black (c1900)	H.20	£55.00	—
A	C		*Beauties, with frameline — 'CHOAB' (c1900):	H.21		
		25	A Blue typeset back		£75.00	—
		50	B Overprinted in black on Bradford cards		£70.00	—

Size	Print-ing	Number in set		Handbook reference	Price per card	Complete set

JAS. BIGGS & SONS, London *(continued)*

C	C		*Beauties, no framelines — selection 'BOCCA' (c1900):	H.39		
		25	A Blue back		£75.00	—
		25	B Black back		£75.00	—
C	C	30	*Colonial Troops (c1901)	H.40	£32.00	—
C	C	30	*Flags and Flags with Soldiers (c1903)	H.41	£30.00	—
A1	C	25	*Star Girls (c1900)	H.30	£250.00	—

J.S. BILLINGHAM, Northampton

D	C	30	*Army Pictures, Cartoons etc (c1916)	H.12	£120.00	—

R. BINNS, Halifax

A	U	? 17	*Halifax Footballers (c1924)	H.531	£200.00	—

BLANKS CIGARETTES

A	C	50	Keystrokes in Break-Building (c1935)	H.647	£450.00	—

THE BOCNAL TOBACCO CO., London

A2	U	25	Luminous Silhouettes of Beauty and Charm (1938)		£2.80	£70.00
A2	C	25	Proverbs Up-to-Date (1938)		£2.40	£60.00

ALEXANDER BOGUSLAVSKY LTD, London

—	C	12	Big Events on the Turf (133 × 70mm) (1924)		£45.00	—
A2	C	25	Conan Doyle Characters (1923):			
			A Back in black, white board		£7.00	—
			B Back in grey, cream board		£7.00	—
			C Back in green		£7.00	—
A2	C	25	Mythological Gods and Goddesses (1924)		£3.00	£75.00
A	C	25	*Sports Records, Nd. 1-25 (1925)		£2.00	£50.00
A	C	25	Sports Records, Nd. 26-50 (1925)		£2.00	£50.00
	C	25	Winners on the Turf (1925):			
A			A Small size, captions 'sans serif'		£3.40	£85.00
A			B Small size, captions with 'serif'		£5.00	—
B			C Large size		£5.50	—

R. & E. BOYD LTD, London

—	U	25	Places of Interest (c1938):			
			A Size 67 × 35mm		£65.00	—
			B Size 71 × 55mm		£65.00	—
—	U	25	Wild Birds at Home (75 × 57mm) (c1938)	H.626	£65.00	—

WM. BRADFORD, Liverpool

C	C	50	*Beauties 'CHOAB' (c1900)	H.21	£35.00	—
D	U	? 7	Beauties — 'Jersey Lily Cigarettes' (c1900)	H.488	£500.00	—
D2	BW	20	Boer War Cartoons (c1901)	H.42	£120.00	—

T. BRANKSTON & CO., London

C	C	30	*Colonial Troops (c1901):	H.40		
			A Golf Club Mixture		£32.00	—
			B Red Virginia		£32.00	—
			C Sweet as the Rose		£32.00	—
A2	C	12	*Pretty Girl Series 'RASH' (c1900)	H.8	£350.00	—

Size	Printing	Number in set		Handbook reference	Price per card	Complete set

BRIGHAM & CO., Reading

Size	Printing	Number in set		Handbook reference	Price per card	Complete set
B	U	16	Down the Thames from Henley to Windsor (c1912)		£150.00	–
A	U	16	Reading Football Players (c1912)		£400.00	–
–	BW	3	Tobacco Growing in Hampshire (89 × 79mm) (1915)	H.470	£16.00	£50.00

BRITANNIA ANONYMOUS SOCIETY

Size	Printing	Number in set		Handbook reference	Price per card	Complete set
–	C	? 31	*Beauties and Scenes (60 × 40mm) (c1914)	H.532	£80.00	–

BRITISH & COLONIAL TOBACCO CO., London

Size	Printing	Number in set		Handbook reference	Price per card	Complete set
A1	C	25	*Armies of the World (c1900)	H.43	£200.00	–

J.M. BROWN, Derby

Size	Printing	Number in set		Handbook reference	Price per card	Complete set
D	C	30	*Army Pictures, Cartoons etc (c1916)	H.12	£120.00	–

ROBERT BRUCE LTD, Birmingham & Wolverhampton

Size	Printing	Number in set		Handbook reference	Price per card	Complete set
A	C	18	Motor Cycle Series (c1912)	H.469	£150.00	–

JOHN BRUMFIT, London

Size	Printing	Number in set		Handbook reference	Price per card	Complete set
A	C	50	The Public Schools' Ties Series (Old Boys) (1925)		£4.00	£200.00

G.A. BULLOUGH, Castleford

Size	Printing	Number in set		Handbook reference	Price per card	Complete set
D	C	30	*Army Pictures, Cartoons etc (c1916)	H.12	£120.00	–

BURSTEIN, ISAACS & CO., London

(The BI-CO Company, B.I. & Co. Ltd)

Size	Printing	Number in set		Handbook reference	Price per card	Complete set
D	BW	25	Famous Prize-Fighters, Nd. 1-25 (1923):			
			A Front caption upper and lower case lettering		£7.00	–
			B Front caption small capital letters		£7.00	–
D	BW	25	Famous Prize-Fighters, Nd. 26-50 (1924):			
			A Front caption upper and lower case lettering		£7.00	–
			B Front caption small capital letters		£7.00	–
D	P	28	London View Series (1922)		£4.00	–

BYRTWOOD & CO., Bristol

Size	Printing	Number in set		Handbook reference	Price per card	Complete set
A2	U	? 37	*Pretty Girl Series — 'BAGG' (c1900)	H.45	£140.00	–

CABANA CIGAR CO., London

Size	Printing	Number in set		Handbook reference	Price per card	Complete set
–	BW	2	Advertisement Card — 'Little Manturios' (63 × 49mm) (1905)	H.719	£325.00	–
A2	C	40	*Home and Colonial Regiments (c1900)	H.69	£325.00	–

PERCY E. CADLE & CO. LTD, Cardiff

Size	Printing	Number in set		Handbook reference	Price per card	Complete set
A1	BW	20	*Actresses 'BLARM' (c1900)	H.23	£38.00	–
C	U	26	*Actresses — 'FROGA A' (c1900):	H.20		
			A Printed Back		£36.00	–
			B Rubber — Stamped Back		£200.00	–
C	C	26	*Actresses — 'FROGA B' (c1900)	H.20	£50.00	–
C	BW	12	*Boer War and Boxer Rebellion Sketches (c1901)	H.46	£60.00	–
C	BW	10	*Boer War Generals — 'FLAC' (c1901)	H.47	£70.00	–
A	BW	20	*Footballers (c1904)	H.4	£70.00	–

Size	Print-ing	Number in set		Handbook reference	Price per card	Complete set

CARRERAS LTD, London

Size	Print-ing	Number in set		Handbook reference	Price per card	Complete set
A	CP	24	Actresses and Their Pets (1926) (export)	H.648	£5.00	—
	C	48	Alice in Wonderland (1930):			
A			A Small size, rounded corners		£1.50	£75.00
A			B Small size, square corners		£3.00	—
B2			C Large size		£1.80	£90.00
		1	D Instruction Booklet		—	£18.00
A	C	50	Amusing Tricks and How to Do Them (1937)		£1.50	£75.00
	C		Battle of Waterloo (1934):	H.533		
C		1	1 Paper insert, with instructions		—	£12.00
—		15	*2 Soldiers and Guns, large size (67 × 70mm)		£4.00	—
A			*3 Soldiers and Guns, small size:			
		10	Soldiers — Officers' Uniforms		£2.00	—
		12	Soldiers and Guns		£2.00	—
C1	C	50	Believe it or Not (1934)		70p	£35.00
A	C	50	Birds of the Countryside (1939)		£1.00	£50.00
D1	BW	200	The Black Cat Library (Booklets) (c1910)		£12.00	—
A	C	50	Britain's Defences (1938)		70p	£35.00
A	C	50	British Birds (1976)		20p	£3.75
	C	25	British Costumes (1927):			
C2			A Small size		£1.40	£35.00
B2			B Large size		£1.40	£35.00
A	P	27	British Prime Ministers (1928) (export)		£1.80	£50.00
A1	C	1	Calendar for 1934		—	£30.00
A	C	50	Celebrities of British History (1935):			
			A Brown on cream back (two shades of ink)		90p	£45.00
			B Pale brown on bluish back		90p	£45.00
A	C	25	Christie Comedy Girls (1928) (export)		£2.00	£50.00
A	U		Cricketers (1934):			
		30	A 'A Series of Cricketers'		£3.30	£100.00
		50	B 'A Series of 50 Cricketers':			
			1 Front in brown and white		£3.50	£175.00
			2 Front in black and white		£35.00	—
A	BW	50	Dogs and Friend (1936)		50p	£25.00
A	C	50	Do You Know? (1939)		30p	£15.00
A	C	50	Famous Airmen and Airwomen (1936)		£1.70	£85.00
	C		Famous Escapes (1926):			
A		25	A Small size		£1.60	£40.00
B2		25	B Large size		£1.40	£35.00
—		10	C Extra-large size (133 × 70mm)		£3.00	£30.00
A2	C	96	Famous Film Stars (1935)	H.534	£1.30	£125.00
A	C		Famous Footballers (1935):			
		48	A Set of 48		£1.40	£70.00
		24	B Nos. 25-48 redrawn		£1.80	£45.00
A	C	25	Famous Men (1927) (export)		£1.60	£40.00
B2	P	24	Famous Naval Men (1929) (export)		£2.00	£50.00
—	C	6	Famous Posters (folders) (65 × 41mm) (1923)	H.606	£25.00	—
B2	P	12	Famous Soldiers (1928) (export)		£5.50	£65.00
A	P	27	Famous Women (1929) (export)		£1.30	£35.00
A	C	25	Figures of Fiction (1924)		£2.00	£50.00
	P	54	Film and Stage Beauties (1939):			
A2			A Small size		50p	£27.00
—			B Medium size (70 × 60mm):			
			(a) Without full point after 'Carreras Ltd'		65p	£35.00
			(b) With full point after 'Carreras Ltd.'		80p	£42.00
	P	36	Film and Stage Beauties:			
B1			A Large size (1939)		£1.00	£36.00
J2			B Extra-large size (1938)		£1.50	£55.00

Size	*Print-ing*	*Number in set*		*Handbook reference*	*Price per card*	*Complete set*

CARRERAS LTD, London *(continued)*

A	C	50	Film Favourites (1938)		£1.50	£75.00
A	P	54	Film Stars — 'A Series of 54' (1937)		85p	£45.00
	P	54	Film Stars (1938):			
A			A Small size, 'Second Series of 54'		50p	£27.00
—			B Medium size (68 × 60mm), 'A Series of 54'		£1.00	£55.00
J2	P		Film Stars (export):			
		36	'A Series of 36' (c1935)		£2.75	—
		36	'Second Series of 36' (c1936)		£2.75	—
		36	'Third Series of 36' (c1937)		£2.75	—
		36	'Fourth Series of 36' (c1938)		£2.75	—
A2	C	50	Film Stars, by Florence Desmond (1936)		90p	£45.00
—		72	Film Stars, oval (70 × 30mm) (1934):			
	P		A Inscribed 'Real Photos'		£2.50	—
	U		B Without 'Real Photos'		£1.50	£110.00
A	C	60	Flags of All Nations (unissued) (c1960)		50p	£30.00
—	C		*Flags of the Allies (shaped) (c1915):	H.49		
		1	Grouped Flags:'Black Cat' Cigarettes		£50.00	—
		5	Allies Flags: 'Black Cat' Cigarettes		£50.00	—
A	C	50	Flowers (1936)		50p	£25.00
A	C	50	Flowers All the Year Round (1977)		20p	£10.00
A2	C	75	*Footballers (1934):			
			A 'Carreras Cigarettes' on front 27mm long		£2.00	£150.00
			B 'Carreras Cigarettes' on front 26mm long		£2.00	£150.00
	C	36	'Fortune Telling' (1926):			
A			A Small size:			
			1 Card inset		55p	£20.00
			2a Head inset, black framelines		55p	£20.00
			2b Head inset, brown framelines		£1.00	£36.00
B2			B Large size:			
			1 Card inset		55p	£20.00
			2 Head inset		55p	£20.00
		1	C Instruction Booklet:			
			1 Address 23 New North Street		—	£20.00
			2 Address 12 Bath Street		—	£11.00
	P		Glamour Girls of Stage and Films (1939):			
A2		54	A Small size		55p	£30.00
—		54	B Medium size (70 × 60mm)		65p	£35.00
—		36	C Large size (76 × 70mm)		£1.00	£36.00
J2		36	D Extra-large size		£1.25	£45.00
	C	50	'Gran-Pop' by Lawson Wood (1934):			
C1			A Small size		50p	£25.00
B			B Large size		40p	£20.00
	C	52	Greyhound Racing Game (1926):			
A			A Small size		25p	£12.50
B2			B Large size		25p	£12.50
		1	C Instruction Leaflet		—	£11.00
—	C		Guards Series (68 × 50mm):			
		4	A Military Mug Series (1971)		£1.00	—
		8	B Order Up the Guards (1970)		£1.00	—
		16	C Send for the Guards (1969)		£1.00	—
D1	BW	5	The Handy Black Cat English-French Dictionary (Booklets) (1915)		£25.00	—
	C	48	Happy Family (1925):			
A1			A Small size		40p	£20.00
B2			B Large size		40p	£20.00
A	C	25	Highwaymen (1924)		£2.40	£60.00

Size	*Printing*	*Number in set*		*Handbook reference*	*Price per card*	*Complete set*
			CARRERAS LTD, London *(continued)*			
A	C	50	History of Army Uniforms (1937)		£1.50	£75.00
A	C	50	History of Naval Uniforms (1937)		90p	£45.00
	C		Horses and Hounds (1926)			
A		25	A Small size		£2.00	£50.00
B2		20	B Large size		£2.00	£40.00
—		10	C Extra-large size (133 × 70mm)		£4.00	£40.00
	C	50	Kings and Queens of England (1935):			
A			A Small size		£1.60	£80.00
B2			B Large size		£2.40	£120.00
A	C	50	Kings and Queens of England (1977)		30p	£15.00
A	U	50	A 'Kodak' at the Zoo 'Series of Fifty' (1924)		70p	£35.00
A	U	50	A 'Kodak' at the Zoo '2nd Series' (1925)		70p	£35.00
A	P	27	Malayan Industries (1929) (export)		80p	£20.00
	P	24	Malayan Scenes (1928):			
A			A Small size		£3.00	—
—			B Medium size (70 × 60mm)		75p	£18.00
A	C	50	Military Uniforms (1976)		20p	£4.00
—	C	7	Millionaire Competition Folders (68 × 30mm) (1971)		£2.00	—
—	C	53	*Miniature Playing Cards (44 × 32mm) (c1935)	H.535-1A	20p	£9.00
	C	50	The 'Nose' Game (1927):			
A			A Small size		50p	£25.00
B2			B Large size		50p	£25.00
		1	C Instruction Leaflet		—	£11.00
	C	50	Notable MPs (1929):			
A			A Small size		£1.20	£60.00
—			B Medium size (69 × 60mm)		60p	£30.00
A	P	25	Notable Ships — Past and Present (1929) (export)		£1.40	£35.00
	C		Old Staffordshire Figures (1926):			
A		24	A Small size		£1.25	£30.00
—		12	B Extra-large size (134 × 71mm)		£3.00	£36.00
B	C	24	Old Staffordshire Figures (different subjects) (1926)		£1.50	£36.00
	C	24	Orchids (1925):			
A			A Small size		£1.00	£25.00
B			B Large size		£1.00	£25.00
—			C Extra-large size (133 × 70mm)		£3.40	—
A	C		Our Navy (1937):			
		20	A Thick card, selected numbers		£1.20	£24.00
		50	B Thin card		£1.20	£60.00
C1	C	50	Palmistry (1933)		60p	£30.00
A	C	50	Palmistry (1980)		£1.00	—
A	P	27	Paramount Stars (1929) (export)		£1.70	£45.00
A	C	25	Picture Puzzle Series (1923)	H.649	£1.60	£40.00
—	C	53	Playing Cards (68 × 42mm) (c1925)	H.535-1B	£1.20	—
	C		*Playing Cards and Dominoes (1929):	H.535-IC		
C		52	A Small size — (a) Numbered		50p	—
			(b) Unnumbered		50p	—
—		26	B Large size (77 × 69mm):			
			(a) Numbered		80p	£20.00
			(b) Unnumbered		80p	£20.00
A	C	48	Popular Footballers (1936):			
			A White back		£1.10	£55.00
			B Cream back		£1.10	£55.00
—	C		Popular Personalities, oval (70 × 30mm) (1935):	H.629		
		72	1 Normal issue		85p	£60.00
		10	2 Replaced subjects (Nos. 1-10) for issue in Eire		£20.00	—
A	U	50	Radio & Television Favourites (unissued) (c1955)		£8.00	—

Size	Printing	Number in set		Handbook reference	Price per card	Complete set
			CARRERAS LTD, London *(continued)*			
	C		Races — Historic and Modern (1927):			
A		25	A Small size		£2.40	£60.00
B		25	B Large size		£2.40	£60.00
—		12	C Extra-large size (133 × 69mm)		£5.00	£60.00
A	C	140	Raemaekers War Cartoons (1916):			
			A 'Black Cat' Cigarettes		£1.30	£185.00
			B Carreras Cigarettes		£3.75	—
	C		Regalia Series (1925):			
A		25	A Small size		50p	£12.50
B		20	B Large size		60p	£12.00
—		10	C Extra-large size (135 × 71mm)		£2.00	£20.00
—	C	50	'Round the World' Scenic Models (folders) (83 × 73mm) (c1930)		80p	£40.00
	C		School Emblems (1929):			
A		50	A Small size		90p	£45.00
B		40	B Large size		75p	£30.00
—		20	C Extra-large size (134 × 76mm)		£2.25	£45.00
A	C	50	The Science of Boxing (c1916):			
			A 'Black Cat' back		£3.00	£150.00
			B 'Carreras Ltd' back		£5.00	—
A	C	50	Sport Fish (1978)		20p	£3.75
C1	C	48	Tapestry Reproductions of Famous Paintings (sectional) (1938)		70p	£35.00
A	C	50	Tools — And How to Use Them (1935)		£2.00	£100.00
A	C	80	Types of London (1919)		£1.70	£135.00
A	P	27	Views of London (1929) (export)		40p	£11.00
A	P	27	Views of the World (1927) (export)		75p	£20.00
A	C	50	Vintage Cars (1976):			
			A With word 'Filter' in white oval:			
			i Thin card, bright red oblong at top		20p	£9.00
			ii Thick card, bright red oblong at top		20p	£7.50
			iii Thin card, dull red oblong at top		40p	—
			B Without word 'Filter' in white oval		20p	£5.00
A	C	25	Wild Flower Art Series (1923)		£1.20	£30.00
A	C	50	Women on War Work (c1916)		£7.00	£350.00
TURF SLIDE ISSUES						
A	U	50	British Aircraft (1953)		£1.60	£80.00
A	U	50	British Fish (1954)		70p	£35.00
A	U	50	British Railway Locomotives (1952)		£1.60	£80.00
A	U	50	Celebrities of British History (1951)		£1.20	£60.00
A	U	50	Famous British Fliers (1956)		£6.00	—
A	U	50	Famous Cricketers (1950)		£6.00	—
A	U	50	Famous Dog Breeds (1952)	H.889	£1.80	£90.00
A	U	50	Famous Film Stars (1949)		£3.20	—
A	U	50	Famous Footballers (1951)		£5.00	—
A	U	50	Film Favourites (1948)		£4.00	—
A	U	50	Film Stars (1947)		£3.20	—
A	U	50	Footballers (1948)		£5.00	—
A	U	50	Olympics (1948)		£6.00	—
A	U	50	Radio Celebrities (1950)		£1.20	£60.00
A	U	50	Sports Series (1949)		£3.50	—
A	U	50	Zoo Animals (1955)		50p	£25.00

(N.B. These prices are for the full slides. If only the cut slides are required these will be half Catalogue price.)

Size	Printing	Number in set		Handbook reference	Price per card	Complete set

CARRERAS LTD, London *(continued)*

SILKS

Size	Printing	Number in set		Handbook reference	Price per card	Complete set
			Lace Motifs (c1915):	H.506		
—	—	79	A Size 63 × 63mm		£8.00	—
—	—	15	B Size 125 × 63mm		£40.00	—
—	—	7	C Size 125 × 125mm		£80.00	—
—	C	12	Miscellaneous Series Cabinet size (1915)	H.505-18	£180.00	—

OVERSEAS ISSUES (AUSTRALIA & CANADA)

Size	Printing	Number in set		Handbook reference	Price per card	Complete set
—	C	20	Canadian Fish (69 × 50mm) (1985)		£2.00	—
—	C	20	Canadian Wild Animals (69 × 50mm) (1984):			
			A Complete set		£2.00	—
			B 15 Different		30p	£4.50
C2	U	72	Film Star Series (1933):			
			A Smile Away back		£3.00	—
			B Standard back		£1.50	—
C2	C	72	Football Series (1933)		£2.75	—
C2	C	24	Personality Series (1933)		£2.50	—
C2	U	72	Personality Series Film Stars (1933)		£1.50	—
C2	C	72	Personality Series Footballers (1933)		£2.75	—
—	C	216	Sportsman's Guide — Fly Fishing (Package Issue) (c1955):			
			A 25 Package (103 × 75mm)		£2.00	—
			B 20 Package (82 × 75mm)		£2.00	—

CARRICK & CO., Hull

Size	Printing	Number in set		Handbook reference	Price per card	Complete set
D	C	12	*Military Terms (1901)	H.50	£75.00	—
—	U	1	Queen Victoria Jubilee 1887 (105 × 67mm)	H.720	—	£300.00

P.J. CARROLL & CO. LTD, Dundalk, Glasgow and Liverpool

Size	Printing	Number in set		Handbook reference	Price per card	Complete set
D	C	25	Birds (prepared but not issued) (c1940)	H.537	70p	£17.50
D	C	25	British Naval Series (c1915)	H.51	£40.00	—
A	P	20	County Louth G.R.A. Team and Officials (1913)		£32.00	—
D	BW	25	*Derby Winners (1914-15):	H.52		
			A Back in black		£100.00	—
			B Back in green		£100.00	—
K2	BW	26	Grand Slam Spelling Bee Cards (c1935)		£15.00	—
D	C	25	Ship Series (1937)		£9.00	£225.00
D	U	24	Sweet Afton Jig-Saw Puzzles (1935)	H.650	£20.00	—

THE CASKET TOBACCO & CIGARETTE CO. LTD, Manchester

Size	Printing	Number in set		Handbook reference	Price per card	Complete set
A2	U	? 1	Bowling Fixture Cards, Coupon Back (1907)	H.53	£500.00	—
A2	U	? 5	Cricket Fixture Cards, Coupon back (1905-10)	H.53	£500.00	—
A2	U	? 2	Cyclists Lighting-up Table (1909-10)		£500.00	—
A2	U	? 18	*Football Fixture Cards, Coupon back (1905-11)	H.53	£500.00	—
A2	BW	? 7	Road Maps (c1910)	H.54	£450.00	—

S. CAVANDER & CO., London and Portsea

Size	Printing	Number in set		Handbook reference	Price per card	Complete set
D	BW	50	*Beauties — selection from 'Plums' (1898)	H.186	£500.00	—

CAVANDERS LTD, London and Glasgow

Size	Printing	Number in set		Handbook reference	Price per card	Complete set
A	C	25	Ancient Chinese (1926)		£1.80	£45.00
A	C	25	Ancient Egypt (1928)		£1.60	£40.00
B	C	25	Ancient Egypt (different subjects) (1928)		£1.40	£35.00
A	P	36	Animal Studies (1936)		40p	£14.00

Size	*Printing*	*Number in set*		*Handbook reference*	*Price per card*	*Complete set*

CAVANDERS LTD, London and Glasgow *(continued)*

	CP	50	Beauty Spots of Great Britain (1927):			
A			A Small size		40p	£20.00
—			B Medium size (76 × 52mm)		40p	£20.00
	CP		Camera Studies (1926):			
A		54	A Small size		25p	£12.50
—		56	B Medium size (77 × 51mm)		28p	£15.00
A	C	30	Cinema Stars — Set 6 (1934)	GP.55	£1.20	£36.00
—	CP	30	The Colonial Series (77 × 51mm) (1925):	GP.330		
			A Small caption, under lmm high		50p	£15.00
			B Larger caption, over lmm high		50p	£15.00
—	C	25§	Coloured Stereoscopic (77 × 51mm) (1931)		60p	£30.00
D	C	25	Feathered Friends or Foreign Birds (1926):	GP.70		
			A Titled 'Feathered Friends'		£2.40	—
			B Titled 'Foreign Birds'		£1.60	£40.00
—	C	25§	Glorious Britain (76 × 51mm) (1930)		60p	£30.00
			The Homeland Series (1924-26):	GP.333		
A			Small size:			
	CP	50	A Back in blue		£1.00	£50.00
	CP	50	B Back in black, glossy front		£1.00	£50.00
	CP	54	C Back in black, matt front		40p	£20.00
			Medium size (77 × 51mm):			
	CP	50	D Back inscribed 'Hand Coloured Real Photos'		30p	£15.00
	CP	56	E As D, with 'Reprinted ...' at base		50p	£28.00
	CP	56	F Back inscribed 'Real Photos'		50p	£28.00
	P	56	G Back inscribed 'Real Photos'		50p	£28.00
A	C	25	Little Friends (1924)	GP.89	£1.20	£30.00
—	C	25	The Nation's Treasures (77 × 51mm) (1925)		50p	£12.50
	P		Peeps into Many Lands — 'A Series of ...' (1927):			
D		36§	A Small size		50p	£36.00
—		36§	B Medium size (75 × 50mm)		80p	£55.00
—		36	C Extra-large size (113 × 68mm)		£2.00	—
	P	36§	Peeps into Many Lands — 'Second Series ...' (1928):			
D			A Small size		£1.00	£75.00
—			B Medium size (75 × 50mm)		£1.00	£75.00
	P	24§	Peeps into Many Lands — 'Third Series ...' (1929):			
D			A Small size		40p	£20.00
			B Medium size (75 × 50mm)		90p	£45.00
—			C As B, but inscribed 'Reprinted by Special Request'		£1.50	£75.00
	P	24§	Peeps into Prehistoric Times — 'Fourth Series ...' (1930):			
D			A Small size		90p	£45.00
—			B Medium size (75 × 50mm)		£1.40	£65.00
—	P		*Photographs (54 × 38mm) (1924):	GP.337		
		30	1 Animal Studies		£1.50	—
		3	2 Royal Family		£3.30	—
—	C	48	Regimental Standards (76 × 70mm) (c1924)		£12.00	—
C	C	25	Reproductions of Celebrated Oil Paintings (1925)	GP.245	£1.20	£30.00
	CP	108	River Valleys (1926):			
A			A Small size		35p	£37.50
—			B Medium size (75 × 50mm)		35p	£37.50
A	C	25	School Badges (1928):	GP.121		
			A Back in dark blue		£1.00	£25.00
			B Back in light blue		£1.00	£25.00
—	CP	30	Wordsworth's Country (76 × 51mm) (1926)		£1.00	£30.00

§ Stereoscopic series, consisting of a Right and a Left card for each number, a complete series is thus **double** the number shown.

Size	Printing	Number in set		Handbook reference	Price per card	Complete set

R.S. CHALLIS & CO. LTD, London

D1	C	50	Comic Animals (1936)		70p	£35.00
A	BW	44	Flickits (Greyhound Racing Flickers) (1936)	Ha.589-1	£40.00	—
D1	U	36	Wild Birds at Home (1935):	H.626		
			A Inscribed 'Issued with Baldric Cigarettes'		60p	£22.00
			B Above wording blocked out in black		£1.25	£45.00

H. CHAPMAN & Co.

D	C	30	*Army Pictures, Cartoons, etc (c1916)	H.12	£200.00	—

CHARLESWORTH & AUSTIN LTD, London

C	U	50	*Beauties — 'BOCCA' (c1900)	H.39	£32.00	—
C	BW	16	*British Royal Family (1902)	H.28	£45.00	—
C	C		Colonial Troops (c1900):	H.40		
		50	A Black back		£35.00	—
		30	B Brown back		£35.00	—
A1	BW	20	Cricketers Series (1901)	H.29	£320.00	—
C	C	30	*Flags and Flags with Soldiers (c1903)	H.41	£32.00	—

CHESTERFIELD CIGARETTES

—	C	6	Chesterfield Collection (76 × 45mm) (1979)		£3.00	—
—	C	6	Cocktails (76 × 45mm) 1980		50p	£3.00

CHEW & CO., Bradford

D	C	30	*Army, Pictures, Cartoons etc (c1916)	H.12	£120.00	—

W.A. & A.C. CHURCHMAN, Ipswich

36 page reference book — £4.50

C	C	26	*Actresses — 'FROGA A' (c1900)	H.20	£35.00	—
C	C	26	*Actresses — 'FROGA B' (c1900)	H.20	£42.00	—
C	U	24	*Actresses, 'For the Pipe' back (c1900)	H.55	£80.00	—
—	C	48	Air-Raid Precautions (68 × 53mm) (1938)	H.544	50p	£25.00
A	C	25	Army Badges of Rank (1916)	H.56	£5.00	£125.00
A	U	50	Association Footballers (1938)		70p	£35.00
A	U	50	Association Footballers, 2nd series (1939)		£1.20	£60.00
A	C	12	*Beauties — 'CERF' (1904)	H.57	£60.00	—
			*Beauties — 'CHOAB' (c1900):	H.21		
—	C	3	I Circular cards, 55mm diameter		£1200.00	—
C	C	25	II Five different backs		£120.00	—
C	U	25	*Beauties — 'FECKSA'(c1902)	H.58	£90.00	—
C	C	25	*Beauties — 'GRACC' (c1900)	H.59	£100.00	—
A	C	50	Birds and Eggs (1906)	H.60	£6.50	£325.00
D	BW	20	*Boer War Cartoons (c1901)	H.42	£100.00	—
		20	*Boer War Generals' — 'CLAM' (c1901):	H.61		
A2	BW		A Black front		£35.00	—
A	U		B Brown front		£35.00	—
A	C	25	Boxing (1922)	H.311	£6.00	—
A	U	50	Boxing Personalities (1938)		£1.80	£90.00
A	C	50	Boy Scouts (1916)	H.62	£7.00	£350.00
A	C	50	Boy Scouts, 2nd series (1916)	H.62	£7.00	£350.00
A	C	50	Boy Scouts, 3rd series (1916):	H.62		
			A Brown back		£7.00	£350.00
			B Blue back		£10.00	—
A	U	25	British Film Stars (1934)		£2.40	£60.00

Size	*Print-ing*	*Number in set*		*Handbook reference*	*Price per card*	*Complete set*
W.A. & A.C. CHURCHMAN, Ipswich *(continued)*						
A	C	55	Can You Beat Bogey at St Andrews? (1933):			
			A Without overprint		£3.00	—
			B Overprinted in red 'Exchangeable'		£3.00	—
	U		Cathedrals and Churches (1924):	H.545		
A		25	A Small size		£2.00	£50.00
J		12	B Extra-large size		£10.00	—
A	C	50	Celebrated Gateways (1925)	H.347	£2.00	£100.00
D	P	41	*Celebrities — Boer War Period (c1901)	H.63	£20.00	—
—	BW	1	Christmas Greetings Card (68 × 53mm) (1938)		—	£2.00
A	C	25	Civic Insignia and Plate (1926)		£1.80	£45.00
A	C	50	Contract Bridge (1935)		80p	£40.00
A	C	50	Cricketers (1936)		£3.40	—
	C		Curious Dwellings:			
A		25	A Small size (1926)		£2.00	£50.00
B		12	B Large size (1925)		£6.00	—
A	C	25	Curious Signs (1925)		£2.00	£50.00
A	C	38	Dogs and Fowls (1908)	H.64	£7.50	—
	C		Eastern Proverbs:	H.521		
			A Small size:			
A		25	1 'A Series of 25' (1931)		80p	£20.00
A		25	2 '2nd Series of 25' (1932)		£1.20	£30.00
			B Large size:			
B		12	1 'A Series of 12' (1931)		£4.00	—
B		12	2 '2nd Series of 12' (1933)		£3.00	£36.00
B		12	3 '3rd Series of 12' (1933)		£3.00	£36.00
B		12	4 '4th Series of 12' (1934)		£1.50	£18.00
A		50	East Suffolk Churches:			
	BW		A Black front, cream back (1912)		£2.00	£100.00
	BW		B Black front, white back (1912)		£2.00	£100.00
	U		C Sepia front (1917)		£2.00	£100.00
A	C	50	Empire Railways (1931)		£2.40	£120.00
A	C	25	Famous Cricket Colours (1928)		£3.80	£95.00
	U		Famous Golfers:			
A		50	A Small size (1927)		£9.00	—
			B Large size:			
B		12	1 'A Series of 12' (1927)		£30.00	—
B		12	2 '2nd Series of 12' (1928)		£30.00	—
	C		Famous Railway Trains:			
A		25	A Small size (1929)		£2.60	£65.00
			B Large size:			
B		12	1 'Series of 12' (1928)		£7.00	—
B		12	2 '2nd Series of 12' (1929)		£7.00	—
A	C	50	Fish and Bait (1914)	H.65	£6.50	£325.00
A	C	50	Fishes of the World (1911):	H.66	—	£250.00
			30 cards as re-issued 1924		£1.65	£50.00
			20 cards not re-issued		£10.00	—
A	C	50	Flags and Funnels of Leading Steamship Lines (1912)	H.67	£7.00	—
A	C	50	Football Club Colours (1909)	H.68	£10.00	£500.00
A	U	50	*Footballers — Photogravure Portraits (c1910)		£32.00	—
A	C	50	Footballers — Action Pictures & Inset (1914)		£16.00	£800.00
A	C	52	'Frisky' (1935)		£3.50	—
A	C	50	History and Development of the British Empire (1934)		£2.00	£100.00
—	U	48	Holidays in Britain (Views and Maps) (68 × 53 mm) (1937)		40p	£20.00
—	C	48	Holidays in Britain (views only) (68 × 53mm) (1938)		50p	£25.00

Size	*Print-ing*	*Number in set*		*Handbook reference*	*Price per card*	*Complete set*

W.A. & A.C. CHURCHMAN, Ipswich *(continued)*

C	C	40	*Home and Colonial Regiments (1902)	H.69	£50.00	—
A	C	25	The Houses of Parliament and Their Story (1931)		£2.00	£50.00
	C		Howlers:			
A		40	A Small size (1937)		40p	£16.00
B		16	B Large size (1936)		50p	£8.00
A	C	25	The Inns of Court (1932)		£2.80	£70.00
A	C	50	Interesting Buildings (1905)	H.70	£8.00	£400.00
A	C	25	Interesting Door-Knockers (1928)		£2.40	£60.00
A	C	25	Interesting Experiments (1929)		£1.60	£40.00
A	C	50	'In Town To-night' (1938)		40p	£20.00
B	C	12	Italian Art Exhibition, 1930 (1931)		£2.50	£30.00
B	C	12	Italian Art Exhibition, 1930 — '2nd Series' (1931)		£2.50	£30.00
	C		The King's Coronation (1937):			
A		50	A Small size		30p	£12.50
B		15	B Large size		80p	£12.00
A	U	50	Kings of Speed (1939)		60p	£30.00
	C		Landmarks in Railway Progress:			
A		50	A Small size (1931)		£2.80	£140.00
			B Large size:			
B		12	1 '1st Series of 12' (1932)		£5.50	£65.00
B		12	2 '2nd Series of 12' (1932)		£5.50	£65.00
	U		Lawn Tennis (1928):	H.546		
A		50	A Small size		£3.60	£180.00
B		12	B Large size		£11.00	—
	C		Legends of Britain (1936):			
A		50	A Small size		90p	£45.00
B		12	B Large size		£1.50	£18.00
	C		Life in a Liner (1930):			
A		25	A Small size		£1.60	£40.00
B		12	B Large size		£6.00	—
A	C	50	*Medals (1910)	H.71	£7.00	£350.00
	C		Men of the Moment in Sport:			
A		50	A Small size (1928)		£5.00	£250.00
			B Large size:			
B		12	1 '1st Series of 12' (1929)		£8.00	—
B		12	2 '2nd Series of 12' (1929)		£8.00	—
—	C	48	Modern Wonders (68 × 53mm) (1938)		40p	£20.00
A	C	25	Musical Instruments (1924)	H.547	£3.40	£85.00
	C		Nature's Architects (1930):			
A		25	A Small size		£1.40	£35.00
B		12	B Large size		£2.50	£30.00
—	U	48	The Navy at Work (68 × 53mm) (1937)		50p	£24.00
—	U	55	Olympic Winners Through The Years (Package Designs, 30 small, 25 large) (1960)	H.891	£2.00	—
A	C	50	*Phil May Sketches (1912):	H.72		
			A 'Churchman's Gold Flake Cigarettes'		£7.00	£350.00
			B 'Churchman's Cigarettes'		£8.00	—
A	C	25	Pipes of the World (1927)		£3.00	£75.00
	C		Prominent Golfers (1931):			
A		50	A Small size		£8.00	—
B		12	B Large size		£20.00	—
	C		The 'Queen Mary' (1936):			
A		50	A Small size		£1.50	£75.00
B		16	B Large size		£3.00	£50.00
A	C	50	Racing Greyhounds (1934)		£2.60	£130.00

W.A. & A.C. CHURCHMAN, Ipswich *(continued)*

Size	Print-	Number		Handbook	Price	Complete
—	C	48	The RAF at Work (68 × 53mm) (1938)		90p	£45.00
	C		Railway Working	H.548		
			A Small size:			
A		25	1 'Series of 25' (1926)		£3.60	£90.00
A		25	2 '2nd Series of 25' (1927)		£2.40	£60.00
			B Large size:			
B		12	1 'Series of 12' (1926)		£10.00	—
B		13	2 '2nd Series, 13' (1927)		£10.00	—
B		12	3 '3rd Series, 12' (1927)		£10.00	—
A	C	50	*Regimental Colours and Cap Badges (1911)	H.73	£7.00	£350.00
A	BW	50	Rivers and Broads (1922):			
			A Titled 'Rivers & Broads'		£6.00	—
			B Titled 'Rivers & Broads of Norfolk & Suffolk'		£5.00	—
A	C	50	Rugby Internationals (1935)		£1.80	£90.00
A	C	50	Sectional Cycling Map (1913)	H.74	£6.00	£300.00
A	C	50	Silhouettes of Warships (1915)		£9.00	—
A	C	50	Sporting Celebrities (1931)		£3.00	£150.00
	C		Sporting Trophies (1927):			
A		25	A Small size		£2.40	£60.00
B		12	B Large size		£6.00	—
A	C	25	Sports and Games in Many Lands (1929)	H.651	£5.00	£125.00
	C		The Story of London (1934):			
A		50	A Small size		£1.80	£90.00
B		12	B Large size		£3.00	£36.00
	C		The Story of Navigation:			
A		50	A Small size (1936)		40p	£20.00
B		12	B Large size (1935)		£1.25	£15.00
A	C		3 Jovial Golfers in search of the perfect course (1934):			
		36	A Home issue		£3.50	—
		72	B Irish issue, with green over-printing		£8.00	—
A	C	50	A Tour Round the World (1911)	H.75	£7.00	£350.00
	C		Treasure Trove:			
A		50	A Small size (1937)		40p	£20.00
B		12	B Large size (1935)		£1.50	£18.00
A1	C	25	*Types of British and Colonial Troops (c1900)	H.76	£45.00	—
	C		Warriors of All Nations:			
A		25	A Small size (1929)		£3.00	£75.00
			B Large size:			
B		12	1 'A Series of 12' (1929)		£4.00	£50.00
B		12	2 '2nd Series of 12' (1931)		£4.00	£50.00
	C		Well-known Ties (1934):			
A		50	A Small size		90p	£45.00
			B Large size:			
B		12	1 'A Series of 12'		£1.75	£21.00
B		12	2 '2nd Series of 12'		£1.75	£21.00
A	C	50	Well-known Ties, '2nd Series' (1935)		70p	£35.00
A	U	25	Wembley Exhibition (1924)		£2.60	£65.00
A	U	50	West Suffolk Churches (1919)		£1.80	£90.00
A	C	50	Wild Animals of the World (1907)	H.77	£8.00	£400.00
—	C	48	Wings Over the Empire (68 × 53mm) (1939)		40p	£20.00
	C		Wonderful Railway Travel (1937):			
A		50	A Small size		60p	£30.00
B		12	B Large size		£1.50	£18.00
—	U	40	The World of Sport (Package Designs, 30 small, 10 large) (1961)	H.892	£2.00	—
A	C	50	World Wonders Old and New (prepared but not issued) (c1955)		40p	£20.00

Size	Printing	Number in set		Handbook reference	Price per card	Complete set

W.A. & A.C. CHURCHMAN, Ipswich *(continued)*

OVERSEAS ISSUES (CHANNEL ISLANDS)

(All cards without I.T.C. clause)

Size	Printing	Number in set		Handbook reference	Price per card	Complete set
—	C	48	Air Raid Precautions (68 × 53) (1938)	H.544	£1.80	—
—	U	48	Holidays in Britain (68 × 53) (1937)		£1.80	—
—	C	48	Holidays in Britain (68 × 53) (1938)		£1.80	—
—	C	48	Modern Wonders (68 × 53) (1938):			
			A I.T.C. clause blocked out in silver		£5.00	—
			B Reprinted without I.T.C. clause		£1.80	—
—	U	48	The Navy at Work (68 × 53) (1937)		£1.80	—
—	C	48	The RAF at Work (68 × 53) (1939)		£1.80	—
—	C	48	Wings Over the Empire (68 × 53) (1939)		£1.80	—

WM. CLARKE & SON, Dublin

Size	Printing	Number in set		Handbook reference	Price per card	Complete set
A	C	25	Army Life (1915)	H.78	£12.00	£300.00
A1	BW	16	*Boer War Celebrities — 'CAG' (c1901)	H.79	£25.00	—
A	C	50	Butterflies and Moths (1912)	H.80	£8.00	£400.00
A	BW	30	Cricketer Series (1901)		£160.00	—
A1	BW	66	Football Series (1902)	H.81	£30.00	—
A	C	25	Marine Series (1907)		£14.00	£350.00
A	C	50	Royal Mail (1914)	H.82	£11.00	£550.00
	C	50	Sporting Terms (38 × 58mm) multi-backed (c1900):	H.83		
			14 Cricket Terms		£45.00	—
			12 Cycling Terms		£45.00	—
			12 Football Terms		£45.00	—
			12 Golf Terms		£45.00	—
—	C	20	*Tobacco Leaf Girls (shaped) (c1898)	H.84	£450.00	—
—	C	25	Well-known Sayings (71 × 32mm) (c1900)	H.85	£24.00	£600.00

J. CLAYTON, Wakefield

Size	Printing	Number in set		Handbook reference	Price per card	Complete set
—	C	? 6	*Play Up Sporting Shields (c1895)	H.718	£175.00	—

J.H. CLURE, Keighley

Size	Printing	Number in set		Handbook reference	Price per card	Complete set
D	C	30	*Army Pictures, Cartoons, etc (c1900):	H.12		
			A 'These Cigarettes' back		£120.00	—
			B 'Try Clure's Havana Mixture' back		£120.00	—
A	U	50	War Portraits (1916)	H.86	£100.00	—

J. LOMAX COCKAYNE, Sheffield

Size	Printing	Number in set		Handbook reference	Price per card	Complete set
A	U	50	War Portraits (1916)	H.86	£100.00	—

COHEN WEENEN & CO. LTD, London

Size	Printing	Number in set		Handbook reference	Price per card	Complete set
—	P	40	*Actresses, Footballers and Jockeys (26 × 61mm) (c1901)	GP.350	£50.00	—
A1	U	26	*Actresses — 'FROGA A' (c1900)	H.20/GP.351	£65.00	—
A	C	25	*Beauties — selection from 'BOCCA' (c1900)	H.39/GP.353	£75.00	—
A1	C	25	*Beauties — 'GRACC' (c1900)	H.59/GP.354	£100.00	—
D2	BW	25	*Boxers (c1912):	H.721/GP.362		
			A Black back		£16.00	—
			B Green back		£11.00	£275.00
			C *Without Maker's Name*		£17.00	—
A	BW		*Celebrities — Black and white (1901):	GP.356		
		65	A 'Sweet Crop, over 250 ...' back		£5.50	—
		? 20	B 'Sweet Crop, over 500 ...' back		£10.00	—

Size	Printing	Number in set		Handbook reference	Price per card	Complete set

COHEN WEENEN & CO. LTD, London *(continued)*

Size	Printing	Number in set		Handbook reference	Price per card	Complete set
A	C		*Celebrities — Coloured (1901):	GP.357		
		45	I 1-45 Boer War Generals etc. 'Sweet Crop, over 100 …' back:		—	£250.00
			A Toned back		£5.50	—
			B White back		£5.50	—
			C *Plain Back*		£8.00	—
		121	II 1-121 Including Royalty, etc. 'Sweet Crop, over 250 …' back:			
			1-45 as in I		£8.00	—
			46-121 additional subjects		£5.50	—
—	C		*Celebrities — 'GAINSBOROUGH I' (1901):	GP.358		
—		? 21	A In metal frames (46 × 67mm)		£100.00	—
D2		39	B 'Sweet Crop, over 250 …' back		£50.00	—
D		30	C 'Sweet Crop, over 400 …' back		£12.00	£360.00
		2	D *1902 Calendar Back gilt border to front*		£130.00	—
D1		39	*E Plain Back*		£12.00	£475.00
—	P	? 177	*Celebrities — 'GAINSBOROUGH II' (c1901):	GP.359		
			A In metal frames (46 × 67mm)		£18.00	—
			B Without frames showing Frame Marks		£5.00	—
			C Without Frames no Frame Marks (as issued)		£10.00	—
D2	U	25	*Cricketers (1926)		£15.00	—
A2	C	20	*Cricketers, Footballers, Jockeys (c1900):	GP.361		
			A Caption in brown		£22.00	£440.00
			B Caption in grey-black		£22.00	£440.00
D	C	40	Fiscal Phrases (c1905):	GP.363		
			A 'Copyright Regd.' on front		£11.00	£440.00
			B Without 'Copyright Regd.'		£11.00	£440.00
A2	C	60	Football Captains, 1907-8 — Series No. 5	GP.364	£14.00	—
A2	BW	100	*Heroes of Sport (c1898)	GP.365	£90.00	—
A	C	40	*Home and Colonial Regiments (c1901):	H.69/GP.366		
			A 'Sweet Crop, over 100 …' back		£9.00	£360.00
			B 'Sweet Crop, over 250 …' back		£13.00	—
			C *1902 Calendar Back Gilt Border*		£130.00	—
A2	C	20	*Interesting Buildings and Views (1902):	GP.367		
			A No Framelines		£11.00	£220.00
			B *Gilt Framelines 1902 Calendar back*		£130.00	—
K2	C	52	*Miniature Playing Cards — Bandmaster Cigarettes (c1910)		£4.00	—
D2	C		*Nations:	GP.369		
		20	A Blue 'Sweet Crop, over 250 …' back (c1902)		£12.00	£240.00
		20	*B Plain back – gilt border* (c1902)		£100.00	—
		? 1	*C 1902 Calender back* (c1902)		£130.00	—
		20	D Text back (1923)		£4.50	£90.00
D	C	40	Naval and Military Phrases (c1904):	H.14/GP.370		
			A Red back, 'Series No. 1'		£16.00	£640.00
			B 'Sweet Crop, over 250 …' back:			
			i White Border		£28.00	—
			ii Gilt Border		£130.00	—
D2	C	50	Owners, Jockeys, Footballers, Cricketers — Series No. 2 (c1906)	GP.371	£14.00	£700.00
D2	C	20	Owners, Jockeys, Footballers, Cricketers — Series No. 3 (c1907)	GP.372	£15.00	£300.00
D	C	30	*Proverbs, 'Sweet Crop, over 400 …' back (c1905)	H.15/GP.373	£15.00	—
A	C	20	Russo-Japanese War Series (1904)	H.100/GP.120	£20.00	—
A	BW	25	*Silhouettes of Celebrities (c1905)	GP.374	£12.00	£300.00

Size	Print-ing	Number in set		Handbook reference	Price per card	Complete set

COHEN WEENEN & CO. LTD, London *(continued)*

D1	C	50	Star Artistes — Series No. 4 (c1905):	GP.375		
			20 With stage background		£11.00	£220.00
			30 No stage, plain background		£11.00	£330.00
D	C	50	V.C. Heroes (of World War I), Nd. 51-100 (1915):			
			51-75 — dull greyish card		£11.00	£275.00
			Without Maker's Name on back		£14.00	—
			76-100 — glossy white card		£11.00	£275.00
D	U	50	*War Series (World War I) (1915):	H.103/GP.376		
			1-25 Admirals and Warships:			
			A Thick card		£10.00	£250.00
			B Thin card		£10.00	£250.00
			26-50 Leaders of the War:			
			A Maker's Name on back		£10.00	£250.00
			B *Without Maker's Name on back*		£14.00	—
D1	C	30	Wonders of the World:	GP.378		
			A Inscribed 'Series 6', white borders (c1908)		£7.00	£210.00
			B Without 'Series 6', gilt borders (1923)		£3.00	£90.00
SILKS						
—	C	16	*Victoria Cross Heroes II (72 × 70mm) (paper-backed) (c1915)	GP.251	£40.00	—

T.H. COLLINS, Mansfield

A1	U	25	Homes of England (1924):			
			A Dark mauve front		£6.00	£150.00
			B Grey front		£20.00	—
A	C	25	Sports and Pastimes — Series I (1923)	H.225	£7.00	£175.00

F. COLTON Jun., Retford

D	C	30	*Army Pictures, Cartoons, etc (c1916):	H.12		
			A 'Best House' back		£120.00	—
			B 'Our Hand-filled Cigarettes' back		£120.00	—
A	U	50	War Portraits (1916)	H.86	£100.00	—

T.W. CONQUEST, London

D	C	*30	Army Pictures, Cartoons etc (c1916)	H12	£120.00	—

THE CONTINENTAL CIGARETTE FACTORY, London

A	C		Charming Portraits (c1925):	H.549		
		25	A Back in blue, with firm's name		£5.00	—
		25	B Back in blue, inscribed 'Club Mixture Tobacco'		£7.00	—
		4	C Back in brown, inscribed 'Club Mixture Tobacco'		£10.00	—
		25	*D *Plain back*		£5.00	—

COOPER & CO'S STORES LTD, London

A	BW	25	*Boer War Celebrities — 'STEW' (c1901):	H.105		
			A 'Alpha Mixture' back		£150.00	—
			B 'Gladys Cigars' back		£150.00	—

CO-OPERATIVE WHOLESALE SOCIETY LTD, Manchester

A2	C	? 6	*Advertisement Cards (c1915)	H.106	£400.00	—
A	C	24	African Types (1936)		50p	£12.00
—	C	? 2	*Beauties (102 × 68mm) (c1915)	H.722	£100.00	—
—	U	50	Beauty Spots of Britain (76 × 51mm) (1936)		40p	£20.00

Size	*Print-ing*	*Number in set*		*Handbook reference*	*Price per card*	*Complete set*

CO-OPERATIVE WHOLESALE SOCIETY LTD, Manchester *(continued)*

A2	C	50	Boy Scout Badges (1939)		£1.40	£70.00
A	C	25	Boy Scout Series (c1915)		£36.00	—
A	C	48	British and Foreign Birds (1938)		80p	£40.00
A	C	50	British Sport Series§ (c1914)		£30.00	—
D	C	25	*Cooking Recipes (1923)		£2.20	£55.00
A	C	28	*Co-operative Buildings and Works (c1914)	H.107	£14.00	£400.00
A	C	24	English Roses (1924)		£4.00	£100.00
A	C	50	Famous Bridges (48 + 2 added) (1937)		90p	£45.00
A	C	48	Famous Buildings (1935)		80p	£40.00
A2	C	25	How to Do It (1924):			
			A 'Anglian Mixture' back		£3.00	—
			B 'Equity Tobacco' back		£3.00	—
			C 'Jaycee Brown Flake' back		£3.00	—
			D 'Raydex Gold Leaf' back		£3.00	—
A	C	48	Musical Instruments (1934)		£3.80	£190.00
A	C	25	Parrot Series (1910)		£40.00	—
A	C	48	Poultry (1927)		£7.50	£375.00
A	C	48	Railway Engines (1936)		£3.20	£160.00
A	C	24	Sailing Craft (1935)		£1.60	£40.00
A	C	18	War Series (c1915)		£28.00	—
A2	C	48	Wayside Flowers, brown back (1923)		£2.00	£100.00
A2	C	48	Wayside Flowers, grey back (1928)		80p	£40.00
A2	C	48	Wayside Woodland Trees (1924)		£2.50	£125.00
A	C	24	Western Stars (1957)		65p	£16.00

§Note: Cards advertise non-tobacco products, but are believed to have been packed with cigarettes and/or tobacco.

COPE BROS. & CO. LTD, Liverpool

	BW	20	*Actresses — 'BLARM' (c1900):	H.23		
A1			A Plain backs. Name panel ¼" from border		£35.00	—
A1			B Black design back. Name ¼" from border		£35.00	—
D			C Black design back. Name panel 1/16" from border		£35.00	—
A	U	? 6	*Actresses — 'COPEIS' (c1900)	H.108	£300.00	—
A	U	26	*Actresses 'FROGA A' (c1900)	H.20	£90.00	—
D1	P	50	*Actresses and Beauties (c1900)	H.109	£15.00	—
KI	P	? 46	*Beauties, Actors and Actresses (c1900)	H.110	£30.00	—
A	C	52	*Beauties — P.C. inset (c1898)	H.111	£45.00	—
A	C	15	*Beauties 'PAC' (c1898)	H.2	£75.00	—
A1	C	50	Boats of the World (c1910)		£15.00	£750.00
D2	BW	126	Boxers (c1915):			
			1-25 Boxers		£18.00	£450.00
			26-50 Boxers		£15.00	£375.00
			51-75 Boxers		£15.00	£375.00
			76-100 Boxers		£20.00	£500.00
			101-125 Army Boxers		£15.00	£375.00
			126 'New World Champion'		—	£45.00
D	BW	25	Boxing Lessons (1935)		£4.00	£100.00
A1	C	35	*Boy Scouts and Girl Guides (c1910)	H.132	£12.00	£420.00
—	C	25	Bridge Problems (folders) (85 × 50mm) (1924)		£27.00	—
D	BW	25	British Admirals (c1915)	H.103	£13.00	£325.00
A2	C	50	British Warriors (c1912):			
			A Black on white backs		£8.00	£400.00
			B Grey on toned backs		£10.00	£500.00
A1	U	25	Castles§ (1939)		£1.20	£30.00
A1	U	25	Cathedrals§ (May, 1939)		£1.60	£40.00

Size	Printing	Number in set		Handbook reference	Price per card	Complete set
			COPE BROS. & CO. LTD, Liverpool *(continued)*			
A	C	50	Characters from Scott (c1900):			
			A Wide card		£12.00	£600.00
			B Narrow card — officially cut		£12.00	—
	U	115	Chinese Series (c1903):			
A1			Nos 1-20		£12.00	—
A1			Nos-21-40:			
			A 'Bond of Union Tobacco' back		£12.00	—
			B 'Cope's Courts' back		£12.00	—
			C 'Golden Cloud' back		£12.00	—
			D 'Golden Magnet' back		£12.00	—
			E 'Solace' back		£12.00	—
			Nos 41-65:			
D			A Picture 56mm long		£12.00	—
Al			B Picture 58mm long		£12.00	—
A2			Nos 66-115:			
			A 'Bond of Union'/'Bond of Union' back		£12.00	—
			B 'Bond of Union'/'Golden Magnet' back		£12.00	—
			C 'Golden Magnet'/'Golden Magnet' back		£12.00	—
			D 'Golden Magnet'/'Bond of Union' back		£12.00	—
—	C	6	*Comic Hunting Scenes (c1890)	H.723	£300.00	—
A	C	50	Cope's Golfers (1900):			
			A Wide card		£80.00	—
			B Narrow card — officially cut		£80.00	—
—	C	25	Dickens' Character Series (75 × 58mm) (1939)		£1.00	£25.00
—	C	50	Dickens' Gallery (1900):			
A			A Back listed		£11.00	£550.00
—			B Size 70 × 43mm, 'Solace' back		£120.00	—
A	C	50	Dogs of the World (by Cecil Aldin) (c1910)		£13.00	£650.00
A	C	25	Eminent British Regiments Officers' Uniforms (c1908):		—	£300.00
			A Yellow-brown back		£12.00	—
			B Claret back		£12.00	—
A2	C	30	*Flags of Nations (c1903):	H.114		
			A 'Bond of Union' back		£12.00	£360.00
			B *Plain back*		£9.00	—
D	C	24	*Flags, Arms and Types of Nations (c1904):	H.115		
			A Numbered		£8.00	£200.00
			B Unnumbered		£100.00	—
—	C	25	The Game of Poker§ (75 × 58mm) (1936)		50p	£12.50
—	C	50	General Knowledge§ (70 × 42mm) (1925)		£4.00	—
—	BW	32	Golf Strokes (70 × 45mm) (1923)		£14.00	—
A1	C	60	'Happy Families' (1937)		£1.50	£90.00
—	C	50	Household Hints§ (advertisement fronts) (70 × 45mm) (1925)		£1.60	£80.00
—	U	20	*Kenilworth Phrases (80 × 70mm) (c1910)	H.116	£400.00	—
C	BW	30	Lawn Tennis Strokes (1924):			
			A Numbers 1 to 25		£6.00	—
			B Numbers 26 to 30		£20.00	—
—	U	50	Modern Dancing (folders) (74 × 43mm) (1926)		£15.00	—
A2	C	50	Music Hall Artistes (c1910):			
			A Inscribed 'Series of 50'		£35.00	—
			B Without the above		£12.00	£600.00
A	U	472	Noted Footballers — 'Clips Cigarettes' (c1910):	H.474		
			1 Unnumbered — Wee Jock Simpson		—	£60.00
			120 Series of 120:			
			A Greenish-blue frame		£20.00	—
			B Bright blue frame		£20.00	—

Size	Printing	Number in set		Handbook reference	Price per card	Complete set

COPE BROS. & CO. LTD, Liverpool *(continued)*

Size	Printing	Number in set		Handbook reference	Price per card	Complete set
			162 Series of 282:			
			A Greenish-blue frame		£20.00	—
			B Bright blue frame		£20.00	—
			471 Series of 500. Bright blue frame		£20.00	—
D	P	195	Noted Footballers — 'Solace Cigarettes' (c1910)	H.474	£20.00	—
A	C	24	*Occupations for Women (1897)	H.117	£100.00	—
—	C	6	*Phases of the Moon (111 × 74mm) (c1890)	H.725	£300.00	—
—	C	24	Photo Albums for the Million (c1898):	H.119		
			12 Buff cover (25 × 39mm)		£16.00	—
			12 Green cover (25 × 39mm)		£16.00	—
A2	C	25	Pigeons (c1926)		£8.00	£200.00
A	C	52	*Playing Cards. Blue backs (c1902):			
			A Rounded Corners		£16.00	—
			B Square Corners		£12.00	—
—	C	7	The Seven Ages of Man (114 × 78mm) (c1885)	H.726	£300.00	—
A	C	50	Shakespeare Gallery (c1900):			
			A Wide card		£12.00	£600.00
			B Narrow card — officially cut		£12.00	—
A2	C	25	Song Birds (c1926)		£7.00	£175.00
A1	C	25	Sports and Pastimes (1925)	H.551	£4.00	£100.00
—	C	25	Toy Models (The Country Fair) (73 × 66mm) (c1930)	H.552	40p	£10.00
A1	C	25	*Uniforms of Soldiers and Sailors (c1900):	H.120		
			A Circular Medallion back, wide card		£28.00	—
			B Square Medallion back, wide card		£50.00	—
			C Square Medallion back, narrow card, officially cut		£24.00	—
D	BW		VC and DSO Naval and Flying Heroes:			
		50	Unnumbered (1916)	H.121	£9.00	£450.00
		25	Numbered 51-75 (1917)		£10.00	£250.00
D	BW	20	*War Pictures (1915)	H.122	£12.50	£250.00
D	BW	25	*War Series (War Leaders and Warships) (c1915)	H.103	£13.00	—
A1	C	25	Wild Animals and Birds (c1908)		£16.00	—
A	C	25	The World's Police (c1935)		£5.00	£125.00

§Joint Cope and Richard Lloyd issues.

OVERSEAS ISSUES

Size	Printing	Number in set		Handbook reference	Price per card	Complete set
A2	C	30	Flags of Nations (c1903)		£80.00	—
A	C	50	Jordklodens Hunde (1912)		£35.00	—
D	C	30	Scandinavian Actors and Actresses (1910)		£40.00	—
A	C	35	Speider Billeder I Hver Pakke (1910)		£35.00	—
A	C	25	Uniformer A F Fremragende Britiske Regimenter (1908)		£30.00	—
A	C	25	Vilde Dyr Og Fugle (1907)		£35.00	—

E. CORONEL, London

Size	Printing	Number in set		Handbook reference	Price per card	Complete set
A	C	25	*Types of British and Colonial Troops (1900)	H.76	£60.00	—

DAVID CORRE & CO., London

Size	Printing	Number in set		Handbook reference	Price per card	Complete set
—	C	1	Advertisement Card — The New Alliance (70 × 42mm) (c1915)		—	£375.00
D	C	40	*Naval and Military Phrases (1900):	H.14		
			A With border		£80.00	—
			B Without border		£80.00	—

JOHN COTTON LTD, Edinburgh

Size	Printing	Number in set		Handbook reference	Price per card	Complete set
—	C	50	*Bridge Hands (folders) (82 × 66mm) (1934)		£11.00	—
A1	U	50	*Golf Strokes — A/B (1936)		£8.00	—
A1	U	50	*Golf Strokes— C/D (1937)		£9.00	—

Size	*Print-ing*	*Number in set*		*Handbook reference*	*Price per card*	*Complete set*

JOHN COTTON LTD, Edinburgh *(continued)*

A1	U	50	*Golf Strokes— E/F (1938)		£13.00	—
A1	U	50	*Golf Strokes — G/H (1939)		£500.00	—
A1	U	50	*Golf Strokes — I/J (1939)		£500.00	—

A. & J. COUDENS LTD, London

A1	P	60	British Beauty Spots (1923):	H.553		
			A Printed back, numbered		£1.70	£100.00
			B Printed back, unnumbered		£2.50	—
			*C Back rubber stamped 'Cymax Cigarettes ...'		£4.00	—
			*D *Plain back*		£4.00	—
A	P	60	Holiday Resorts in East Anglia (1924)		£1.25	£75.00
A2	BW	25	Sports Alphabet (1924)	H.551	£9.00	£225.00

THE CRAIGMILLAR CREAMERY CO. LTD, Midlothian

H	C	1	*Views of Craigmillar (c1901)	H.727	—	£900.00

W.F. DANIELL, Bristol

—	BW	? 1	*Puzzle Cards (108 × 73mm) (c1900)	H.729	£500.00	—

W.R. DANIEL & CO., London

—	C	1	Advertisement Card (85 × 55mm) (c1901)	H.728	—	£600.00
A2	C	30	*Colonial Troops (c1902):	H.40		
			A Black back		£90.00	—
			B Brown back		£90.00	—
A2	C	25	*National Flags and Flowers — Girls (c1901)	H.123	£160.00	—

W.T. DAVIES & SONS, Chester

A	C	50	*Actresses — 'DAVAN' (c1902)	H.124	£90.00	—
A2	U	42	Aristocrats of the Turf (1924):	H.554		
			1 Nos 1-30 — 'A Series of 30'		£6.00	—
			2 Nos 31-42 — 'A Series of 42'		£20.00	—
A2	U	36	Aristocrats of the Turf, Second Series (1924)	H.554	£5.50	—
A	C	25	Army Life (1915)	H.78	£12.00	—
A	BW	12	*Beauties (1903)	H.125	£60.00	—
A	C	25	Boxing (1924)	H.311	£4.40	£110.00
A	C	50	Flags and Funnels of Leading Steamship Lines (1913)	H.67	£12.00	—
A	BW	? 13	Newport Football Club (c1904)	H.126	£400.00	—
A	BW	5	Royal Welsh Fusiliers (c1904)	H.127	£400.00	—

S.H. DAWES, Luton

D	C	30	*Army Pictures, Cartoons, etc (c1916)	H.12	£120.00	—

J.W. DEWHURST, Morecambe

D	C	30	*Army Pictures, Cartoons, etc (c1916)	H.12	£120.00	—

R.I. DEXTER & CO., Hucknall

D2	U	30	*Borough Arms (1900)	H.128	£1.30	£40.00

A. DIMITRIOU, London

—	C	? 3	Advertisement Cards (100 × 65mm) (c1930)		£125.00	—

Size	Printing	Number in set		Handbook reference	Price per card	Complete set

GEORGE DOBIE & SON LTD, Paisley

—	C	? 22	Bridge Problems (folders) (circular 64mm diam.) (c1933)		£50.00	—
—	C	32	Four-Square Book (Nd 1-32) (75 × 50mm) (1959)		£2.00	—
—	C	32	Four-Square Book (Nd 33-64) (75 × 50mm) (1959)		£2.00	—
—	C	32	Four-Square Book (Nd 65-96) (75 × 50mm) (1960)		£1.50	£50.00
A	C	25	Weapons of All Ages (1924)		£7.00	£175.00

DOBSON & CO. LTD

A	C	8	The European War Series (c1917)	H.129	£45.00	—

THE DOMINION TOBACCO CO. (1929) LTD, London

A	U	25	Old Ships (1934)		£2.60	£65.00
A	U	25	Old Ships (Second Series) (1935)		80p	£20.00
A	U	25	Old Ships (Third Series) (1936)		£1.00	£25.00
A	U	25	Old Ships (Fourth Series) (1936)		£2.20	£55.00

JOSEPH W. DOYLE LTD, Manchester

—	P	18	*Beauties, Nd X.1-X.18 (89 × 70mm) (c1925)	H.653	£14.00	—
D	P	12	Dirt Track Riders Nd. CC.A.1-CC.A.12 (c1925)	H.635	£50.00	—
D	P	12	Views Nd. CC.B.1-CC.B.12 (c1925)	H.635	£28.00	—
D	P	12	Views Nd CC.C.1-CC.C.12 (c1925)	H.635	£28.00	—
D	P	12	*Beauties Nd. CC.D.1-CC.D.12 (c1925)	H.635	£28.00	—
D	P	12	*Beauties Nd CC.E.1-CC.E.12 (c1925)	H.635	£28.00	—

MAJOR DRAPKIN & CO., London

D	BW	12	**Actresses 'FRAN'* (c1910)	H.175/GP.400	£8.00	—
C	C	8	*Advertisement Cards (c1925):	GP.401		
			1 Packings (4)		£7.50	£30.00
			2 Smokers (4)		£6.50	£26.00
—	BW	? 1	*Army Insignia (83 × 46mm) (c1915)	GP.402	£750.00	—
	BW	50	Around Britain (1929) (export):			
C			A Small size		£1.30	£65.00
B1			B Large size		£2.80	—
	C	50	Around the Mediterranean (1926) (export):	GP.404		
C			A Small size		£1.50	£75.00
B1			B Large size		£2.80	—
A2	P	40	Australian and English Test Cricketers (1928)		£2.00	£80.00
—	—	? 111	'Bandmaster' Conundrums (58 × 29mm) (c1910)	GP.352	£10.00	—
A2	BW	? 32	Boer War Celebrities 'JASAS' — 'Sweet Alva Cigarettes' (c1901)	H.133	£180.00	—
A1	U	25	British Beauties (1930) (export)		£3.00	£75.00
A1	P		*Celebrities of the Great War (1916):	GP.409		
		36	A Printed back		70p	£25.00
		34	B *Plain back*		£1.00	£34.00
—	BW	96	Cinematograph Actors (42 × 70mm) (1913)	GP.410	£13.00	—
	C	15	Dogs and Their Treatment (1924):			
A			A Small size		£5.50	£85.00
B2			B Large size		£6.50	£100.00
A	C	40	The Game of Sporting Snap (1928)		£4.00	—
			Instruction Leaflet		—	£11.00
	C	50	Girls of Many Lands (1929):			
D			A Small size		£4.00	—
—			B Medium size (76 × 52mm)		50p	£25.00
A	C	1	'Grey's' Smoking Mixture Advertisement Card (plain back) (c1935)		—	£7.00

MAJOR DRAPKIN & CO., London *(continued)*

Size	*Printing*	*Number in set*		*Handbook reference*	*Price per card*	*Complete set*
A	C	25	How to Keep Fit — Sandow Exercises (c1912):	H.136		
			A 'Drapkin's Cigarettes'		£16.00	£400.00
			A1 'Drapkin's Cigarettes' short cards, cut officially		£16.00	—
			B 'Crayol Cigarettes'		£16.00	£400.00
A2	BW	54	Life at Whipsnade Zoo (1934)	GP.415	50p	£27.00
D2	C	50	'Limericks' (1929):	GP.416		
			A White card		£1.50	£75.00
			B Cream card		£1.50	£75.00
A2	P	36	National Types of Beauty (1928)	GP.417	85p	£30.00
	C	25	Optical Illusions (1926):			
A			A Small size. Home issue, name panel (23 × 7mm)		£3.40	£85.00
A			B Small size. Export issue, name panel (26 × 10mm)		£3.00	£75.00
B2			C Large 'size. Home issue		£3.60	£90.00
	C	25	Palmistry:			
A			A Small size (1927)		£3.00	£75.00
B			B Large size (1926)		£3.00	£75.00
D	U	48	Photogravure Masterpieces (1915)	GP.420	£10.00	—
	C	25	Puzzle Pictures (1926):			
A			A Small size		£4.00	£100.00
B			B Large size		£4.40	£110.00
—	C	25	*Soldiers and Their Uniforms, die cut (1914):	H.138/GP.423		
			A 'Drapkin's Cigarettes':			
			i 23 Different		£1.00	—
			ii 1st Life Guards		£30.00	—
			iii South Wales Borderers		£30.00	—
			B 'Crayol Cigarettes':			
			i 22 Different		£1.00	£22.00
			ii Durham Light Infantry		£20.00	—
			iii 1st Life Guards		£30.00	—
			iv South Wales Borderers		£30.00	—
A2	P	36	Sporting Celebrities in Action (1930) (export)		—	£300.00
			35 different (No. 18 withdrawn)		£5.00	£175.00
D	BW		**Views of the World* (c1912):	H.176/GP.425		
		12	A Caption in two lines		£5.00	£60.00
		8	B Caption in one line		£30.00	—
D	BW	8	**Warships* (c1912)	GP.426	£12.00	—

SILKS

Size	*Printing*	*Number in set*		*Handbook reference*	*Price per card*	*Complete set*
—	C	40	Regimental Colours and Badges of the Indian Army (70 × 50mm) (paper-backed) (c1915):	H.502-5/GP.422		
			A The Buffs' back		£5.00	—
			B No brand back		£35.00	—

DRAPKIN & MILLHOFF, London

Size	*Printing*	*Number in set*		*Handbook reference*	*Price per card*	*Complete set*
A	U		*Beauties 'KEWAI' (c1898):	H.139-1		
		? 2	A 'Eldona Cigars' back		£300.00	—
		? 1	B 'Explorer Cigars' back		£300.00	—
A	BW	25	*Boer War Celebrities — 'PAM' (c1901):	H.140		
			A With PTO on front 'Pick-Me-Up Cigarettes', multi-backed		£30.00	—
			B Without PTO on front 'Pick-Me-Up Cigarettes', multi-backed		£30.00	—
			C Plain back		£50.00	—
C	C	30	*Colonial Troops, multi-backed (c1902)	H.40	£50.00	—
—	BW	? 7	*'Pick-me-up' Paper Inserts (112 × 44mm) (c1900)		£250.00	—
—	U	? 2	**Portraits* (48 × 36mm) (c1900)	H.461	£250.00	—
A2	U	? 3	*Pretty Girl Series — 'BAGG' (c1900)	H.45	£300.00	—

Size	*Printing*	*Number in set*		*Handbook reference*	*Price per card*	*Complete set*

J. DUNCAN & CO. LTD, Glasgow

D1	C	50	'Evolution of the Steamship' (c1925)	H.559	—	£75.00
			47 different		75p	£35.00
			'Olympia II'		£25.00	—
			'Castalia' and 'Athenia'		£7.50	—
D1	C	48	*Flags, Arms and Types of Nations (c1910):	H.115		
			A Back in Blue		£27.00	—
			B Back in Green		£50.00	—
A	C	20	Inventors and Their Inventions (c1915)	H.213	£60.00	—
A	C	30	Scottish Clans, Arms of Chiefs and Tartans (c1910):	H.142		
			A Back in black		£250.00	—
			B Back in green		£20.00	—
—	C		Scottish Gems: (58 × 84mm):	H.143		
—	C	72	1st series (c1912)		£13.00	—
—	C	50	2nd series (c1913)		£13.00	—
—	C	50	3rd series (c1914)		£13.00	—
H1	BW	50	Scottish Gems (known as '4th Series') (c1925)	H.143	60p	£30.00
D	C	25	*Types of British Soldiers (c1910)	H.144	£45.00	—

G. DUNCOMBE, Buxton

D	C	30	*Army Pictures, Cartoons, Etc (c1916)	H.12	£120.00	—

ALFRED DUNHILL LTD, London

—	U	25	Dunhill Kingsize Ransom (75 × 45mm) (1985)		£1.60	—

EDWARDS, RINGER & CO., Bristol

—	BW	50	How to Count Cribbage Hands (79 × 62mm) (c1908)		£300.00	—

EDWARDS, RINGER & BIGG, Bristol

A	U	25	Abbeys and Castles — Photogravure series (c1912):			
			A Type-set back		£8.00	£200.00
			B 'Statue of Liberty' back		£8.00	£200.00
			C 'Stag Design' back		£8.00	£200.00
A	U	25	Alpine Views — Photogravure series (c1912):			
			A 'Statue of Liberty' back		£8.00	£200.00
			B 'Stag Design' back		£8.00	£200.00
A	C	12	*Beauties — 'CERF' (1905)	H.57	£70.00	—
A	U	25	*Beauties — 'FECKSA', 1900 Calendar back	H.58	£40.00	—
A	C	50	*Birds and Eggs (1906)	H.60	£12.00	£600.00
A	BW	? 2	Boer War and Boxer Rebellion Sketches (c1901)	H.46	£150.00	—
A	BW	25	*Boer War Celebrities — 'STEW' 1901 Calendar back	H.105	£45.00	—
A	C	25	British Trees and Their Uses (1933)	H.654	£2.60	£65.00
A	C	1	Calendar for 1899	H.730	—	£500.00
A	C	1	Calendar (1905), Exmore Hunt Stag design back	H.730	—	£400.00
A	C	2	Calendar (1910)	H.730	£400.00	—
A	C	50	Celebrated Bridges (1924)	H.346	£2.40	£120.00
	U		Cinema Stars (1923):			
A2		50	A Small size		£1.60	£80.00
—		25	B Medium size (67 × 57mm)		£1.80	£45.00
A	U	25	Coast and Country — Photogravure series (1911):			
			A 'Statue of Liberty' back		£8.00	£200.00
			B 'Stag Design' back		£8.00	£200.00
A	C	23	*Dogs series (1908):	H.64		
			A 'Exmoor Hunt' back		£9.00	—
			B 'Klondyke' back		£4.50	£105.00

Size	Print-ing	Number in set		Handbook reference	Price per card	Complete set

EDWARDS, RINGER & BIGG, Bristol *(continued)*

A	C	3	Easter Manoeuvres of Our Volunteers (1897)	H.146	£325.00	—
A	C	25	Flags of All Nations, 1st series (1906)	H.37	£8.00	£200.00
A	C	12	Flags of All Nations, 2nd series (1907)	H.37	£11.00	£135.00
A	C	37	*Flags of All Nations (1907):	H.37		
			A Globe and Grouped Flags back		£8.00	—
			B 'Exmoor Hunt' back:			
			i 4½d per oz		£8.00	—
			ii Altered to 5d by hand		£8.00	—
			iii 5d label added		£9.00	—
			C 'Stag' design back		£8.00	£300.00
			D Upright titled back		£8.00	—
A	C	25	Garden Life (1934)	H.449	£3.20	£80.00
A	C	25	How to Tell Fortunes (1929)		£4.00	£100.00
A	C	50	Life on Board a Man of War (1905)	H.38	£10.00	—
—	C	1	'Miners Bound for Klondyke' (41 × 81mm) (1897)		—	£500.00
A	C	50	Mining (1925)	H.450	£2.40	£120.00
A	C	25	Musical Instruments (1924)	H.547	£4.00	£100.00
A	C	25	Optical Illusions (1936)	H.560	£3.00	£75.00
A	C	25	Our Pets (1926)	H.561	£2.40	£60.00
A	C	25	Our Pets, 2nd series (1926)	H.561	£2.40	£60.00
A	C	25	Past and Present (1928)		£3.40	£85.00
A	C	10	Portraits of His Majesty the King in Uniforms of the British and Foreign Nations (1902)	H.147	£40.00	£400.00
A	C	25	Prehistoric Animals (1924)		£5.00	£125.00
A	C	25	Sports and Games in Many Lands (1935)	H.651	£5.00	£125.00
A	C	50	A Tour Round the World (Mar. 1909)	H.75	£11.00	£550.00
A	C	56	War Map of the Western Front (1916)		£11.00	—
A	U	54	War Map of the Western Front, etc Series No. 2 (1917):			
			A 'Exmoor Hunt' back		£11.00	—
			B 'New York Mixture' back		£11.00	—

S. EISISKI, Rhyl

D	U	? 25	*Actresses 'ANGOOD' (c1900)	H.187	£350.00	—
A	U	? 6	*Actresses — 'COPEIS' (c1900)	H.108	£350.00	—
A	U	? 23	*Beauties — 'FENA' (c1900)	H.148	£350.00	—
A	U	? 2	*Beauties — 'KEWA I', back inscribed 'Eisiski's New Gold Virginia Cigarettes' (c1900)	H.139	£350.00	—
A	U	? 2	*Beauties — 'KEWA I', back inscribed 'Eisiski's Rhyl Best Bird's Eye Cigarettes' (c1900)	H.139	£350.00	—
A	U	? 2	*Beauties — 'KEWA I' Rubber-stamped back (c1900)	H.139	£350.00	—

ELDONS LTD

A1	C	30	*Colonial Troops — 'Leon de Cuba' Cigars (c1900)	H.40	£160.00	—

R.J. ELLIOTT & CO. LTD, Huddersfield

A2	C	? 2	Advertisement Card — Bulldog (c1910)		£300.00	—

EMPIRE TOBACCO CO., London

D	C	? 6	Franco-British Exhibition (c1907)	H.471	£350.00	—

THE EXPRESS TOBACCO CO. LTD, London

—	U	50	'How It is Made'(Motor Cars) (76 × 51mm) (1931)		£3.00	—

Size	Print-ing	Number in set		Handbook reference	Price per card	Complete set

L. & J. FABIAN, London

—	P		The Elite Series (Beauties) (c1935):			
D1		24	A Numbered LLF 1 to 24		£35.00	—
A1		? 47	B Plain Numerals		£35.00	—

FAIRWEATHER & SONS, Dundee

A	C	50	Historic Buildings of Scotland (c1914)		£45.00	—

W. & F. FAULKNER, London

12 page reference book — £4.50

C	C	26	*Actresses — 'FROGA A' (c1900)	H.20	£50.00	—
A	C	25	Angling (1929)	H.655	£8.00	—
D2	C	12	*'Ation Series (1901)		£24.00	—
C	C	25	*Beauties (c1898)	H.150	£75.00	—
A	U	49	*Beauties — 'FECKSA' (1901)	H.58	£22.00	—
A	BW	16	*British Royal Family (1901)	H.28	£40.00	—
A	C	50	Celebrated Bridges (1925)	H.346	£2.50	£125.00
D2	C	12	*Coster Series (1900)	H.151	£30.00	—
A	BW	20	Cricketers Series (1901)	H.29	£275.00	—
D2	C	12	Cricket Terms (1899)	H.152	£80.00	—
D2	C	12	Football Terms, 1st Series (1900)	H.153	£32.00	—
D2	C	12	Football Terms, 2nd Series (1900)	H.153	£32.00	—
D2	C	12	*Golf Terms (1901)	H.155	£100.00	—
D2	C	12	Grenadier Guards (1899)	H.156	£27.00	—
A2	C	40	*Kings and Queens (1902)	H.157	£24.00	—
D2	C	12	Kipling Series (1900)	H.158	£27.00	—
D2	C	12	The Language of Flowers (1900):	H.159		
			A 'Grenadier' Cigarettes		£30.00	—
			B 'Nosegay' Cigarettes		£30.00	—
D2	C	12	*Military Terms, 1st series (1899)	H.50	£24.00	—
D2	C	12	*Military Terms, 2nd series (1899)	H.160	£24.00	—
D2	C	12	*Nautical Terms, 1st series (1900)	H.161	£24.00	—
D2	C	12	*Nautical Terms, 2nd series (1900):	H.162		
			A 'Grenadier' Cigarettes		£24.00	—
			B 'Union Jack Cigarettes'		£24.00	—
A	C	25	Old Sporting Prints (1930)	H.563	£3.60	£90.00
A	C	25	Optical Illusions (1935)	H.560	£3.00	£75.00
D2	C		'Our Colonial Troops' (1900):			
			A Grenadier Cigarettes:			
		30	i With copyright Nos 1-30		£30.00	—
		90	ii Without copyright Nos 1-90		£16.00	—
		60	B Union Jack Cigarettes Nos 31-90		£18.00	—
A	C	20	Our Gallant Grenadiers, 1-20:	H.163		
			A Without I.T.C. clause (1901):			
			i Thick card		£16.00	£320.00
			ii Thin card		£16.00	£320.00
			B With I.T.C. clause, thin card (1902)		£27.00	£540.00
A	C	20	Our Gallant Grenadiers, 21-40 (1903)		£25.00	£500.00
A	C	25	Our Pets (1926)	H.561	£3.00	£75.00
A	C	25	Our Pets, 2nd series (1926)	H.561	£2.80	£70.00
D2	C	12	*Policemen of the World (1899):	H.164		
			A 'Grenadier' Cigarettes		£200.00	—
			B 'Nosegay' Cigarettes		£35.00	—
D2	C	12	*Police Terms (1899)	H.165	£30.00	—
A	C	25	Prominent Racehorses of the Present Day (1923)		£3.20	£80.00

Size	*Print-ing*	*Number in set*		*Handbook reference*	*Price per card*	*Complete set*

W. & F. FAULKNER, London *(continued)*

A	C	25	Prominent Racehorses of the Present Day, 2nd series (1924)		£5.00	£125.00
D2	C	12	*Puzzle series (1897):	H.166		
			A 'Grenadier Cigarettes		£225.00	—
			B 'Nosegay Cigarettes		£65.00	—
A	BW	25	*South African War Scenes (1901)	H.167	£16.00	£400.00
D2	C	12	Sporting Terms (1900)	H.168	£35.00	—
D2	C	12	Street Cries (1902)	H.169	£24.00	—

FIELD FAVOURITES CIGARETTES

D	P	? 1	*Footballers (c1895)	H.731	£2000.00	—

THE FIGARO CIGARETTE

—	C	12	Caricatures of Celebrities (101 × 57mm) (c1880)	H.732	£800.00	—

FINLAY & CO. LTD, Newcastle-on-Tyne and London

D1	BW	? 28	Our Girls (c1910)	H.170	£150.00	—
A	U	30	World's Aircraft (c1912)		£70.00	—

FLYNN, Dublin

A	C	26	*Beauties — 'HOL' (c1900)	H.192	£500.00	—

C.D. FOTHERGILL, St Helens

—	C	? 1	*'Play Up' Sporting Shields (c1895)	H.718	£175.00	—

FRAENKEL BROS., London

A2	C	? 2	*Beauties — 'Don Jorg (c1898)	H.733	£750.00	—
A	U	? 23	*Beauties — 'FENA' (c1898)	H.148	£130.00	—
A	C	25	*Beauties — 'GRACC' (c1898)	H.59	£160.00	—
A	U	24	*Beauties — 'HUMPS' (c1900)	H.222	£140.00	—
A	U	26	*Music Hall Artistes (c1900):	H.171		
			A Pink card		£100.00	—
			B White card		£100.00	—
A2	C	25	*Types of British and Colonial Troops (c1900)	H.76	£70.00	—

FRANKLYN, DAVEY & CO., Bristol

A	C	12	*Beauties — 'CERF' (1905)	H.57	£70.00	—
D2	C	50	*Birds (c1895)		£70.00	—
A2	BW	10	*Boer War Generals — 'FLAC' (1901)	H.47	£85.00	—
A	C	25	Boxing (1924)	H.311	£3.20	£80.00
A	C	25	Ceremonial and Court Dress (Oct. 1915)	H.145	£12.00	—
A	C	50	Children of All Nations (1934)	H.656	90p	£45.00
—	C	? 1	Comic Dog Folder (opens to 183 × 65mm) (1898)	H.490	—	£600.00
A	C	50	*Football Club Colours (1909)	H.68	£16.00	£800.00
A	C	50	Historic Events (1924)	H.464	£2.50	£125.00
A	U	25	Hunting (1925)		£1.00	£25.00
A	U	50	Modern Dance Steps (1929)		£5.00	£250.00
A	U	50	Modern Dance Steps, 2nd series (1931)		80p	£40.00
A	C	50	Naval Dress and Badges (1916)	H.172	£12.00	—
A	C	50	Overseas Dominions (Australia) (1923)	H.451	£4.50	£225.00
A	C	25	*Star Girls (c1898)	H.30	£250.00	—

Size	*Print-ing*	*Number in set*		*Handbook reference*	*Price per card*	*Complete set*

FRANKLYN, DAVEY & CO., Bristol *(continued)*

A	C	10	Types of Smokers (c1898)		£55.00	£550.00
A	C	50	Wild Animals of the World (c1902)	H.77	£12.00	£600.00

A.H. FRANKS & SONS, London

D1	BW	56	*Beauties — 'Beauties Cigarettes' (c1900)	H.173	£75.00	—
D	C	24	*Nautical Expressions (c1900)	H.174	£80.00	—
A1	C	25	*Types of British and Colonial Troops (c1900)	H.76	£65.00	—

J.J. FREEMAN, London

D	BW	12	*Actresses — 'FRAN' (c1912)	H.175	£45.00	—
D	BW	12	*Views of the World (c1910)	H.176	£45.00	—

J.R. FREEMAN, London

C1	U	33	Football Challenge (1969)		£6.00	—
—	U	12	*'Manikin' Cards (77 × 49mm) (c1920)	H.481	£75.00	—

C. FRYER & SONS LTD, London

A2	C		*Boer War and General Interest: (c1900)	H.13		
		? 10	A Brown leaf design back		£150.00	—
		? 5	B Green leaf design back		£150.00	—
		? 2	C Green daisy design back		£150.00	—
—	—	50	Clan Sketches (101 × 74mm) (paper folders with wording only) — 'Pibroch Virginia' (c1936)		£14.00	—
D	C	40	*Naval and Military Phrases (c1905)	H.14	£65.00	—
A2	BW	? 14	*'Vita Berlin' series (c1902)	H.177	£450.00	—

FRYER & COULTMAN, London

D	BW	50	*Beauties — PLUMS (c1900)	H.186	£800.00	—
—	C	12	*French Phrases, 1893 Calendar back (96 × 64 mm)	H.178	£800.00	—

J. GABRIEL, London

A	BW	10	*Actresses — 'HAGG A' (1900)	H.24	£75.00	—
A2	C	25	*Beauties — 'GRACC' (c1898)	H.59	£200.00	—
A	BW	20	Cricketers series (1901)	H.29	£400.00	—
A	C	40	*Home and Colonial Regiments (c1902)	H.69	£85.00	—
A	U	? 56	*Pretty Girl series — 'BAGG' (c1898)	H.45	£70.00	—
A2	C	25	*Types of British and Colonial Troops (c1900)	H.76	£65.00	—

GALA CIGARETTES

D1	U	? 1	Stamp Card c1910	H.589	—	£170.00

GALLAHER LTD, Belfast and London

40 page reference book — £4.50

D	P	110	*Actors and Actresses (c1900)	H.179	£5.50	—
D	C	48	Aeroplanes (1939)		90p	£45.00
A2	C	25	Aesop's Fables (1931):	H.518		
			A Inscribed 'Series of 25'		£1.40	£35.00
			B Inscribed 'Series of 50'		£1.20	£30.00
D	C	25	The Allies Flags: (1914):			
			A Toned card		£5.00	—
			B White card		£5.00	—

Size	Printing	Number in set		Handbook reference	Price per card	Complete set
			GALLAHER LTD, Belfast and London *(continued)*			
D	C	100	Animals and Birds of Commercial Value (1921)		80p	£80.00
D	C	48	Army Badges (1939)		80p	£40.00
—	U	24	Art Treasures of the World (76 × 56mm) (1930)		80p	£20.00
D	C	100	Association Football Club Colours (1910):			
			A Grey border		£9.00	—
			B Brown border		£9.00	—
A	C	52	*Beauties (c1900):	H.180		
			A Without inset		£12.00	—
			B With Playing Card inset		£12.00	—
—	P	48	Beautiful Scotland (77 × 52mm) (1939)	H.564-1	90p	£45.00
D	C	50	*Birds and Eggs (c1905)	H.60		
			A 'Gallaher Ltd' Label		£50.00	—
			B 'Manufactured by Gallaher' Label		£9.00	—
D	C	100	Birds' Nests and Eggs series (1919):			
			A White card		£1.50	£150.00
			B Toned card		£1.50	—
D	C		Boy Scout Series grey-green back (1911):	H.630		
		100	A 'Belfast and London'		£2.50	£250.00
		86	B 'London and Belfast'		£2.70	—
D	C	100	Boy Scout Series brown back (1922)	H.630	£2.25	£225.00
D	C	48	British Birds (1937)		50p	£25.00
D	C	100	British Birds by Rankin (1923):	H.537		
			A 'By Rankin'		£20.00	—
			B 'By George Rankin'		£1.50	£150.00
D	C	75	British Champions of 1923 (1924)		£2.00	£150.00
D	U	50	British Naval series (1914)		£6.00	£300.00
D	C	48	Butterflies and Moths (1938)		40p	£20.00
D	C	25	Champion Animals & Birds of 1923 (1924)		£2.00	£50.00
D	C	48	Champions (1934):			
			A Front without letterpress		90p	£45.00
			B Front with captions, subjects re-drawn		80p	£40.00
D	C	48	Champions, 2nd Series (1935)		60p	£30.00
D	C	48	Champions of Screen & Stage (1934):			
			A Red back		70p	£35.00
			B Blue back, 'Gallaher's Cigarettes' at base		£1.20	£60.00
			C Blue back, 'Gallaher Ltd' at base		£2.00	£100.00
D	U	100	Cinema Stars (1926)	H.658	£1.60	£160.00
—	P	48	Coastwise (77 × 52mm) (1938)	H.564-2	£1.00	£50.00
	C	24	Dogs (1934):			
			A Captions in script letters on front:			
D			1 Small size		£2.00	£50.00
B			2 Large size		£2.00	£50.00
			B Captions in block letters on front:			
D			1 Small size		£1.00	£24.00
B			2 Large size		£1.25	£30.00
D	C	48	Dogs (1936)		60p	£30.00
D	C	48	Dogs Second Series (1938)		50p	£24.00
D	P	100	English and Scotch Views (c1910)		£3.20	£320.00
D	C	100	Fables and Their Morals:			
			A Numbered Outside Set Title Panel (1912)		£1.60	£160.00
			B & C numbered in set title panel			
			B Thin numerals (1922)			
			1 White card		80p	£80.00
			2 Yellow card		80p	£80.00
			C Thick numerals (1922)		80p	£80.00
D	U	100	Famous Cricketers (1926)		£3.00	£300.00
D	C	48	Famous Film Scenes (1935)		70p	£35.00

Size	*Print-ing*	*Number in set*		*Handbook reference*	*Price per card*	*Complete set*

GALLAHER LTD, Belfast and London *(continued)*

D	U	100	Famous Footballers, green back (1925)		£2.30	£230.00
D	C	50	Famous Footballers, brown back (1926)		£2.50	£125.00
D	C	48	Famous Jockeys (1936):			
			A Blue text		£1.20	£60.00
			B Mauve text		£2.50	—
D	C	48	Film Episodes (1936)		70p	£35.00
D	C	48	Film Partners (1935)		80p	£40.00
—	P	48	Flying (77 × 52mm) (1938)	H.564-3	£1.50	—
D	C	100	Footballers, red back (1928):	H.659		
			1 Nos. 1-50 — Action pictures		£3.00	£150.00
			2 Nos. 51-100 — Portraits		£3.00	£150.00
D	C	50	Footballers in Action (1928)		£3.00	£150.00
D	C	48	Garden Flowers (1938)		20p	£10.00
D	C	100	The Great War series (1915)		£3.00	£300.00
D	C	100	The Great War series — Second Series (1916)		£3.00	£300.00
D	C		The Great War, Victoria Cross Heroes (1915-16):	H.735		
		25	1st series 1-25		£5.00	£125.00
		25	2nd series 26-50		£5.00	£125.00
		25	3rd series 51-75		£5.00	£125.00
		25	4th series 76-100		£5.00	£125.00
		25	5th series 101-125		£5.00	£125.00
		25	6th series 126-150		£5.00	£125.00
		25	7th series 151-175		£5.00	£125.00
		25	8th series 176-200		£5.00	£125.00
—	C	20	£½ Million Berkeley Star Competition (90 × 33mm) (1996)		£1.50	—
D	C	100	How to do it (1916)		£3.50	£350.00
D		100	Interesting Views:			
	P		A Uncoloured, glossy (1923)		£1.80	£180.00
	CP		B Hand-coloured, matt (1925)		£2.75	£275.00
D			Irish View Scenery (c1910):	H.181		
	BW	400	1-400, matt:			
			A Numbered on back		£2.00	—
			B Unnumbered, plain back		£3.00	—
	P	400	1-400, glossy — see H.181-A			
			A Black photo		90p	£360.00
			B Brown photo		£3.00	—
			C As A, but series title and No. omitted		£2.00	—
			D Numbered 1-200 plain back		£3.00	—
	P	600	1-600, glossy — see H.181-B			
			A Nos 1 to 500		90p	£450.00
			B Nos 501 to 600		£5.00	—
B2	P	48	Island Sporting Celebrities (Channel Islands) (1938)		£2.80	—
D	C	100	'Kute Kiddies' series (1916)		£4.00	£400.00
D	P	50	Latest Actresses (1910):			
			A Black photo		£13.00	—
			B Chocolate photo		£20.00	—
D	C	50	Lawn Tennis Celebrities (1928)		£4.50	—
A	C	24	Motor Cars (1934)		£4.50	£110.00
D	C	48	My Favourite Part (1939)		60p	£30.00
D	C	48	The Navy (1937):			
			A 'Park Drive ...' at base of back		60p	£30.00
			B 'Issued by ...' at base of back		£1.20	£60.00
—	P	48	Our Countryside (72 × 52mm) (1938)	H.564-4	£1.25	—
D	C	100	Plants of Commercial Value (1923)		90p	£90.00
D	C	48	Portraits of Famous Stars (1935)		£1.00	£50.00
D	C	48	Racing Scenes (1938)		60p	£30.00

Size	*Print-ing*	*Number in set*		*Handbook reference*	*Price per card*	*Complete set*

GALLAHER LTD, Belfast and London *(continued)*

D	C	100	The Reason Why (1924)		80p	£80.00
A	C	50	*Regimental Colours and Standards (Nd 151-200) (1899)		£6.50	£325.00
D	C	100	Robinson Crusoe (1928)		£1.80	£180.00
A	C	50	Royalty series (1902)		£7.00	£350.00
B2	P	48	Scenes from the Empire (1939) (export)	H.565	30p	£15.00
—	P	24	Shots from the Films (77 × 52mm) (1936)	H.566	£3.50	—
D	C	48	Shots from Famous Films (1935)		60p	£30.00
D	C	48	Signed Portraits of Famous Stars (1935)		£2.50	—
C1	C	20	Silk Cut Advertisements (1993)		£1.50	—
A	C	111	The South African series (Nd 101-211) (1901):			
			A White back		£6.00	—
			B Cream back		£6.00	—
D	C	48	Sporting Personalities (1936)		40p	£20.00
D	C	100	'Sports' series (1912)		£7.00	£700.00
D	U	? 98	*Stage and Variety Celebrities (collotype) (c1898):	H.182		
			A 'Gallager' back		£85.00	—
			B 'Gallaher' back		£85.00	—
			C As B but larger lettering, etc		£85.00	—
D	C	48	Stars of Screen & Stage (1935):			
			A Back in green		60p	£30.00
			B Back in brown		£1.60	£80.00
G2	C	5	Telemania (1989)		£2.00	£10.00
D	C	48	Trains of the World (1937)		£1.00	£50.00
D	C	100	Tricks and Puzzles Series, green back (1913)		£5.00	£500.00
D	C	100	Tricks & Puzzles Series, black back (1933):			
			Nos. 1-50		£1.00	£50.00
			Nos. 51-100		£1.00	£50.00
A	C	50	*Types of the British Army — unnumbered (1897):	H.183		
			A 'Battle Honours' back		£11.00	—
			B 'The Three Pipe ...' — green back		£11.00	—
A	C	50	*Types of the British Army — Nd 1-50 (1898):	H.183		
			A 'The Three Pipe ...' — brown back		£10.00	—
			B 'Now in Three ...' — brown back		£10.00	—
A	C	50	*Types of British and Colonial Regiments — Nd 51-100 (1900):			
			A 'The Three Pipe ...' — brown back		£10.00	—
			B 'Now in Three ...' — brown back		£10.00	—
D	C	100	Useful Hints series (1915)		£3.00	£300.00
	C	20	Views – Berkeley Superkings Panoramic (1994):			
G2			A Blue border (90 × 45mm)		£1.50	—
—			B Blue border (90 × 33mm)		£1.50	—
G2			C Green border (90 × 45mm)		£1.50	—
—			D Green border (90 × 33mm)		£1.50	—
G2			E Red border (90 × 45mm)		£1.50	—
—			F Red border (90 × 33mm)		£1.50	—
D	U	25	Views in North of Ireland (1912)		£60.00	—
D	C	50	Votaries of the Weed (1916)		£7.00	£350.00
D	C	100	'Why is it?' series (1915):			
			A Green back		£3.20	£320.00
			B Brown back		£3.20	£320.00
D	C	48	Wild Animals (1937)		40p	£20.00
D	C	48	Wild Flowers (1939)		60p	£30.00
D	C	100	Woodland Trees series (1912)		£5.00	£500.00
D	C	100	The 'Zoo' Aquarium (1924)		£1.20	£120.00
D	C	50	'Zoo' Tropical Birds, 1st Series (1928)		£1.50	£75.00
D	C	50	'Zoo' Tropical Birds, 2nd Series (1929)		£1.50	£75.00

Size	Print-ing	Number in set		Handbook reference	Price per card	Complete set

GALLAHER LTD, Belfast and London *(continued)*

SILKS

—	C	25	Flags — Set 1 (68 × 48mm) (paper-backed) (1916)	H.501-1	£7.50	—

SAMUEL GAWITH, Kendal

—	BW	25	The English Lakeland (90 × 70mm) (1926)		£24.00	—

F. GENNARI LTD, London

A	U	50	War Portraits (1916)	H.86	£100.00	—

LOUIS GERARD LTD, London

D1	U	50	Modern Armaments (1936):	H.567		
			A Numbered		£1.00	£50.00
			B Unnumbered		£1.20	£60.00
D1	U	24	Screen Favourites (1937):	H.568		
			A Inscribed 'Louis Gerard & Company'		£3.50	—
			B Inscribed 'Louis Gerard Limited'		£3.50	—
D1	C	48	Screen Favourites and Dancers (1937):	H.569		
			A Matt front		£2.50	£125.00
			B Varnished front		£4.00	—

W.G. GLASS & CO. LTD, Bristol

A	BW	20	*Actresses — 'BLARM' (c1900)	H.23	£70.00	—
A2	BW	10	*Actresses — 'HAGG A' (c1900)	H.24	£70.00	—
A	U	25	*Beauties — 'FECKSA (c1901)'	H.58	£110.00	—
D1	BW	20	*Boer War Cartoons ('Roseland Cigarettes') (c1901)	H.42	£120.00	—
A	BW	25	*Boer War Celebrities — 'STEW' (c1901)	H.105	£90.00	—
A	BW	16	*British Royal Family (1901)	H.28	£70.00	—
A2	BW	20	Cricketers Series (1901)	H.29	£350.00	—
D	C	40	*Naval and Military Phrases (c1902)	H.14	£110.00	—
A	BW	19	*Russo-Japanese Series (1904)	H.184	£65.00	—

R.P. GLOAG & CO, London

(Cards bear advertisements for 'Citamora' and/or 'The Challenge Flat Brilliantes' without maker's name)

A2	U	? 9	*Actresses — 'ANGLO' (c1896):	H.185		
			A 'Citamora' on front		£400.00	—
			B 'The Challenge Flat' on front		£400.00	—
D			*Beauties — Selection from 'Plums' (c1898):	H.186		
	BW	60	A 'The Challenge Flat' front in black and white		£100.00	—
			B 'Citamora' front:			
	BW	? 10	(a) front in black and white		£130.00	—
	U	? 11	(b) front in brown printed back		£250.00	—
	U	? 10	(c) front in brown, plain back		£250.00	—
A	C	40	*Home and Colonial Regiments (c1900)	H.69	£45.00	—
D	C	30	*Proverbs (c1901)	H.15	£100.00	—
A2	C	25	*Types of British and Colonial Troops (c1900)	H.76	£60.00	—

GLOBE CIGARETTE CO.

D	BW	25	*Actresses — French (c1900)	H.1	£350.00	—

GOLDS LTD, Birmingham

A2	BW	1	Advertisement Card (Chantecler) (c1905)	H.737	—	£600.00

Size	Printing	Number in set		Handbook reference	Price per card	Complete set

GOLDS LTD, Birmingham *(continued)*

C	C	18	Motor Cycle Series (c1914):	H.469		
			A Back in blue, numbered		£50.00	—
			B Back in grey, numbered		£60.00	—
			C Back in grey, unnumbered		£60.00	—
—	BW	? 21	*Prints from Noted Pictures (68 × 81mm) (c1908):	H.216		
			A With firm's name, 5 brands listed back		£140.00	—
			B With firm's name, 3 brands listed back		£140.00	—
			C Without firm's name, 'Gibson Girl' back		£140.00	—

T.P. & R. GOODBODY, Dublin and London

—	U	? 4	*Actresses — 'ANGOOD' (36 × 60mm) (c1898)	H.187	£350.00	—
A2	U	? 10	*Beauties — 'KEWA' (c1898):	H.139		
			A Back rubber stamped in mauve		£300.00	—
			B Back rubber stamped in red		£300.00	—
D	BW		*Boer War Celebrities — 'CAG' (1901)	H.79		
		25	See H.79 — Fig. 79-B		£35.00	—
		16	See H.79 — Fig. 79-C		£35.00	—
		16	See H.79 — Fig. 79-D		£35.00	—
		16	See H.79 — Fig. 79-E		£35.00	—
	C	50	Colonial Forces (c1900):	H.188		
A2			A Brown back		£75.00	—
A2			B Black back		£75.00	—
—			C Size 80 × 50mm		£500.00	—
—	U	? 67	*Dogs (1910) (36 × 60mm):	H.189		
			A 'Brown Flake' back		£100.00	—
			B 'Celebrated Greenville Plug' back		£100.00	—
			C 'Eblana Flake' back		£100.00	—
			D 'Furze Blossom Cigarettes' back		£100.00	—
			E 'Furze Blossom Navy Cut' back		£100.00	—
			F 'Golden Flake' back:			
			i Text 44mm deep		£100.00	—
			ii Text 50mm deep		£100.00	—
			G 'Silk Cut Cigarettes' back		£100.00	—
			H 'Specialities in Tins & Packets' back		£100.00	—
			I 'Two Flakes' back:			
			i Text 44mm deep		£100.00	—
			ii Text 50mm deep		£100.00	—
C	C	26	Eminent Actresses — 'FROGA A' (c1900):	H.20		
			A Front 'Goodbody' at base		£50.00	—
			B Front 'Goodbody' at top		£250.00	—
C	C	20	Irish Scenery (Five Printings) (c1905)	H.190	£40.00	—
A2	U	? 14	*Pretty Girl Series — 'BAGG' (c1898):	H.45		
			A 10 'Gold and Silver Medals' back		£300.00	—
			B 'Furze Blossom':			
			i Mauve back		£300.00	—
			ii Red back		£300.00	—
			iii Grey back		£300.00	—
D	C	50	Questions & Answers in Natural History (1924)		£2.60	£120.00
A	C	25	Sports & Pastimes — Series 1 (1925)	H.225	£7.00	£175.00
A	C	25	Types of Soldiers (c1914)	H.144	£60.00	—
D	U	20	*War Pictures (c1915)	H.122	£35.00	—
C	C	12	'With the Flag to Pretoria' (c1901)	H.191	£110.00	—

GORDON'S, Glasgow

A2	BW	? 4	Billiards — By George D. Gordon (c1910)		£1000.00	—

Size	Print-ing	Number in set		Handbook reference	Price per card	Complete set

F. GOUGH, Blackley

—	C	? 1	*Play Up Sporting Shields (c1895)	H.718	£125.00	—

GRAVESON, Mexboro'

A2	C	30	*Army Pictures, Cartoons, Etc (c1916):	H.12		
			A 'Wholesale Tobacconist' back		£120.00	—
			B 'Wholesale and Retail Tobacconist' back		£120.00	—
			C 'Wholesale and Retail Tobacconist Flash Cards etc.' back		£120.00	—
A	U	50	War Portraits (1916)	H.86	£100.00	—

FRED GRAY, Birmingham

A	C	25	*Types of British Soldiers (c1914)	H.144	£150.00	—

GRIFFITHS BROS., Manchester

—	P	18	*Beauties (89 × 70mm) (c1925)	H.653	£150.00	—

W.J. HARRIS, London

A2	C	26	*Beauties 'HOL' (c1900)	H.192	£40.00	—
C	C	30	*Colonial Troops (c1900)	H.40	£100.00	—
A1	C	25	*Star Girls (c1899)	H.30	£275.00	—

JAS. H. HARRISON, Birmingham

C	C	18	Motor Cycle Series (c1914)	H.469	£90.00	—

HARVEY & DAVEY, Newcastle-on-Tyne

D1	C	50	*Birds and Eggs (c1905)	H.60	£4.50	£225.00
A1	C	35	*Chinese and South African Series (c1901)	H.193	£130.00	—
C	C	30	*Colonial Troops (c1900)	H.40	£80.00	—
A1	C	25	*Types of British and Colonial Troops (c1901)	H.76	£90.00	—

HARVEY'S NAVY CUT

—	C	? 3	*Play Up Sporting Shields (c1895)	H.718	£125.00	—

W. & H. HEATON, Birkby

—	BW	? 6	Birkby Views (70 × 39mm) (c1912)	H.226	£400.00	—

HENLY & WATKINS LTD, London

A1	C	25	Ancient Egyptian Gods — 'Matossian's Cigarettes' (1924)	H.570		
			*A Plain back		£7.00	£175.00
			B Back in blue		£7.00	£175.00

HIGNETT BROS. & CO., Liverpool

A	C	50	Actors — Natural and Character Studies (1938)	H.571-1	£1.60	£80.00
C	C	26	*Actresses — 'FROGA A' (c1900)	H.20	£60.00	—
A2	U	25	*Actresses — Photogravure (c1900)	H.194	£27.00	—
D1	BW	28	*Actresses — 'PILPI I' (c1901)	H.195	£20.00	—
D1	P	50	*Actresses — 'PILPI II' (c1901)	H.196	£12.00	—
—	C	? 3	Advertisement Cards. (c1885)		£500.00	—
A	C	50	A.F.C. Nicknames (1933)	H.571-2	£6.50	—
A	C	50	Air-Raid Precautions (1939)	H.544	£1.20	£60.00

Size	Printing	Number in set		Handbook reference	Price per card	Complete set

HIGNETT BROS. & CO., Liverpool *(continued)*

Size	Printing	Number in set		Handbook reference	Price per card	Complete set
—	C	60	Animal Pictures ... (38 × 70mm) (c1900)	H.197	£35.00	—
A	C	50	Arms and Armour (1924)	H.273	£3.00	£150.00
C	C	? 25	*Beauties — 'CHOAB' (c1900)	H.21	£200.00	—
D	U	50	*Beauties — gravure (c1898):	H.198		
			A 'Cavalier' back		£75.00	—
			B 'Golden Butterfly' back		£75.00	—
—	C	? 8	*Beauties, multi-backed (168 × 109mm) (c1900)	H.708	£350.00	—
A	C	50	British Birds and Their Eggs (1938)	H.571-3	£2.80	—
A	U	50	Broadcasting (1935)	H.571-4	£2.80	—
A1	C	19	Cabinet, 1900	H.199	£90.00	—
A	C	25	Cathedrals and Churches (1909)	H.545	£4.40	£110.00
A	U	50	Celebrated Old Inns (1925)		£3.00	£150.00
A	C	50	Champions of 1936 (1937)	H.571-5	£3.40	£170.00
A	C	25	Common Objects of the Sea-Shore (1924)		£2.40	£60.00
A	C	25	Company Drill (1915)		£4.40	£110.00
A	C	50	Coronation Procession (sectional) (1937)	H.571-6	£2.50	—
—	BW	6	Diamond Jubilee 1897 (156 × 156mm)	H.740	£600.00	—
A	C	50	Dogs (1936)	H.571-7	£2.20	£110.00
A	C	50	Football Caricatures (1935)	H.571-8	£3.50	£175.00
A	C	50	Football Club Captains (1935)	H.571-9	£3.50	£175.00
A	C	25	Greetings of the World (1907 — re-issued 1922)		£3.00	£75.00
A	U	25	Historical London (1926)		£2.60	£65.00
A	C	50	How to Swim (1935)	H.571-10	£1.20	£60.00
A	C	50	Interesting Buildings (1905)	H.70	£6.50	£325.00
A	C	25	International Caps and Badges (1924)		£4.40	£110.00
A	C	25	Life in Pond & Stream (1925)		£3.00	£75.00
—	C	40	*Medals (34 × 72mm) (1901):	H.200		
			A 'Butterfly Cigarettes'		£25.00	—
			B Officially cut for use in other brands		£25.00	—
A	BW	25	Military Portraits (1914)	H.201	£5.00	£125.00
A	C	50	Modern Railways (1936)	H.571-11	£2.50	£125.00
A	C	25	Modern Statesmen (1906):			
			A 'Butterfly' back		£5.00	£125.00
			B 'Pioneer' back		£5.00	£125.00
A	C	20	*Music Hall Artistes (c1900)	H.202	£65.00	—
A	C	50	Ocean Greyhounds (1938)	H.571-12	£1.60	£80.00
	U	1	Oracle Butterfly (shaped) (c1898):			
			A Orange gold cellophane:			
			i Size 65 × 57mm		£125.00	—
			ii Size 51 × 40mm		£125.00	—
			iii Size 49 × 43mm		£125.00	—
			B Yellow and gold cellophane, size 51 × 38mm		£125.00	—
			C Purple and gold cellophane, size 48 × 38mm		£125.00	—
A	C	25	Panama Canal (1914)		£6.00	£150.00
A2	C	12	*Pretty Girl Series — 'RASH' (c1900)	H.8	£55.00	—
A	U	25	*The Prince of Wales' Empire Tour (1924)		£2.40	£60.00
A	U	50	Prominent Cricketers of 1938 (1938)	H.571-13	£3.50	£175.00
A	C	50	Prominent Racehorses of 1933 (1934)	H.571-14	£2.60	£130.00
A	C	50	Sea Adventure (1939)	H.571-15	50p	£25.00
A	C	25	Ships Flags & Cap Badges (1926)		£4.80	£120.00
A	C	25	Ships Flags & Cap Badges, 2nd Series (1927)		£4.80	£120.00
A	C	50	Shots from the Films (1936)	H.571-16	£3.50	—
—	C	6	*Story of a Boy Who Robs a Stork's Nest (118 × 88mm) (c1890)	H.742	£600.00	—
A	C	50	Trick Billiards (1934)	H.571-17	£6.00	—
A	U	25	Turnpikes (1927)		£2.60	£65.00
—	BW	25	*V.C. Heroes (35 × 72mm) (1901)	H.203	£55.00	—

Size	*Print-ing*	*Number in set*		*Handbook reference*	*Price per card*	*Complete set*

HIGNETT BROS. & CO., Liverpool *(continued)*

A	C	20	*Yachts (c1902):	H.204		
			A Gold on black back		£70.00	—
			B Black on white back		£70.00	—
A	C	50	Zoo Studies (1937)	H.571-18	£1.00	£50.00

OVERSEAS ISSUES (NEW ZEALAND)

D1	P	50	Beauties, Set 1 (1926):			
			A Back without framelines, no brand mentioned		£2.00	—
			B Back with framelines, 'Chess Cigarettes'		£1.50	£75.00
D1	P	50	Beauties, Set 2 (1927)		£1.80	£90.00

R. & J. HILL LTD, London

28 page reference book — £4.50

A	C	26	*Actresses — 'FROGA A' (c1900)	H.20	£60.00	—
D	BW	30	*Actresses, Continental (c1905):	H.205		
			A 'The Seven Wonders' back		£18.00	—
			B 'Black and White Whisky' back		£25.00	—
			C Plain back		£18.00	—
D	BW	16	*Actresses — 'HAGG B' (c1900):	H.24		
			A 'Smoke Hill's Stockrider ...'		£35.00	—
			B 'Issued with Hill's High Class'		£35.00	—
—	BW	25	*Actresses (Belle of New York Series) (1899):	H206		
			A White back (41 × 75mm)		£25.00	—
			B Toned back, thick card (39 × 74mm)		£25.00	—
D1	U	20	*Actresses, chocolate tinted (1917):	H.207		
			A 'Hill's Tobaccos' etc back		£18.00	—
			B 'Issued with Hill's ...' back		£20.00	—
			C Plain back		£18.00	—
C	U	30	The All Blacks (1924)		£6.50	£200.00
C	C	20	*Animal Series (1909):	H.743		
			A 'R. & J. Hill Ltd.' back		£27.00	—
			B 'Crowfoot Cigarettes' back		£27.00	—
			C 'The Cigarettes with which ...' back		£32.00	—
			D Space at back		£27.00	—
			E Plain Back		£27.00	—
A	BW	25	Aviation Series (1934):			
			A 'Issued by R. & J. Hill ...'		£3.40	£85.00
			B 'Issued with "Gold Flake Honeydew" ...'		£3.60	£90.00
A	BW	? 17	*Battleships (c1908):	H.208		
			A 'For the Pipe Smoke Oceanic ...' back		£350.00	—
			B Plain back		£50.00	—
A	C	25	*Battleships and Crests (1901)		£20.00	£500.00
D2	C	12	*Boer War Generals ('Campaigners') (c1901)	H.209	£35.00	£420.00
A1	C	20	Breeds of Dogs (1914):	H.211		
			A 'Archer's M.F.H.' back		£24.00	—
			B 'Hill's Badminton' back		£24.00	—
			C 'Hill's Verbena Mixture' back		£24.00	—
			D 'Spinet Tobacco' back		£24.00	—
D1	BW	? 48	*British Navy Series (c1902)	H.210	£27.00	—
	U	50	Caricatures of Famous Cricketers (1926):			
C			A Small size		£3.20	£160.00
B1			B Large size		£2.20	£110.00
A	BW	? 1	*Celebrated Pictures (c1905)	H.744	£700.00	—
D1	C	50	Celebrities of Sport (1939):			
			A 'Issued by R. & J. Hill ...'		£2.20	£110.00
			B 'Issued with "Gold Flake Honeydew" ...'		£4.00	—

Size	Printing	Number in set		Handbook reference	Price per card	Complete set

R. & J. HILL LTD, London *(continued)*

Size	Printing	Number in set		Handbook reference	Price per card	Complete set
A2	C	35	Cinema Celebrities (1936):	H.572		
			A Inscribed 'These Cigarettes are guaranteed'		£1.15	£40.00
			B Inscribed 'The Spinet House'		£1.30	£45.00
C	C		*Colonial Troops (c1900):	H.40		
		30	A i 'Hill's Leading Lines ...' back		£24.00	—
		30	A ii 'Perfection vide Dress ...' back		£24.00	—
		50	B 1-50. 'Sweet American' back		£24.00	—
D1	BW	40	Crystal Palace Souvenir:			
			A Front matt (1936)		£2.50	£100.00
			B Front varnished (1937)		£2.00	£80.00
D1	C	48	Decorations and Medals (1940):			
			A 'Issued by R. & J. Hill ...'		£1.50	£75.00
			B 'Issued with Gold Flake Cigarettes'		£3.00	—
	P		Famous Cinema Celebrities (1931):			
		? 48	Set 1:			
—			A Medium size (74 × 56mm) inscribed 'Series A':			
			1 'Kadi Cigarettes' at base of back		£5.00	—
			2 Space at base of back blank		£4.00	—
A			B1 Small size, inscribed 'Spinet Cigarettes'		£4.50	—
A			B2 Small size, without 'Spinet Cigarettes'		£4.50	—
		50	Set 2:			
—			C Small size (66 × 41mm) inscribed 'Series C':			
			1 'Devon Cigarettes' at base of back		£7.00	—
			2 'Toucan Cigarettes' at base of back		£7.00	—
			3 Space at base of back blank		£4.00	—
			D Medium size (74 × 56mm) inscribed 'Series D':			
			1 'Kadi Cigarettes' at base of back		£4.00	—
			2 Space at base of back blank		£4.00	—
D1	U	28	Famous Cricketers Series (1912):			
			A Red back, blue picture		£65.00	—
			B Deep blue back, brown picture		£65.00	—
			C Blue back, black picture		£65.00	—
C	U	40	Famous Cricketers (1923)	H.633	£5.00	£200.00
	U	50	Famous Cricketers, including the S. Africa Test Team — 'Sunripe Cigarettes' (1924):			
C			A Small size		£5.00	£250.00
B1			B Large size		£5.50	£275.00
A	U	50	Famous Dog Breeds 1954 (Airmail Cigarettes Slides)	H.889	£8.00	—
—	C	30	Famous Engravings — Series XI (80 × 61mm) (c1920)		£4.50	—
A2	BW	40	Famous Film Stars (1938):	H.634-1		
			A Text in English		£1.25	£50.00
			B *Text in Arabic, caption in English (see also Modern Beauties)*		£1.00	£40.00
D1	BW	20	Famous Footballers Series (1912)		£25.00	£500.00
C	U	50	Famous Footballers (1923)		£3.50	£175.00
D	C	50	Famous Footballers (1939):	H.574		
			A Shoreditch address		£2.50	£125.00
			B 'Proprietors of Hy. Archer ...'		£2.60	£130.00
D	C	25	Famous Footballers, Nd. 51-75 (1939)		£3.00	£75.00
—	U	25	Famous Pictures: (41 × 70mm) (c1912):			
			A 'Prize Coupon' back		£4.00	£100.00
			B Without 'Prize Coupon' back		£4.00	£100.00
D	C	50	Famous Ships:			
			A Front matt (1939)		£1.10	£55.00
			B Front varnished (1940)		90p	£45.00
D	C	48	Film Stars and Celebrity Dancers (1935)		£1.50	£75.00
C	C	30	*Flags and Flags with Soldiers (c1902)	H.41	£24.00	—

Size	Printing	Number in set		Handbook reference	Price per card	Complete set

R. & J. HILL LTD, London *(continued)*

Size	Printing	Number in set	Title	Handbook reference	Price per card	Complete set
—	C	24	*Flags, Arms and Types of Nations, 'Black & White' Whisky advert back (41 × 68mm) (c1910)	H.115	£12.50	£300.00
D	BW	20	Football Captain Series. Nd. 41-60 (1906):			
			A Small title		£45.00	—
			B Larger title, back re-drawn		£60.00	—
—		10	Fragments from France (38 × 67mm) (1916):	H.212		
	C		A Coloured, caption in script		£25.00	£250.00
	U		B Sepia-brown on buff, caption in block		£30.00	£300.00
	U		C As B, but black and white		£90.00	—
—	C	10	Fragments from France, different subjects, caption in block (38 × 67mm) (1916)	H.212	£25.00	£250.00
A1	U	25	Hill's War Series (c1916)	H.35	£12.00	£300.00
	C		Historic Places from Dickens' Classics (1926):			
D		50	A Small size		70p	£35.00
B1			B Large size:			
			1 Nos. 2-26, small numerals		70p	£17.50
			2 Nos. 1-50, large numerals		60p	£30.00
	U	50	Holiday Resorts (1925):			
C			A Small size:			
			1 Back in grey		90p	£45.00
			2 Back in brown		£1.50	—
B1			B Large size:			
			1 Back in grey		80p	£40.00
			2 Back in brown		£1.50	—
C2	C	20	Inventors and Their Inventions Series, Nd. 1-20, (1907):	H.213		
			A Black back, white card		£4.50	£90.00
			B Black back, toned card (shorter)		£6.00	—
C2	C	20	Inventors and Their Inventions Series, Nd. 21-40, (1907)		£7.00	£140.00
A	BW	20	**Inventors and Their Inventions (plain back)* (1934)	H.213	£1.50	£30.00
—			*Japanese Series (40 × 66mm) (1904):	H.214		
	C	15	A 'Hills' on red tablet		£65.00	—
	C	1	B 'Hills' on blue tablet		£300.00	—
	BW	15	C 'Hills' on black tablet:			
			i With 'E F Lind Sydney'		£300.00	—
			ii Without 'E F Lind Sydney'		£50.00	—
—	C	20	Lighthouse Series — without frame lines to picture (42 × 68mm) (c1903)		£35.00	—
—	C	30	Lighthouse Series — with frame line. Nos. 1-20 retouched and 10 cards added (c1903)		£35.00	—
			Magical Puzzles — see 'Puzzle Series'			
A2	BW		Modern Beauties (1939):	H.634-2		
		50	A Titled 'Modern Beauties'. Text in English		£1.00	£50.00
		40	B *Titled 'Famous Film Stars' (selection):*			
			i Text in Arabic, No Captions, Numbered		£2.00	—
			ii Text in Arabic, No Captions, Unnumbered		£12.00	—
	C	30	Music Hall Celebrities — Past and Present (1930):			
D1			A Small size		£2.50	£75.00
B1			B Large size		£2.50	£75.00
D	C	20	National Flag Series (1914):	H.473		
			A Printed back		£8.00	£160.00
			B *Plain back*		£7.00	—
D	C	30	Nature Pictures — 'The Spotlight Tobaccos' (c1930)		£1.20	£36.00
C2	C	30	Nautical Songs (1937)		£1.50	£45.00
—	BW	25	*Naval Series unnumbered (42 × 64mm) (1901)	H.215	£45.00	—
D1	BW	30	Naval Series Nd. 21-50 (1902):	H.215		
			A Numbered 21-40		£13.00	—
			B Numbered 41-50		£60.00	—

Size	Printing	Number in set		Handbook reference	Price per card	Complete set

R. & J. HILL LTD, London *(continued)*

Size	Printing	Number in set		Handbook reference	Price per card	Complete set
	U	30	'Our Empire' (1929):			
D1			A Small size		40p	£12.00
B1			B Large size		80p	£24.00
—	BW		Popular Footballers — Season 1934-5 (68 × 49mm):			
		30	'Series A' — Nd. 1-30		£3.20	£95.00
		20	'Series B' — Nd. 31-50		£3.50	£70.00
C	C	20	Prince of Wales Series (1911)	H.22	£12.00	£240.00
	U		Public Schools and Colleges (1923):	H.575		
		50	A 'A Series of 50':			
C			1 Small size		70p	£35.00
B1			2 Large size		70p	£35.00
		75	B 'A Series of 75':			
C			1 Small size		90p	£70.00
B1			2 Large size		90p	£70.00
A1	C	50	Puzzle Series:	H.660		
			A Titled 'Puzzle Series' (1937)		£1.20	£60.00
			B Titled 'Magical Puzzles' (1938)		£2.00	£100.00
	U	50	The Railway Centenary — 'A Series of 50' (1925):			
C			A Small size		£1.30	£65.00
B1			B Large size:			
			1 Back in brown		£1.30	£65.00
			2 Back in grey		£3.30	—
	U	25	The Railway Centenary — '2nd Series — 51 to 75' (1925):			
C			A Small size		£2.00	£50.00
B1			B Large size		£2.00	£50.00
C2	P	42	Real Photographs — Set 1 (Bathing Beauties) (c1930):	H.576-1		
			A 'London Idol Cigarettes' at base of back:			
			1 Front black and white, glossy		£2.50	—
			2 Front brown, matt		£2.50	—
			B Space at base of back blank:			
			1 Front black and white, glossy		£2.50	—
			2 Front brown, matt		£2.50	—
C2	P	42	Real Photographs — Set 2 (Beauties) (c1930)	H.576-2	£3.00	—
—	BW	20	Rhymes — black and white sketches (c1905)	H.217	£28.00	—
			The River Thames — see 'Views of the River Thames'			
D1	P	50	Scenes from the Films (1932):			
			A Front black and white		£3.30	—
			B Front sepia		£3.30	—
A2	BW	40	Scenes from the Films (1938)		80p	£32.00
D1		35	Scientific Inventions and Discoveries (1929):	H.213		
	C		A Small size, 'The Spinet House ...' back		£1.20	£42.00
	BW		B Small size, 'The Spotlight Tobaccos ...' back		£1.20	£42.00
B1	C		C Large size		£1.20	£42.00
Dl	P	50	Sports (1934):			
			A Titled 'Sports', numbered front and back		£5.00	—
			B Titled 'Sports Series', numbered front only		£12.00	—
			*C Untitled, numbered front only		£15.00	—
A1	BW	30	*Statuary — Set 1 (c1900):	H.218-1		
			A Black and white front, matt		£50.00	—
	BW		B Black and white front, varnished		£12.00	—
A	BW	30	*Statuary — Set 2 (c1900)	H.218-2	£8.00	£240.00
C1	BW		*Statuary — Set 3 (c1900):	H.218-3		
		? 26	A Name panel white lettering on black background		£25.00	—
		? 4	B Name panel black lettering on grey background		£50.00	—
		? 26	C Name panel black lettering on white background		£50.00	—
D1	C	100	*Transfers (c1935)		£6.00	—

Size	*Print-ing*	*Number in set*		*Handbook reference*	*Price per card*	*Complete set*

R. & J. HILL LTD, London *(continued)*

D	C	20	*Types of the British Army (1914):			
			A 'Badminton' back		£30.00	—
			B 'Verbena' back		£30.00	—
B2	CP		Views of Interest:			
		48	'A First Series ...' Nd. 1-48 (1938):			
			A 'The Spinet House ...' back		30p	£15.00
			B 'Sunripe & Spinet Ovals ...' back		25p	£12.50
		48	'Second Series ...' Nd. 49-96 (1938)		25p	£12.50
		48	'Third Series ...' Nd. 97-144 (1939)		25p	£12.50
		48	'Fourth Series ...' Nd. 145-192 (1939)		50p	£25.00
		48	'Fifth Series ...' Nd. 193-240 (1939)		60p	£30.00
B2	CP		Views of Interest — British Empire Series ...:			
		48	'1st Issue — Canada — Nos. 1-48' (1940)		40p	£20.00
		48	'2nd Issue — India — Nos. 49-96' (1940)		£2.50	£120.00
	U	50	Views of London (1925):	H.577		
C			A Small size		80p	£40.00
B1			B Large size		90p	£45.00
	C	50	Views of the River Thames (1924):			
D			A Small size:			
			Nos. 1-25		£1.80	£45.00
			Nos. 26-50		£1.40	£35.00
B1			B Large size:			
			1 Back in green (thin card)		£1.50	£75.00
			2 Back in green and black (thick card)		£1.50	£75.00
	U	50	Who's Who in British Films (Nov. 1927):			
A2			A Small size		£1.60	£80.00
B2			B Large size		£1.60	£80.00
C	C	84	Wireless Telephony (1923)		£1.50	£125.00
B1	U	20	Wireless Telephony — Broadcasting Series (1923)		£2.50	£50.00
A	U	25	World's Masterpieces — 'Second Series' (c1915)		£2.00	£50.00
	U	50	Zoological Series (1924):	H.578		
C			A Small size:			
			1 Back in light brown		80p	£40.00
			2 Back in grey		90p	£45.00
B1			B Large size:			
			1 Back in light brown		90p	£45.00
			2 Back in dark brown		90p	£45.00

CANVASES. Unbacked canvases. The material is a linen fabric, glazed to give the appearance of canvas. Specimens are found rubber stamped in red on back 'The Pipe Tobacco de Luxe Spinet Mixture'.

—	C	30	'Britain's Stately Homes' (78 × 61mm) (c1915)		£3.70	—
—	C		*Canvas Masterpieces — Series 1 (73 × 61mm) (c1915):			
			A 'Badminton Tobacco Factories ...' back:			
		40	1 'H.T. & Co., Ltd., Leeds' at right base		£1.50	—
		20	2 Cardigan Press, Leeds' at right base (Nos. 21-40)		£1.50	—
		10	3 Without printers' credit (Nos. 21-30)		£1.50	—
		3	4 As 3, but size 73 × 53mm (Nos. 23-25)		£1.50	—
		40	B 'The Spinet House ...' back		£2.00	£80.00
—	C	40	*Canvas Masterpieces — Series 2, Nd. 41-80 (73 × 61mm) (c1915)	H.509	£2.50	£100.00
—	C	10	*Canvas Masterpieces — Series 2, Nd. 1-10 (c1915):			
			Nos. 1 to 5		£2.00	£10.00
			Nos. 6 to 10		£3.00	£15.00
—	C	5	Chinese Pottery and Porcelain — Series 1 (132 × 108mm) (c1915)		—	£40.00
			4 Different (minus No. 5)		60p	£2.50

Size	Print-ing	Number in set		Handbook reference	Price per card	Complete set

R. & J. HILL LTD, London *(continued)*

—	C	11	Chinese Pottery and Porcelain — Series 2 (107 × 62mm) (c1915)		£6.00	—
—	C	23	*Great War Leaders — Series 10 (73 × 60mm) (1919)		£6.00	—

OVERSEAS ISSUE

A2	C	10	Chinese Series (c1912)		£80.00	—

L. HIRST & SON, Leeds

—	C	? 5	*Soldiers and their Uniforms (cutouts) (c1915)	H.138	£250.00	—

J.W. HOBSON, Huddersfield

C2	C	18	Motor Cycle Series (c1914)	H.469	£100.00	—

J. & T. HODGE, Glasgow

—	C	? 5	*British Naval Crests (70 × 38mm) (c1896)	H.219	£700.00	—
A	BW	16	British Royal Family (c1901)	H.28	£250.00	—
—	U		*Scottish Views (c1898):	H.220		
		? 11	A Thick card (74 × 39mm)		£200.00	—
		? 14	B Thin card (80 × 45mm)		£200.00	—

HOOK OF HOLLAND CIGARETTES

A	U	? 5	*Footballers (c1905)	H.745	£650.00	—

HUDDEN & CO. LTD, Bristol

C	C	26	*Actresses — 'FROGA A' (c1900)	H.20	£65.00	—
C	C	25	*Beauties — 'CHOAB' (c1900)	H.21	£55.00	—
A2	U	20	*Beauties — 'Crown Seal Cigarettes' (c1898)	H.221	£140.00	—
A	U	24	*Beauties — 'HUMPS' (c1898):	H.222		
			A Blue scroll back		£75.00	—
			B Orange scroll back		£60.00	—
			C Typeset back in brown		£400.00	—
D1	C	? 12	Comic Phrases (c1900)	H.223	£100.00	—
D	U	25	Famous Boxers (1927)	H.721	£35.00	—
A	C	25	*Flags of All Nations (c1905)	H.37	£26.00	£650.00
—	C	48	*Flowers and Designs (55 × 34mm) (c1900):	H.224		
			A 'Hudden Cigarettes' back		£85.00	—
			B 'Hudden's — Dandy Dot' back		£200.00	—
A	C	18	*Pretty Girl Series — 'RASH' (c1900)	H.8	£90.00	—
C	U	50	Public Schools and Colleges (c1925)	H.575	£2.00	£100.00
A	C	25	Soldiers of the Century, Nd. 26-50 (1901)		£50.00	—
A	C	25	Sports and Pastimes Series 1 (c1925)	H.225	£55.00	—
A	C	25	*Star Girls (c1900)	H.30	£100.00	—
A	C	25	Types of Smokers (c1903)		£50.00	—

HUDSON

D	U	? 1	*Actresses — 'ANGOOD' (c1900)	H.187	£600.00	—
C	C	25	*Beauties — selections from 'BOCCA' (c1900)	H.39	£500.00	—

HUNTER, Airdrie

A	BW	? 11	*Footballers (c1910)	H.227	£2000.00	—

J.T. ILLINGWORTH & SONS, Kendal

—	P	48	Beautiful Scotland (77 × 52mm) (1939)	H.564-1	£2.00	—

Size	Print-ing	Number in set		Handbook reference	Price per card	Complete set

J.T. ILLINGWORTH & SONS, Kendal *(continued)*

C1	C	25	*Cavalry (1924)		£6.00	£150.00
—	P	48	Coastwise (77 × 52mm) (1938)	H.564-2	£1.00	£50.00
A	C	25	'Comicartoons' of sport (1927)		£7.00	£175.00
—	P	48	Flying (77 × 52mm) (1938)	H.564-3	£1.80	£90.00
A	C	25	*Motor Car Bonnets (1925)		£8.00	£200.00
A	C	25	*Old Hostels (1926)		£6.00	£150.00
—	P	48	Our Countryside (77 × 52mm) (1938)	H.564-4	£2.00	£100.00
—	P	24	Shots from the Films (1937)	H.566	£4.50	—
A	BW	25	Views from the English Lakes (c1895)	H.228	£225.00	—

THE IMPERIAL TOBACCO CO. (of Great Britain & Ireland) Ltd, Bristol

A	C	50	British Birds (c1910)	H.229	£5.00	—
C	C	1	Folder — Coronation of His Majesty King Edward VII (1902)		—	£100.00
—	C	10	Out of the Blue — Richmond Adverts (2002):			
			A Size 75 × 32mm		£2.00	—
			B Size 80 × 47mm		£2.00	—
			C Size 90 × 47mm		£1.50	—
G2	C	12	Supertrivia — Superkings Adverts (c2000)		£2.00	—

INGRAM'S, 1A, 27 & 33 Leigh Road, Eastleigh

D	C	30	*Army Pictures, Cartoons, etc (1916)	H.12	£120.00	—

INTERNATIONAL TOBACCO CO. LTD, London

—	C	28	Domino cards (69 × 35mm) (1938)		25p	£7.00
	U		*Famous Buildings and Monuments of Britain (1934) (bronze metal plaques)	H.580		
		50	'Series A':			
A1			1 Nos. 1-30, small size		£1.00	£30.00
B2			2 Nos. 31-50, large size		£1.00	£20.00
		50	'Series B':			
A1			1 Nos. 51-80, small size		£1.80	£55.00
B2			2 Nos. 81-100, large size		£1.80	£36.00
A2	C	100	Film Favourites (c1937):	H.581		
			A Back in grey		£2.40	—
			B Back in black		£2.40	—
—	C	100	'Gentlemen! The King!' — (60 small, 40 large) (1937):	H.582		
			A Back in blue		50p	£50.00
			B Back in black		20p	£20.00
A	C	50	International Code of Signals (1934)		80p	£40.00
D	C	48	Screen Lovers — 'Summit' (unissued) (c1940)		£3.20	—

*The same plaques were also used for an export issue, with envelopes inscribed 'International Tobacco (Overseas), Ltd.'

J.L.S. TOBACCO CO., London

('Star of the World' Cigarettes)

D	BW	20	*Boer War Cartoons (1901)	H.42	£150.00	—
B2	BW	? 32	*Boer War Celebrities — 'JASAS' (c1901)	H.133	£225.00	—
A2	C	30	*Colonial Troops (c1901)	H.40	£100.00	—

PETER JACKSON, London

	P		Beautiful Scotland (1939):	H.564-1		
D		28	A Small size		£1.25	£35.00
—		48	B Medium size, 77 × 52mm		£1.00	£50.00

Size	Printing	Number in set		Handbook reference	Price per card	Complete set

PETER JACKSON, London *(continued)*

	P		Coastwise (1938):	H.564-2		
D		28	A Small size		£1.25	£35.00
—		48	B Medium size, 77 × 52mm		£1.25	£60.00
D	P	28	Famous Film Stars (1935)		£3.50	£100.00
D	P	27	Famous Films (1934)		£3.50	£100.00
D	P	28	Film Scenes (1936)		£3.50	£100.00
B	P	28	Film Scenes (1936)		£4.50	£125.00
	P		Flying (1938):	H.564-3		
D		28	A Small size		£3.00	—
—		48	B Medium size (77 × 52mm)		£3.50	—
—	C	100	'Gentlemen! The King!' (60 small, 40 large) (1937):	H.582		
			A Overprinted on International black back		£1.00	£100.00
			B Overprinted on International blue back		£1.00	—
			C Reprinted with Jackson's name at base:			
			i Back in black		£1.00	—
			ii Back in blue		£2.00	—
D	P	28	Life in the Navy (1937)		£2.00	£55.00
B	P	28	Life in the Navy (1937)		£2.50	£70.00
	P		Our Countryside (1938):	H.564-4		
D		28	A Small size		£1.00	£28.00
—		48	B Medium size (77 × 52mm)		£1.25	£60.00
—	C	150	The Pageant of Kingship — 90 small, 60 large (1937):			
			A Inscribed 'Issued by Peter Jackson'		50p	£75.00
			B Inscribed 'Issued by Peter Jackson (Overseas), Ltd.':			
			1 Printed on board		50p	£75.00
			2 Printed on paper		33p	£50.00
	P		Shots from the Films (1937):	H.566		
D		28	A Small size		£3.00	£85.00
—		24	B Medium size (77 × 52mm)		£3.25	£80.00
—	C	250	Speed — Through the Ages (170 small, 80 large) (1937)	H.583	30p	£75.00
D	P	28	Stars in Famous Films (1935)		£3.40	£90.00

JACOBI BROS. & CO. LTD, London

A	BW	? 32	*Boer War Celebrities — 'JASAS' (c1901):	H.133		
			A Black and white front		£200.00	—
			B As A, but mauve tinted		£200.00	—

JAMES & CO. (Birmingham) LTD

—	C	20	Arms of Countries (c1915):			
			A Size 70 × 40mm		£150.00	—
			B Size 70 × 49mm		£150.00	—

JAMES'S (GOLD LEAF NAVY CUT)

A	U	? 11	Pretty Girl Series — 'BAGG' (c1898)	H.45	£350.00	—

J.B. JOHNSON & CO., London

A	C	25	*National Flags and Flowers — Girls (c1900)	H.123	£325.00	—

JOHNSTON'S CIGARETTES

A	U	? 3	*British Views (c1910)	H.746	£650.00	—

Size	Print-ing	Number in set		Handbook reference	Price per card	Complete set

JONES BROS., Tottenham

A	BW	20	*Spurs Footballers:	H.230		
			A 12 Small titles (1911):			
			i 10 Different		£14.00	—
			ii F Bentley		£100.00	—
			iii H Middlemiss		£150.00	—
			B 6 Large titles (1912):			
			i 4 Different		£14.00	—
			ii E J Lightfoot		£200.00	—
			iii R McTavish		£150.00	—
			C 1 Team Group of 36 (1910-11)		£900.00	—
			D 1 Team Group of 34 (1911-12)		£900.00	—

A.I. JONES & CO. Ltd, London

—	C	1	*Advertisement Card — Alexia Mixture (80 × 46mm) (c1900)	H.748	—	£700.00
D	C	12	Nautical Terms (c1905)	H.231	£45.00	—

A.S. JONES, Grantham

D	C	30	Army Pictures, Cartoons, etc (c1916)	H.12	£120.00	—

ALEX. JONES & CO., London

D2	U		*Actresses — 'ANGOOD' (c1898):	H.187		
		? 15	A Front in brown		£250.00	—
		? 1	B Front in green		£500.00	—
A	BW	1	Portrait of Queen Victoria 1897		—	£150.00

T.E. JONES & CO., Aberavon

D	C	? 2	*Conundrums (c1900)	H.232	£225.00	—
A2	C	50	*Flags of All Nations (c1899)	H.233	£85.00	—
D	C	12	Well-known Proverbs (c1900)	H.235	£200.00	—
—	BW	52	Welsh Rugby Players (64 × 34mm) (1899)	H.234	£225.00	—

C.H. JORDEN LTD, London

—	P	? 12	*Celebrities of the Great War (c1915) (35 × 64mm)	H.236	£90.00	—

J. & E. KENNEDY, Dublin

A	U	25	*Beauties — 'FECKSA' (c1900)	H.58	£50.00	—

RICHARD KENNEDY, Dundee

—	C	? 25	*Naval & Military Cartoons (130 × 90mm) (c1905)	H.701	£500.00	—
A	U	50	War Portraits (1916)	H.86	£100.00	—

KINNEAR LTD, Liverpool

A	C	? 13	*Actresses (c1898)	H.237	£120.00	—
D1	BW	? 15	*Australian Cricketers (1897)	H.238	£225.00	—
—	BW	? 1	Cricket Fixture Folder (89 × 69mm) (1903)	H.750	£1500.00	—
A	C	? 18	*Cricketers (c1895)	H.269	£500.00	—
A2	C	25	*Footballers and Club Colours (c1898)	H.239	£220.00	—
—	U	1	The Four Generations (Royal Family) (65 × 70mm) (1897)	H.749	—	£500.00
—	BW	1	'A Gentleman in Kharki' (44 × 64mm) (1900)		—	£80.00

Size	Print-ing	Number in set		Handbook reference	Price per card	Complete set
KINNEAR LTD, Liverpool *(continued)*						
A	C		*Jockeys (1896):	H.240		
		12	— see H.240—I-1		£60.00	—
		1	— see H.240—I-2		£100.00	—
		25	— see H.240—II-A		£100.00	—
		4	— see H.240—II-B		£100.00	—
A	C	? 2	*Prominent Personages (c1902)	H.479	£800.00	—
D1	U	13	*Royalty (1897)	H.241	£45.00	—
—	U	? 32	Views (49 × 35mm) (c1899)	H.751	£400.00	—
B. KRIEGSFELD & CO., Manchester						
—	C	1	*Advertisement Card— Apple Blossom (c1900)	H.752	—	£1500.00
A2	U		*Beauties — 'KEWA' (c1900):	H.139		
		? 63	A Matt surface		£80.00	—
		? 6	B Glossy surface		£150.00	—
A	C	? 10	Celebrities (c1900):	H.242		
			A Backs Horizontal Format		£200.00	—
			B Backs Vertical Format		£200.00	—
A	C	50	*Flags of All Nations (c1900)	H.233	£65.00	—
A	C	50	*Phrases and Advertisements (c1900)	H.243	£80.00	—
A. KUIT LTD, Manchester						
—	C	? 12	*Arms of Cambridge Colleges* (17 × 25mm) (c1914)	H.458	£120.00	—
—	C	? 12	*Arms of Companies* (30 × 33mm) (c1914)	H.459	£120.00	—
—	C	30	British Beauties — oval card (36 × 60mm) (c1914)	H.244	£50.00	—
—	P	? 44	*'Crosmedo'Bijoucards (55 × 37mm) (c1915)	H.245	£130.00	—
A	U	25	Principal Streets of British Cities and Towns (1916)		£100.00	—
A	CP	50	Types of Beauty (c1914)	H.246	£100.00	—
LAMBERT & BUTLER, London						
			32 page reference book — £4.50			
A1	BW	20	*Actresses — 'BLARM' (c1900)	H.23	£32.50	£650.00
—	C	10	*Actresses and Their Autographs (c1898):	H.247		
			A Wide card (70 × 38mm): 'Tobacco' back		£150.00	—
			B Narrow card (70 × 34mm): 'Cigarettes' back		£125.00	—
A2	BW	50	*Admirals (1900):	H.248		
			A 'Flaked Gold Leaf Honeydew' back		£18.00	—
			B 'May Blossom' back		£18.00	—
			C 'Prize Medal Bird's Eye' back		£18.00	—
			D 'Viking' back		£24.00	—
—	C	12	Advertisement Cards — Facts about Lambert & Butler (2002):			
			A Size 75 × 32mm		£2.00	—
			B Size 80 × 47mm		£1.50	£18.00
C	C	1	*Advertisement Card — Spanish Dancer (1898)	H.249	—	£450.00
A	C	50	Aeroplane Markings (1937)		£1.70	£85.00
A	C	40	Arms of Kings and Queens of England (1906)		£5.00	£200.00
A	C	25	Aviation(1915)		£4.00	£100.00
A2	C	26	*Beauties — 'HOL' (c1900):	H.192		
			A 'Flaked Gold Leaf Honey Dew' back		£32.00	—
			B 'Log Cabin' back		£32.00	—
			C 'May Blossom' back		£32.00	—
			D 'Viking Navy Cut' back		£32.00	—
A	C	50	Birds and Eggs (1906)	H.60	£3.50	£175.00
C	BW	25	*Boer War and Boxer Rebellion — Sketches (1904)	H.46	£32.00	—

Size	Print-ing	Number in set		Handbook reference	Price per card	Complete set

LAMBERT & BUTLER, London *(continued)*

Size	Print-ing	Number in set		Handbook reference	Price per card	Complete set
C	U	20	*Boer War Generals — 'CLAM' (1900):	H.61		
			I 10. No frame lines to back:			
			A Brown back		£35.00	—
			B Black back		£35.00	—
			II 10. With frame lines to back:			
			A Brown back		£35.00	—
			B Black back		£35.00	—
C	B	10	*Boer War Generals — 'FLAC' (1901)	H.47	£40.00	—
C	U	1	*Boer War Series — 'The King of Scouts' (Col. R.S.S. Baden-Powell) (1901)	H.753	—	£450.00
A	C	25	British Trees and Their Uses (1927)	H.654	£2.00	£50.00
A	C	25	Common Fallacies (1928)		£2.00	£50.00
—	C	50	*Conundrums (38 × 57mm) (1901):	H.250		
			A Blue back — thick card		£22.00	—
			B Green back		£16.00	—
A2	C	12	Coronation Robes (1902)	H.251	£18.00	£220.00
A	C	25	Dance Band Leaders (1936)		£4.00	£100.00
A	C	50	Empire Air Routes (1936)		£2.00	£100.00
A	BW	25	Famous British Airmen and Airwomen (1935)		£2.00	£50.00
A	U	25	Fauna of Rhodesia (1929)		£1.20	£30.00
A	C	50	Find Your Way:			
			A Address 'Box No. 152, London' (1932)		£1.50	£75.00
			B Address 'Box No. 152, Drury Lane, London' (1932)		£1.50	£75.00
			C Overprinted in red (1933)		£1.50	£75.00
A	BW	1	D Joker Card:			
			i Without overprint (1932)		—	£12.00
			ii With overprint (1933)		—	£12.00
A	C	50	Footballers 1930-1 (1931)		£4.50	—
A	C	25	Garden Life (1930)	H.449	£1.00	£25.00
A	C	25	Hints and Tips for Motorists (1929)		£4.00	£100.00
A	U	25	A History of Aviation:			
			A Front in green (1932)		£2.00	£50.00
			B Front in brown (1933)		£2.80	£70.00
A	C	50	Horsemanship (1938)		£2.50	£125.00
A	C	25	How Motor Cars Work (1931)		£2.20	£55.00
A	C	50	Interesting Customs and Traditions of the Navy, Army and Air Force (1939)		£1.00	£50.00
A	C	25	Interesting Musical Instruments (1929)		£2.60	£65.00
A	C	50	Interesting Sidelights on the Work of the GPO (1939)		£1.00	£50.00
A	C	20	International Yachts (1902)		£65.00	—
A	C	25	Japanese Series (1904):			
			A Thick toned card		£8.00	£200.00
			B Thin white card		£8.00	£200.00
—	C	4	*Jockeys, no frame lines (35 × 70mm) (c1903)	H.252	£55.00	£220.00
—	C	10	*Jockeys with frame lines (35 × 70mm) (c1903)	H.252	£55.00	£550.00
A	C	50	Keep Fit (1937)		80p	£40.00
A	C	25	London Characters (1934):			
			A With Album Clause		£2.40	£60.00
			B Without Album Clause		£20.00	—
A	C	1	*Mayblossom Calendar, 1900		—	£750.00
A	C	25	Motor Car Radiators (1928)		£6.00	£150.00
A	C	25	Motor Cars — 'A Series of 25', green back (1922)		£2.60	£65.00
A	C	25	Motor Cars — '2nd Series of 25' (1923)		£2.60	£65.00
A	C	50	Motor Cars — '3rd Series of 50' (1926)		£4.00	£200.00
A	C	25	Motor Cars — 'A Series of 25', grey back (1934)		£3.60	£90.00
A	C	50	Motor Cycles (1923)		£3.50	£175.00

Size	Printing	Number in set		Handbook reference	Price per card	Complete set

LAMBERT & BUTLER, London *(continued)*

Size	Printing	Number in set		Handbook reference	Price per card	Complete set
A	C	50	Motor Index Marks (1926)		£2.60	£130.00
A	C	25	Motors (1908):	H.703		
			A Green back		£27.00	—
			B Plain back		£27.00	—
A	BW	25	Naval Portraits (1914)		£4.00	£100.00
A	BW	50	Naval Portraits, incl. above 25 (1915)		£4.00	£200.00
—	C	3	Packet Redesign of The Pack (1998):			
			A Size 75 × 32mm		£2.00	—
			B Size 80 × 47mm		£2.00	—
A	C	25	Pirates and Highwaymen (1926)		£1.40	£35.00
A	U	25	Rhodesian Series (1928)		£1.40	£35.00
A	C	50	The Thames from Lechlade to London:	H.754		
			A Small numerals (1907)		£6.00	£300.00
			B Large numerals (1908)		£6.00	£300.00
			C Plain back		£6.00	—
A	U	25	Third Rhodesian Series (1930)		60p	£15.00
—	C	12	Total Experience Total Trivia — Size 80 × 47mm (1999)		£2.00	—
—	C	4	*Types of the British Army & Navy (35 × 70mm) (c1897):	H.254		
			A 'Specialities' back in brown		£70.00	—
			B 'Specialities' back in black		£70.00	—
			C 'Viking' back in black		£70.00	—
A	C	25	*Waverley series (1904)	H.255	£12.00	£300.00
A	C	25	Winter Sports (1914)		£5.00	£125.00
A	C	25	Wireless Telegraphy (1909)		£5.00	£125.00
A	C	25	Wonders of Nature (1924)		80p	£20.00
A	C	25	World's Locomotives, Nd. 1-25 (1912)		£4.00	£100.00
A	C	50	World's Locomotives Nd. 1-50 (1912)		£5.00	£250.00
A	C	25	World's Locomotives, Nd. 1A-25A (c1913)		£4.60	£115.00

OVERSEAS ISSUES

Size	Printing	Number in set		Handbook reference	Price per card	Complete set
D2	U	50	Actors and Actresses — 'WALP' (1905)		£3.50	—
		250	Actresses — 'ALWICS' (1905):			
D2	U		A Portraits in black, border in red:			
			i Scout back		£5.00	—
			ii With firm's name		£3.50	—
D2	BW		B Portraits and border in black		£7.00	—
D2	U	50	Beauties red tinted (1908):			
			A Scout back		£3.50	—
			B With firm's name		£4.00	—
A	C	83	Danske Byvaabner (c1915)		£15.00	—
	BW	26	Etchings of Dogs (1926):			
A			A Small size		£30.00	—
—			B Medium size (80 × 54mm)		£30.00	—
D2	C	25	Flag Girls of All Nations (1908)		£12.00	—
A2	P	50	Homeland Events (1928)		£2.20	£110.00
A	P	50	London Zoo (1927)		£1.40	—
A	C	50	Merchant Ships of the World (1924)		£2.40	—
D2	BW	30	Music Hall Celebrities (1916)		£6.00	—
A	P	50	Popular Film Stars (1926):			
			A Series title in one line, no brand quoted		£1.40	£70.00
			B Series title in two lines, inscribed 'Varsity Cigarettes'		£2.50	—
			C Series title in two lines, no brand quoted		£1.40	£70.00
A	P	50	The Royal Family at Home and Abroad (1927)		£1.40	£70.00
A	BW	100	Royalty, Notabilities and Events 1900-1902 (1902)	W.28	£14.00	—
D2	BW	100	Russo Japanese series (1905)		£6.00	—

Size	*Print-ing*	*Number in set*		*Handbook reference*	*Price per card*	*Complete set*

LAMBERT & BUTLER, London *(continued)*

D	P	50	Types of Modern Beauty (1927)		£1.40	£70.00
A	P	50	Who's Who in Sport (1926)		£3.00	£150.00
A	P	50	The World of Sport (1927)		£2.00	£100.00
A	U	50	Zoological Studies (c1928)		£10.00	—

LAMBKIN BROS., Cork

A	C	36	*Country Scenes — Small size (1924) (6 sets of 6):			
			Series 1 — Yachting		£7.00	—
			Series 2 — Country		£7.00	—
			Series 3 — Far East		£7.00	—
			Series 4 — Sailing		£7.00	—
			Series 5 — Country		£7.00	—
			Series 6 — Country		£7.00	—
C	C	36	*Country Scenes — Large size (1924) (6 sets of 6):			
			Series 7 — Yachting		£7.00	—
			Series 8 — Country		£7.00	—
			Series 9 — Far East		£7.00	—
			Series 10 — Sailing		£7.00	—
			Series 11 — Country		£7.00	—
			Series 12 — Windmill Scenes		£7.00	—
—	C	? 9	**Irish Views, anonymous. inscribed 'Eagle, Cork'* (68 × 67mm) (c1925)	H.585	£40.00	—
—	C	? 5	*'Lily of Killarney' Views (73 × 68mm) (c1925)	H.586	£200.00	—

LANCS & YORKS TOBACCO MANUFACTURING CO. LTD, Burnley (L. & Y. Tob. Mfg. Co.)

C	C	26	*Actresses — 'FROGA A' (c1900)	H.20	£500.00	—

C. & J. LAW, Hertford

A	C	25	*Types of British Soldiers (c1914)	H.144	£28.00	—
A	U	50	War Portraits (1916)	H.86	£100.00	—

R.J. LEA LTD, Manchester

A	C	1	*Advertisement Card — Swashbuckler (c1913)		—	£1000.00
A1	C	50	Chairman Miniatures 1-50 (1912):			
			A No border		£3.00	£150.00
			B Gilt border		£3.00	£150.00
A1	C	50	Chairman and Vice Chair Miniatures, 51-100 (1912)		£3.00	£150.00
—	C	1	Chairman Puzzles Picture No 1 (diamond shaped 54 × 31mm) (c1910)	H.755	£300.00	—
—	C	12	Chairman Puzzles Picture No 2 (60 × 21mm) (c1910)	H.755	£300.00	—
A1	BW	25	Chairman War Portraits (marked 'War Series' on front) (1915)		£5.00	£125.00
A	C	70	Cigarette Transfers (Locomotives) (1916)		£8.00	—
A	BW	25	Civilians of Countries Fighting with the Allies (1914)		£12.00	£300.00
		48	Coronation Souvenir (1937):			
A2	P		A Small size, glossy:			
			1 Lea's name		60p	£30.00
			2 'Successors to ...'		40p	£20.00
A2	BW		B Small size, matt:			
			1 Lea's name		£1.00	£50.00
			2 Successors to		50p	£25.00
—	P		C Medium size (77 × 51mm)		60p	£30.00

Size	Printing	Number in set		Handbook reference	Price per card	Complete set

R.J. LEA LTD, Manchester *(continued)*

Size	Printing	Number in set		Handbook reference	Price per card	Complete set
A2	C	50	Dogs (1923):			
			1 Nos. 1-25 — A White card		£4.00	—
			B Cream card		£4.00	—
			2 Nos. 26-50		£6.00	—
A2	C	25	English Birds (1922):			
			A Glossy front		£3.00	£75.00
			B Matt front		£6.00	—
A2	C	25	The Evolution of the Royal Navy (1925)		£2.40	£60.00
A2	P	54	Famous Film Stars (1939)		£1.30	£70.00
	CP	48	Famous Racehorses of 1926 (1927):			
A2			A Small size		£3.00	£150.00
			B Medium size (75 × 50mm)		£8.00	—
		48	Famous Views (1936):			
A2	P		A Small size — 1 Glossy		25p	£12.50
	BW		2 Matt		£1.00	£50.00
—	P		B Medium size (76 × 51mm)		50p	£25.00
A2	P	36	Film Stars — 'A First Series ...' (1934)		£3.00	£110.00
A2	P	36	Film Stars — 'A Second Series ...' (1934)		£2.75	£100.00
A2	C	25	Fish (1926)		£2.40	£60.00
A1	C	50	Flowers to Grow (The Best Perennials) (1913)		£4.00	£200.00
A2		48	Girls from the Shows (1935):			
	P		A Glossy front		£2.20	£110.00
	BW		B Matt front		£2.50	£125.00
A1	C	50	Modern Miniatures (1913)	H.756	—	£360.00
			46 different, less 1, 8, 12, 32		£1.75	£80.00
A1	C	12	More Lea's Smokers (1906):	H.256		
			A Green borders		£80.00	—
			B Red borders		£110.00	—
A1	C	50	Old English Pottery and Porcelain, 1-50 (1912)		£2.00	£100.00
A1	C	50	Old Pottery and Porcelain, 51-100 (1912):			
			A 'Chairman Cigarettes'		£1.60	£80.00
			B 'Recorder Cigarettes'		£6.00	—
A1	C	50	Old Pottery and Porcelain, 101-150 (1912):			
			A 'Chairman Cigarettes'		£1.60	£80.00
			B 'Recorder Cigarettes'		£6.00	—
A1	C	50	Old Pottery and Porcelain, 151-200 (1913)		£1.60	£80.00
A1	C	50	Old Pottery and Porcelain, 201-250 (1913)		£1.60	£80.00
—	C	24	Old English Pottery and Porcelain (138 × 89mm) (Inscribed Chairman Cigarette Series or other firms' names, postcard format back) (c1910)	H.257	£6.00	—
A2		54	Radio Stars (1935):			
	P		A Glossy front		£2.20	£120.00
	BW		B Matt front		£3.00	£160.00
A2	C	50	Roses (1924)		£1.60	£80.00
A2	C	50	Ships of the World (1925)		£1.80	£90.00
A	BW	25	War Pictures (1915)		£4.40	£110.00
		48	Wonders of the World (1938):			
A2	P		A Small size — 1 Glossy		60p	£30.00
	BW		2 Matt		£1.40	£65.00
	P		B Medium size (76 × 50mm)		60p	£30.00

SILKS. All paper-backed.

Size	Printing	Number in set		Handbook reference	Price per card	Complete set
—	C		*Butterflies and Moths III (c1925):	H.505-7		
		12	1 Small size (70 × 44mm)		£4.50	£55.00
		12	2 Large size (70 × 88mm)		£4.00	£50.00
		6	3 Extra-large size (143 × 70mm)		£4.50	£27.00
—	C	54	*Old Pottery — Set 1 (68 × 38mm) (c1915)	H.505-14	£1.00	£55.00

Size	Printing	Number in set		Handbook reference	Price per card	Complete set

R. J. LEA LTD, Manchester *(continued)*

Size	Printing	Number in set		Handbook reference	Price per card	Complete set
—	C	72	*Old Pottery — Set 2 (61 × 37mm) (c1915)	H.505-14	£1.00	£75.00
—	C	50	Regimental Crests and Badges — Series I (48mm sq.) (c1920)	H.502-4	£1.80	—
—	C	50	Regimental Crests and Badges — Series II (48 mm sq.) (c1920)	H.502-4	£2.00	—

ALFRED L. LEAVER, London

Size	Printing	Number in set		Handbook reference	Price per card	Complete set
—	U	12	Manikin Cards (79 × 51mm) (c1925)	H.481	£150.00	—

J. LEES, Northampton

Size	Printing	Number in set		Handbook reference	Price per card	Complete set
A	C	? 21	Northampton Town Football Club (No. 301-321) (c1912)		£120.00	—

A. LEWIS & CO. (WESTMINSTER) LTD, London

Size	Printing	Number in set		Handbook reference	Price per card	Complete set
A2	C	52	Horoscopes (1938)	H.587	80p	£42.00

H.C. LLOYD & SON, Exeter

Size	Printing	Number in set		Handbook reference	Price per card	Complete set
A	U	28	Academy Gems (c1900):	H.258		
			A Red-brown tint		£50.00	—
			B Purple tint		£50.00	—
			C Green tint		£50.00	—
D	BW	? 26	*Actresses and Boer War Celebrities (c1900)	H.260	£45.00	—
—	BW		*Devon Footballers and Boer War Celebrities (c1901):	H.259		
		? 42	Set 1 — Without framelines (70 × 41mm)		£50.00	—
		? 6	Set 2 — With framelines (70 × 45mm)		£225.00	—
A1	C	25	*Star Girls — 'Tipsy Loo Cigarettes' (c1898):	H.30		
			A Brand name in capitals:			
			i Black		£400.00	—
			ii Blue		£400.00	—
			iii Red		£400.00	—
			B Brand name in upper and lower case		£400.00	—
—	BW	36	War Pictures (73 × 69mm) (c1914)		£325.00	—

RICHARD LLOYD & SONS, London

Most cards inscribed 'Branch of Cope Bros. & Co., Ltd.' See also under 'Cope Bros'.

Size	Printing	Number in set		Handbook reference	Price per card	Complete set
A	C	25	Atlantic Records (1936)		£3.00	£75.00
—	BW	25	*Boer War Celebrities (35 × 61mm) (1899)	H.261	£37.00	—
A2	P	27	Cinema Stars, glossy — 'A Series of 27', Nd. 1-27 (c1934)		£7.00	—
A2	P	27	Cinema Stars, glossy — 'A Series of 27', Nd. 28-54 (c1934)		£2.50	£70.00
A2	P	27	Cinema Stars, glossy — 'Third Series of 27', Nd. 55-81 (1935)		£7.00	—
A2	U	25	Cinema Stars, matt — 'A Series of 25' (c1937)		£2.00	£50.00
A	BW	25	*Famous Cricketers (Puzzle Series) (1930)	H.661	£6.50	—
—	U	? 23	*General Interest — Actresses, Celebrities and Yachts (62 × 39mm) (c1900)	H.262	£100.00	—
Al	C	96	*National Types, Costumes and Flags (c1900)	H.263	£35.00	—
D	C		Old Inns:			
		25	A1 Titled 'Old English Inns' (1923)		£1.60	£40.00
		25	A2 Titled 'Old Inns — Series 2' (1924)		£3.00	£75.00
		50	B Titled 'Old Inns' (1925)		£1.60	£80.00
A	C	10	*Scenes from San Toy* (c1905)	H.462	£10.00	£100.00

Size	Print-ing	Number in set		Handbook reference	Price per card	Complete set

RICHARD LLOYD & SONS, London *(continued)*

A	BW	25	Tricks and Puzzles (1935)		£1.00	£25.00
A2	U	25	Types of Horses (1926):			
			A Back in light brown		£4.00	£100.00
			B Back in dark brown		£4.00	£100.00
A2	U	25	'Zoo' Series (1926)	H.588	£1.00	£25.00

A. LOWNIE, Abroath

A	C	30	*Army Pictures, Cartoons, etc. (c1916)	H.12	£120.00	—

LUSBY LTD, London

D	C	25	Scenes from Circus Life (c1900)	H.264	£120.00	—

HUGH McCALL, Edinburgh, Glasgow and Aberdeen

C	C	? 1	*RAF Advertisement Card (c1924)	H.594	£400.00	—

D. & J. MACDONALD, Glasgow

A	C	? 10	*Actresses — 'MUTA' (c1891)	H.265	£120.00	—
A	BW	25	*Cricketers (c1902)	H.266	£450.00	—
—	BW	? 24	*Cricket and Football Teams (71 × 69mm) (c1902):	H.267		
			A 'Winning Team' Cigarettes		£475.00	—
			B 'Tontine' Cigarettes		£475.00	—
—	C	? 1	County Cricket Team (71 × 69mm) (1900)	H.267	£2000.00	—

MACKENZIE & CO., Glasgow

—	P	50	*Actors and Actresses (32 × 58mm) (c1902)	H.268	£22.00	—
—	U	50	Victorian Art Pictures — Photogravure (32 × 58mm) (c1908)		£24.00	—
A	BW	50	The Zoo (c1910)		£28.00	—

WM. M'KINNELL, Edinburgh

A	C	12	European War Series (1915)	H.129	£75.00	—
A	U	50	War Portraits (1916)	H.86	£100.00	—

MACNAUGHTON, JENKINS & CO. LTD, Dublin

—	C	50	Castles of Ireland (1924):	H.662		
			A Size 76 × 45mm		£4.00	£200.00
			B Size 74 × 44mm		£4.50	—
D	C	50	Various Uses of Rubber (1924)		£2.60	£130.00

A. McTAVISH, Elgin

D	C	30	*Army Pictures, Cartoons etc (c1916)	H12	£120.00	—

McWATTIE & SONS, Arbroath

D	C	30	*Army Pictures, Cartoons etc (c1916)	H.12	£120.00	—

THE MANXLAND TOBACCO CO., Isle of Man

D	BW	? 6	*Views in the Isle of Man (c1900):	H.491		
			A Varnished front		£500.00	—
			B Matt front		£500.00	—

Size	*Print-ing*	*Number in set*		*Handbook reference*	*Price per card*	*Complete set*

MARCOVITCH & CO., London

A2	P	18	**Beauties (anonymous with plain backs, numbered left base of front)* (1932)	GP.490	£1.00	£18.00
			The Story in Red and White (1955):	GP.494		
A	U	6	A Standard size		£4.00	—
—	U	7	B Size 75 × 66mm		£2.00	£14.00

MARCUS & CO., Manchester

A	C	? 18	*Cricketers, 'Marcus Handicap Cigarettes' (1895)	H.269	£500.00	—
A	C	25	*Footballers and Club Colours (1896)	H.239	£200.00	—
—	BW	1	The Four Generations (Royal Family) (65 × 70mm) (1897)	H.749	—	£350.00

T.W. MARKHAM, Bridgwater

—	BW	? 28	Views of Bridgwater (68 × 42mm) (c1906)	H.709	£120.00	—

MARSUMA LTD, Congleton

A	BW	50	*Famous Golfers and Their Strokes (c1914)		£45.00	—

C. MARTIN, Moseley

D	C	30	*Army Pictures, Cartoons etc. (c1916)	H12	£120.00	—

MARTINS LTD, London

A	C	1	''Arf a Mo', Kaiser!' (c1915)		—	£75.00
—	U		Carlyle Series — folding card (c1918):	H.270		
			A Second page 'Martin Bros.'			
		? 3	i Size 83 × 38mm		£125.00	—
		? 14	ii Size 83 × 78mm		£125.00	—
		? 4	B Third page 'Martin Bros.'		£125.00	—
		? 3	C Second Page 'Martin's Ltd'		£125.00	—
—	U	? 781	The Performer Tobacco Fund Photographs – Celebrities (140 × 88mm) (c1916)		£7.00	—
D	U	25	*VC Heroes (c1916)		£28.00	£700.00

R. MASON & CO., London

C	C	30	*Colonial Troops (c1902)	H.40	£55.00	—
D2	C	40	*Naval and Military Phrases (c1904):	H.14		
			A White Border		£50.00	—
			B No Border		£50.00	—

JUSTUS VAN MAURIK

—	C	12	*Dutch Scenes (108 × 70mm) (c1920)	H.622	£150.00	—

MAY QUEEN CIGARETTES

—	C	12	Interesting Pictures (68 × 48mm) (c1960)		£1.00	—

MENTORS LTD, London

—	C	32	Views of Ireland (42 × 67mm) (c1912)	H.271	£12.00	—

J. MILLHOFF & CO. LTD, London

	CP		Antique Pottery (1927):			
A2		54	A Small size		90p	£50.00
—		56	B Medium size (74 × 50mm)		80p	£45.00

Size	*Print-ing*	*Number in set*		*Handbook reference*	*Price per card*	*Complete set*

J. MILLHOFF & CO. LTD, London *(continued)*

	C		Art Treasures:			
D		30	A Small size (1927)		£1.00	£30.00
B		50	B Large size (1926)		70p	£35.00
B	C	25	Art Treasures — '2nd Series of 50', Nd. 51-75 (1928)		£1.00	£25.00
B	C	25	England, Historic and Picturesque — 'Series of 25' (1928)		£1.20	£30.00
B	C	25	England, Historic and Picturesque — 'Second Series ...' (1928)		£1.00	£25.00
A2	P	27	Famous Golfers (1928)		£13.00	—
	P	27	Famous 'Test' Cricketers (1928):			
A2			A Small size		£5.00	—
			B Medium size (76 × 51mm)		£5.00	—
—	C	25	Gallery Pictures (76 × 51mm) (1928)		£1.20	£30.00
A2	C	50	'Geographia' Map Series (sectional) (1931)	GP.506	£1.80	£90.00
	CP		The Homeland Series (1933):	GP.333		
A2		54	A Small size		30p	£17.00
—		56	B Medium size (76 × 51mm)		50p	£28.00
A2	P	36	In the Public Eye (1930)		£1.50	£55.00
D	C	25	Men of Genius (1924)		£5.00	£125.00
B	C	25	Picturesque Old England (1931)		£1.20	£30.00
A2	P		Real Photographs:	GP.7		
		27	'A Series of 27' —			
			A Matt front (c1931)		80p	£22.00
			B Glossy front (c1931)		40p	£11.00
		27	'2nd Series of 27' (c1931)		80p	£22.00
		27	'3rd Series of 27' (c1932)		40p	£11.00
		27	'4th Series of 27' (c1932)		80p	£22.00
		27	'5th Series of 27' (c1933)		£1.10	£30.00
		27	'6th Series of 27' (c1933)		£1.10	£30.00
C	C	25	Reproductions of Celebrated Oil Paintings (1928)	GP.338	£1.60	£40.00
—	U		'RILETTE' Miniature Pictures (60 × 45mm) (c1925):	GP.512		
		20	A Inscribed Series of 20		£3.50	—
		25	B Inscribed Series of 25		£3.50	—
		30	C Inscribed Series of 30		£3.50	—
		42	D Inscribed Series of 42		£3.50	—
		43	E Inscribed Series of 43		£3.50	—
		56	F Inscribed Series of 56		£3.50	—
		74	G Inscribed Series of 74		£3.50	—
B	C	25	Roses (1927)		£2.80	£70.00
			Theatre Advertisement Cards, multi-backed (c1905):			
—	BW	? 9	A Medium size (83 × 56mm)		£180.00	—
—	BW	? 2	B Large size (108 × 83mm)		£250.00	—
A2	C	50	Things to Make — 'De Reszke Cigarettes' (1935)		60p	£30.00
A2	C	50	What the Stars Say — 'De Reszke Cigarettes' (1934)		80p	£40.00
A2	P	36	Zoological Studies (1929)		40p	£14.00

MIRANDA LTD, London

A	C	20	Dogs (c1925)	H.211	£8.00	—
A	C	25	Sports and Pastimes — Series I (c1925)	H.225	£7.00	£175.00

STEPHEN MITCHELL & SON, Glasgow

C	C	51	*Actors and Actresses — Selection from 'FROGA B and C' (c1900)	H.20	£24.00	—
C	U	25	*Actors and Actresses — 'FROGA C' (c1900)	H.20	£24.00	—
C	U	50	*Actors and Actresses — 'FROGA D' (c1900)	H.20	£24.00	—

Size	Printing	Number in set		Handbook reference	Price per card	Complete set

STEPHEN MITCHELL & SON, Glasgow *(continued)*

C	U	26	*Actresses — 'FROGA B' (c1900)	H.20	£24.00	—
A	U	1	Advertisement Card 'Maid of Honour' (c1900)		—	£750.00
A	C	50	Air Raid Precautions (1938)	H.544	£1.00	£50.00
A	C	25	Angling (1928)	H.655	£7.00	£175.00
A	C	50	Arms and Armour (1916)	H.273	£3.80	£190.00
A	C	25	Army Ribbons and Buttons (1916)		£4.00	£100.00
C	BW	25	*Boxer Rebellion — Sketches (c1904)	H.46	£28.00	—
D1	BW	25	British Warships, 1-25 (1915)		£7.00	£175.00
D1	BW	25	British Warships, Second series 26-50 (1915)		£7.00	£175.00
A	C	50	Clan Tartans — 'A Series of 50' (1927)	H.663	£2.00	£100.00
A	C	25	Clan Tartans — '2nd Series, 25' (1927)		£1.00	£25.00
A	C	25	Empire Exhibition, Scotland, 1938 (1938)		£1.00	£25.00
A2	C	25	Famous Crosses (1923)		70p	£17.50
A	C	50	Famous Scots (1933)		£1.80	£90.00
A	U	50	First Aid (1938)		£1.40	£70.00
A	U	50	A Gallery of 1934 (1935)		£3.00	£150.00
A	U	50	A Gallery of 1935 (1936)		£1.90	£95.00
A	C	50	Humorous Drawings (1924)	H.590	£2.50	£125.00
A	C	50	Interesting Buildings (1905)	H.70	£8.00	£400.00
A	C	40	London Ceremonials (1928)		£1.50	£60.00
A	C	25	Medals (1916)	H.71	£5.00	£125.00
A	C	30	A Model Army (cut-outs) (1932)		£1.20	£36.00
A	C	25	Money (1913)		£5.00	£125.00
A	C	25	Old Sporting Prints (1930)	H.563	£1.40	£35.00
A	U	50	Our Empire (1937)	H.522	50p	£25.00
A	C	25	*Regimental Crests, Nicknames and Collar Badges (1900)	H.274	£14.00	£350.00
A	C	70	River and Coastal Steamers (1925)		£4.00	—
A	C		A Road Map of Scotland (1933):			
		50	A Small numerals		£3.50	£175.00
		50	B Large numerals in circles		£3.50	£175.00
		50	C Overprinted in red		£4.50	£225.00
		1	D Substitute card (Blue)		—	£16.00
A	C	50	Scotland's Story (1929)		£2.80	£140.00
A	C	25	Scottish Clan Series No. 1 (1903)	H.33	£14.00	£350.00
A	U	50	Scottish Footballers (1934)		£3.00	£150.00
A	U	50	Scottish Football Snaps (1935)		£3.00	£150.00
A	C	25	Seals (1911)		£5.00	£125.00
A	C	25	Sports (1907)	H.275	£14.00	£350.00
A	C	25	Stars of Screen and History (1939)		£2.80	£70.00
A	C	25	Statues and Monuments (l914)		£4.60	£115.00
—	C	25	Village Models Series (1925):	H.664		
A			A Small size		£2.20	£55.00
			B Medium size (68 × 62mm)		£5.00	£125.00
—	C	25	Village Models Series — 'Second' (1925):	H.664		
A			A Small size:			
			1 Inscribed 'Second Series'		£2.20	£55.00
			2 Not inscribed 'Second Series'		£5.00	—
			B Medium size (68 × 62mm)		£5.00	£125.00
A	U	50	Wonderful Century (1937)		70p	£35.00
A	U	50	The World of Tomorrow (1936)		£1.80	£90.00

MOORGATE TOBACCO CO., London

—	BW	30	The New Elizabethan Age (20 small, 10 large) (1953):			
			A Matt front		£3.30	—
			B Varnished front		£2.00	£60.00

Size	*Print-ing*	*Number in set*		*Handbook reference*	*Price per card*	*Complete set*

B. MORRIS & SONS LTD, London

—	BW	30	*Actresses (41 × 68mm) (1898)	H.276	£2.00	£60.00
C	U	26	*Actresses — 'FROGA A (c1900):	H.20		
			A 'Borneo Queen' back		£32.00	—
			B 'Gold Seals' back		£32.00	—
			C 'Morris's Cigarettes' back		£32.00	—
			D 'Tommy Atkins' back		£80.00	—
—	C	? 4	*Actresses — selection from 'FROGA B' — 'Morris's High Class Cigarettes' on front (76 × 66mm) (c1900)	H.20	£1500.00	—
A1	P	1	*Advertisement Card (Soldier and Girl) (c1900)	H.758	—	£2000.00
A1	C	50	Animals at the Zoo (1924):	H.520		
			A Back in blue		70p	£35.00
			B Back in grey		80p	£40.00
A1	C	35	At the London Zoo Aquarium (1928)		50p	£17.50
A1	BW	25	Australian Cricketers (1925)		£3.60	£90.00
A	C	50	*Beauties — 'CHOAB' (c1900):	H.21		
			A 'Gold Flake Honeydew' back		£50.00	—
			B 'Golden Virginia' back		£50.00	—
			C 'Levant Favourites' back		£50.00	—
			D 'Reina Regenta' back		£50.00	—
A	U	? 53	*Beauties — Collotype, multi-backed (c1897)	H.278	£175.00	—
A	U	21	*Beauties — 'MOM' (c1900):	H.277		
			A 'Borneo Queen' back		£32.00	—
			B 'Gold Seals' back		£32.00	—
			C 'Morris's Cigarettes' back		£32.00	—
			D 'Tommy Atkins' back		£80.00	—
A	C	20	Boer War, 1900 (VC Heroes)	H.279	£35.00	—
A	BW	25	*Boer War Celebrities — 'PAM' (c1901)	H.140	£30.00	—
A2	C	25	Captain Blood (1937)		£1.10	£27.50
D	U	50	Film Star Series (1923)		£3.40	—
A	C	30	*General Interest — six cards each entitled (c1910):	H.280		
			i Agriculture in the Orient		£6.50	£40.00
			ii Architectural Monuments		£6.50	£40.00
			iii The Ice Breaker		£6.50	£40.00
			iv Schools in Foreign Countries		£6.50	£40.00
			v Strange Vessels		£6.50	£40.00
D	U	25	Golf Strokes Series (1923)		£6.00	£150.00
A1	—	12	Horoscopes (wording only) (1936):			
			A White card		£1.00	—
			B Cream card		70p	£8.50
A2	C	25	How Films are Made (1934):			
			A White card		£1.20	£30.00
			B Cream Card		£1.40	£35.00
A1	BW	50	How to Sketch (1929)		£1.20	£60.00
D	BW	20	London Views (c1905):	H.34		
			A 'American Gold' back		£32.00	—
			B 'Morris's Gold Flake' back		£32.00	—
			C 'Smoke Borneo Queen' back		£32.00	—
			D 'Smoke Reina Regenta' back		£32.00	—
A	C	25	Marvels of the Universe Series (c1912)	H.281	£4.00	£100.00
A1	C	25	Measurement of Time (1924)		£1.40	£35.00
D	U	25	Motor Series (Motor parts) (1922)		£4.40	£110.00
D	C	50	National and Colonial Arms (1917)	H.704	£6.00	£300.00
A1	C	25	The Queen's Dolls' House (1925)		£3.20	£80.00
D	U	25	Racing Greyhounds — 'Issued by Forecasta' (1939)		£1.60	£40.00
A1	BW	24	Shadowgraphs (1925)		£2.60	£65.00
A1	C	13	Treasure Island (1924)		£2.00	£26.00

Size	Print-ing	Number in set		Handbook reference	Price per card	Complete set

B. MORRIS & SONS LTD, London *(continued)*

A1	C	50	Victory Signs (1928)		70p	£35.00
C	U	25	War Celebrities (1915)		£5.00	£125.00
D	C	25	War Pictures (1916)	H.51	£8.00	£200.00
A	C	25	Wax Art Series (1931)		50p	£12.50
A	C	25	Whipsnade Zoo (1932)		60p	£15.00
D	C	25	Wireless Series (1923)		£4.40	£110.00
SILKS						
—	C	24	Battleship Crests (70 × 50mm) (paper backed) (c1915)	H.504-3	£35.00	—
—	C		English Flowers (78 × 56mm) (paper backed) (c1915):	H.505-4		
		25	A Series of 25:			
			i Back text 5th line with 'Crewel'		£4.00	—
			ii Back text 5th line overprinted with 'Cruel'		£9.00	—
			iii Back Without 'Crewel' or 'Cruel'		£7.00	—
		50	B Series of 50		£4.50	—
—	C	25	English and Foreign Birds (78 × 56mm) (paper backed) (c1915)	H.505-1	£5.00	£125.00
—	C	25	**Regimental Colours IV* (75 × 55m) (unbacked and anonymous (c1915))	H.502-9	£3.60	£85.00
—	C	4	**Regimental Colours* (210 × 190mm) (c1915)	H.502-13	£60.00	—

PHILIP MORRIS & CO. LTD, London

	U	50	British Views (1924):			
C			A Small size		£3.00	—
—			B Large size (79 × 67mm)		£3.00	—
C	—	108	Classic Collection (90 × 47mm) (1985)	H.894	£1.25	—
C	—	72	Motormania (75 × 45mm) (1986)		£1.50	—

P. MOUAT & CO., Newcastle-on-Tyne

C	C	30	*Colonial Troops (c1902)	H.40	£300.00	—

MOUSTAFA LTD, London

D2	CP	50	Camera Studies (1923):	GP.541		
			A Front with number and caption, back in black		£3.00	—
			* B *Front without letterpress, plain back*		£3.00	—
D2	C	25	*Cinema Stars — Set 8* (1924)	GP.542	£5.00	—
A2	C	40	Leo Chambers Dogs Heads (1924)		£3.50	£140.00
D2	C	25	*Pictures of World Interest* (1923)		£3.40	—
A2	P	25	Real Photos (Views) (1925)		44p	£11.00

MUNRO, Glasgow

C	C	30	Colonial Troops (c1900)		£500.00	—

B. MURATTI, SONS & CO. LTD, Manchester and London

—	U	? 24	*Actresses, cabinet size, collotype (106 × 69mm) (c1898)	GP.551	£125.00	—
C	C	26	*Actresses — 'FROGA A' (c1900):	H.20		
			A 'To the Cigarette Connoisseur' back		£27.00	—
			B 'Muratti's Zinnia Cigarettes' back		£35.00	—
—	C		*Actresses and Beauties — Green Corinthian column framework — 'Neb-Ka' vertical backs (117 × 67mm) (c1900):			
		? 18	Actresses — selection from 'FROGA C'	H.20	£160.00	—
		? 3	Beauties — selection from 'MOM'	H.277/GP.555	£250.00	—

Size	Print-ing	Number in set		Handbook reference	Price per card	Complete set

B. MURATTI, SONS & CO. LTD, Manchester and London *(continued)*

Size	Print-ing	Number in set		Handbook reference	Price per card	Complete set
—	C		*Actresses and Beauties — brown and yellow ornamental framework (117 × 67mm) (c1900):			
			I 'Neb-Ka' horizontal backs:			
		26	i Actresses — selection from 'FROGA A'	H.20	£140.00	—
		50	ii Beauties — selection from 'CHOAB'	H.21	£140.00	—
		25	II Rubber stamped back. Beauties — selection from 'CHOAB'	H.21	£140.00	—
		25	III Plain back — Beauties — selection from 'CHOAB'	H.21	£140.00	—
—	C		*Advertisement Cards, Globe design back (88 × 66mm) (c1900):	GP.552		
		? 10	i Brown borders to front		£400.00	—
		? 19	ii White borders to front		£400.00	—
A2	P	24	Australian Race Horses (export) (c1930)		£1.00	£25.00
C	C	50	*Beauties — 'CHOAB' (Zinnia back) (c1900):	H.21/GP.554		
			A Black printing on back		£45.00	—
			B Olive green printing on back		£60.00	—
—	C	? 66	*Beautiful Women, Globe design back (54 × 75mm) (c1900)	H.284/GP.32	£90.00	—
—	BW	20	*Boer War Generals — 'CLAM' (35 × 61mm) (c1901)	H.61/GP.556	£37.00	—
—	C	15	*Caricatures (42 × 62mm) (c1903):	GP.558		
			A 'Sole Manufacturers of ...' brown back		£30.00	—
			B 'Muratti's Zinnia Cigarettes' brown back		£32.00	—
			C 'Muratti's Zinnia Cigarettes' black back		£30.00	—
			D 'Muratti's Vassos Cigarettes' (not seen)		—	—
			E As D, but 'Vassos' blocked out, brown back		£50.00	—
—	C	35	Crowned Heads (53 × 83mm) (c1913)		£13.00	—
C	C	52	*Japanese Series, Playing Card inset (c1904)	GP.560	£17.00	—
			Plain back		£15.00	—
—	P		Midget Post Card Series (1902):	GP.561		
		? 124	A Matt Front (90 × 70mm)		£11.00	—
		? 18	B Matt Front (80 × 65mm)		£11.00	—
			C Glossy front (85 × 65mm few 75-80 × 65mm):			
		? 96	i With serial numbers		£11.00	—
		? 136	ii Without serial numbers		£11.00	—
—	P	? 127	'Queens' Post Card Series (90 × 70mm) (c1902):	GP.562		
			A Front in black/sepia		£15.00	—
			B Front in reddish brown		£15.00	—
A1	BW	19	*Russo-Japanese Series (1904)	H.184/GP.563	£14.00	£265.00
A1	C	25	*Star Girls (c1898)	H.30	£225.00	—
A	U	? 51	*Views of Jersey (c1912):	GP.564		
			A Plain back		£16.00	—
			B 'Opera House, Jersey' back		£18.00	—
A	U	25	*War Series — 'MURATTI I', white card (1916)	GP.565	£22.00	—
A	U	50	*War Series — 'MURATTI II', toned card (1917) Nos. 1-25 (and alternative cards)	H.290/GP.566	£14.00	—

SILKS

Size	Print-ing	Number in set		Handbook reference	Price per card	Complete set
—	C		*Flags — Set 3 (70 × 52mm) (paper backed) (c1915):			
		25	1st Series — Series C, Nd. 20-44	GP.579	£3.75	—
		24	2nd Series:			
			Series A, Nd. 26-49	GP.578	£3.75	—
			Series E, Nd. 48-72, paper backing in grey (No. 52 unissued)	GP.582	£3.75	—
			Series E, Nd. 48-72, paper backing in green (No. 52 unissued)	GP.582	£3.75	—

Size	Printing	Number in set		Handbook reference	Price per card	Complete set

B. MURATTI, SONS & CO. LTD, Manchester and London *(continued)*

—	C		*Flags — Set 8 (paper backed) (c1915):			
		3	Series A, Nd. 1-3 (89 × 115mm)	GP.577	£10.00	—
		1	Series B, Nd. 19 (70 × 76mm)	GP.586	—	£12.00
		18	Series C, Nd. 1-18 (89 × 115mm)	GP.580	£10.00	—
		3	Series D, Nd. 45-47 (89 × 115mm)	GP.581	£10.00	—
		6	Series F, Nd. 73-78 (89 × 115mm)	GP.583	£10.00	—
—	C	18	*Great War Leaders — Series P (89 × 115mm) (paper backed) (c1916)	GP.584	£15.00	—
—	C		*Regimental Badges I (paper backed) (c1915):	H.502-1		
		25	Series A, Nd. 1-25 (70 × 52mm)	GP.585	£4.50	—
		48	Series B, Nd. 1-48 (76 × 70mm)	GP.587	£6.00	—
		15	Series B, Nd. 4-18 (76 × 70mm)	GP.586	£6.00	—
		16	Series G, Nd. 79-94 (76 × 70mm)	GP.588	£8.00	—
—	C	25	*Regimental Colours I — Series CB (76 × 70mm) (paper backed) (c1915)	GP.589	£10.00	—
—	C	72	*Regimental Colours V — Series RB (70 × 52 mm) (paper backed) (c1915)	GP.590	£6.00	—

CANVASES. Unbacked canvases. The material is not strictly canvas, but a linen fabric glazed to give the appearance of canvas.

—	C	40	Canvas Masterpieces — Series M (71 × 60mm) (c1915):	H.509/GP.575		
			A Shaded back design, globe 12mm diam		£5.50	—
			B Unshaded back design, globe 6mm diam		£2.50	£100.00
—	C	16	Canvas Masterpieces — Series P (114 × 90mm) (c1915)		£12.00	—

MURRAY, SONS & CO. LTD, Belfast

A	BW	20	*Actresses — 'BLARM' (c1900):	H.23		
			A 'Pineapple Cigarettes' back		£90.00	—
			B 'Special Crown Cigarettes' back		£100.00	—
D1	P	22	Bathing Beauties (1929)		£6.00	—
A1	BW	40	Bathing Belles (1939)	H.592	40p	£16.00
C	C	15	Chess and Draughts Problems — Series F (1912)	H.291	£80.00	—
D1	P	22	Cinema Scenes (1929)		£6.00	—
A	BW	54	*Cricketers and Footballers — Series H (c1912):	H.292		
			20 Cricketers. A Thick card		£75.00	—
			B Thin card		£75.00	—
			C Brown Printing		£175.00	—
			34 Footballers. A Thick card		£50.00	—
			B Thin card		£50.00	—
A1	BW	25	Crossword Puzzles (c1925)		£200.00	—
D1	P	26	Dancers (1929)		£5.00	—
D	P		Dancing Girls (1929):			
		25	A 'Belfast-Ireland' at base		£3.40	£85.00
		25	B 'London & Belfast' at base		£3.40	£85.00
		26	C Inscribed 'Series of 26'		£3.40	—
—	C	? 29	Football Flags (shaped) (60 × 32mm) (c1905):	H.759		
			A Maple Cigarettes		£70.00	—
			B Murray's Cigarettes		£70.00	—
C	C	25	*Football Rules (c1911)		£28.00	—
A	BW	104	*Footballers — Series J (c1910)	H.293	£50.00	—
A	C	20	Holidays by the LMS (1927)	H.593	£10.00	—
A1	C	20	Inventors Series (1924)	H.213	£5.00	£100.00

Size	*Print-ing*	*Number in set*		*Handbook reference*	*Price per card*	*Complete set*

MURRAY, SONS & CO. LTD, Belfast *(continued)*

C	U	25	*Irish Scenery Nd. 101-125 (1905):			
			A 'Hall Mark Cigarettes'		£22.00	—
			B 'Pine Apple Cigarettes'		£22.00	—
			C 'Special Crown Cigarettes'		£22.00	—
			D 'Straight Cut Cigarettes'		£22.00	—
			E 'Yachtsman Cigarettes'		£22.00	—
C	BW	25	Polo Pictures — E Series (1911)	H.294	£25.00	—
—	U	50	Prominent Politicians — B Series (41 × 70mm) (1909):	H.295		
			A Without '... in two strengths' in centre of back		£18.00	—
			B With '... in two strengths' in centre of back		£2.80	£140.00
—	C	50	Puzzle Series (1925):	H.660		
A1			A With coupon attached at top		£20.00	—
			B Without coupon		£7.50	—
C	U	25	Reproduction of Famous Works of Art — D Series (1910)	H.296	£24.00	£600.00
C	U	24	Reproductions of High Class Works of Art — C Series (1910)	H.297	£24.00	£600.00
D2	C	50	Stage and Film Stars — 'Erinmore Cigarettes' (c1926)		£4.00	£200.00
A1	BW	25	Steam Ships (1939)		£1.60	£40.00
A1	C	50	The Story of Ships (1940)		40p	£20.00
A2	C	25	Types of Aeroplanes (1929)		£1.40	£35.00
C	C	20	Types of Dogs (1924):	H.211		
			A Normal back		£6.50	—
			B Normal back, with firm's name rubber-stamped in red		£6.50	—
A1	C	35	*War Series — Series K (1915)	H.298	£27.00	—
C2	U	25	*War Series — Series L, Nd. 100-124 (c1916):			
			A Sepia		£3.00	£75.00
			B Grey-brown		£3.00	—
			C Purple-brown		£3.00	—
SILKS						
—	C	? 16	*Flags, small (70 × 42mm) — 'Polo Mild Cigarettes' (plain paper backing) (c1915)	H.498-1	£20.00	—
—	C	? 3	*Flags and Arms, large (102 × 71mm) — 'Polo Mild Cigarettes' (plain paper backing) (c1915)	H.498-2	£65.00	—
—	C	? 31	*Orders of Chivalry II, 'Series M' (70 × 42mm) (paper backed, Nd. 35-65) (c1915)	H.504-15	£18.00	—
—	C	? 25	*Regimental Badges (70 × 42mm) — 'Polo Mild Cigarettes' (plain paper backing) (c1915)	H.498-3	£18.00	—

H.J. NATHAN, London

D	C	40	Comical Military and Naval Pictures (c1905):	H.14		
			A White Border		£60.00	—
			B No Border		£60.00	—

JAMES NELSON, London

A	P	? 23	*Beauties — 'FENA' (c1899)	H.148	£900.00	—

NETTLETON AND MITCHELL, Ossett

A	C	30	*Army Pictures, Cartoons, etc. (c1916)	H.12	£150.00	—

THE NEW MOSLEM CIGARETTE CO., London

D	C	30	*Proverbs (c1902)	H.15	£100.00	—

E.J. NEWBEGIN, Sunderland

Size	Print-	Number		Handbook	Price	Complete
—	P	50	*Actors and Actresses (39 × 60mm) (c1902)	H.299	£50.00	—
A	BW	10	*Actresses — 'HAGG A' (c1900)	H.24	£180.00	—
D	C	? 4	Advertisement Cards (c1900)	H.761	£900.00	—
A	BW	20	Cricketers Series (1901)	H.29	£500.00	—
A	BW	19	*Russo-Japanese Series (1904)	H.184	£150.00	—
D	C	12	Well-Known Proverbs (c1905)	H.235	£140.00	—
D	C	25	Well-Known Songs (c1905)	H.300	£140.00	—

W.H. NEWMAN, Birmingham

Size	Print-	Number		Handbook	Price	Complete
C	C	18	Motor Cycle Series (c1914)	H.469	£100.00	—

THOS. NICHOLLS & CO., Chester

Size	Print-	Number		Handbook	Price	Complete
A	C	50	Orders of Chivalry (1916)	H.301	£7.50	£375.00

THE NILMA TOBACCO COY., London

Size	Print-	Number		Handbook	Price	Complete
A	C	40	*Home and Colonial Regiments (c1903)	H.69	£120.00	—
D	C	30	*Proverbs (c1903)	H.15	£100.00	—

M.E. NOTARAS LTD, London

Size	Print-	Number		Handbook	Price	Complete
A2	P	36	National Types of Beauty (c1925)	GP.625	£1.00	£36.00
—	U	24	*Views of China (68 × 43mm) (1925)		80p	£20.00

A. NOTON, Sheffield

Size	Print-	Number		Handbook	Price	Complete
—	U	12	'Manikin' Cards (79 × 51mm) (c1920)	H.481	£120.00	—

OGDENS LTD, Liverpool

330 page reference book (updated 2005 Edition) – £27.00

Home Issues (*excluding 'Guinea Gold' and 'Tabs', but including some early issued abroad*).

Size	Print-	Number		Handbook	Price	Complete
A	C	25	ABC of Sport (1927)		£3.20	£80.00
A	C	50	Actors — Natural and Character Studies (1938)	H.571-1	£1.00	£50.00
C	C	25	*Actresses — coloured, 'Ogden's Cigarettes contain no glycerine' back (c1895):	OG.3		
			A Titled in black		£90.00	—
			B Titled in brown		£90.00	—
D2	U	? 1	*Actresses — green, green borders (c1900)	OG.4	£1000.00	—
D1	U	50	*Actresses — green photogravure (c1900)	OG.5	£12.00	—
D	P	? 589	*Actresses — 'Ogden's Cigarettes' at foot (c1900)	OG.6	£3.20	—
D	P		*Actresses and Beauties — collotype (c1895):	OG.12		
		? 83	i named:			
			A *Plain back*		£80.00	—
			B 'Midnight Flake' back		£60.00	—
		? 21	ii unnamed:			
			A *Plain back*		£80.00	—
			B 'Midnight Flake' back:			
			i blue back		£60.00	—
			ii red back		£120.00	—
D	P		*Actresses and Beauties — collotype, 'Ogden's Cigarettes' back (1895):	OG.12		
		? 54	i named		£65.00	—
		? 45	ii unnamed		£65.00	—
A	P	? 205	*Actresses and Beauties — woodbury-type (c1894)	OG.13	£37.00	—

Size	Printing	Number in set		Handbook reference	Price per card	Complete set
OGDENS LTD, Liverpool *(continued)*						
A	C	50	AFC Nicknames (1933)	H.571-2	£4.50	£225.00
A	C	50	Air-Raid Precautions (1938)	H.544	90p	£45.00
A	C	50	Applied Electricity (1928)		£1.20	£60.00
—	C	192	Army Crests and Mottoes (39 × 59mm) (c1902)	OG.20	£5.50	—
A	U	36	Australian Test Cricketers, 1928-29	OG.21	£3.60	£130.00
A	C	28	*Beauties — 'BOCCA' (c1900)	H.39/OG.23	£28.00	—
—	C	50	*Beauties — 'CHOAB' (c1900):	H.21/OG.24		
			Nos 1-25 (size 65 × 36mm)		£30.00	—
			Nos 26-50 (size 67 × 37mm)		£30.00	—
A	C	26	*Beauties — 'HOL' (c1900):	H.192/OG.25		
			A 'Guinea Gold' red rubber stamp back		£250.00	—
			B Blue Castle Design back		£22.00	£570.00
A2	C	52	*Beauties — 'Playing Card' series (c1900):	OG.26		
			A 52 with playing card inset		£30.00	—
			B 26 without playing card inset		£35.00	—
A2	C	52	*Beauties and Military — PC inset (c1898)	OG.29	£30.00	—
—	P	50	Beauty Series, numbered, 'St. Julien Tobacco' (36 × 54mm) (c1900)	OG.30	£3.00	£150.00
D	P	? 83	Beauty Series, unnumbered, issued Australia (c1900)	OG.31	£70.00	—
A	C	50	Billiards, by Tom Newman (1928)	OG.33	£2.20	£110.00
A	C	50	Birds' Eggs (1904):			
			A White back		£2.00	£100.00
			B Toned back		£1.80	£90.00
A	C	50	Bird's Eggs (cut-outs) (1923)		£1.10	£55.00
A	C	50	The Blue Riband of the Atlantic (1929)		£2.50	£125.00
D	P	? 142	*Boer War and General Interest — 'Ogden's Cigarettes' at foot (c1900)	OG.38	£3.20	—
H2	P	? 68	*Boer War and General Interest — 'Ogden's Cigarettes' at foot (c1900)	OG.38	£45.00	—
—	P	? 3	*Boer War & General Interest (Liners) 'Ogdens Cigarettes' at foot (72 × 55mm) (c1900)	OG.38	£175.00	—
A	C	50	Boxers (1915)		£7.00	£350.00
A	C	25	Boxing (1914)	H.311/OG.40	£6.00	£150.00
—	C	? 6	*Boxing Girls (165 × 94mm) (c1895)	OG.69	£600.00	—
A	C	50	Boy Scouts (1911):	H.62/OG.41		
			A Blue back		£3.20	£160.00
			B Green back		£4.50	£225.00
A	C	50	Boy Scouts, 2nd series (1912):	H.62/OG.42		
			A Blue back		£3.20	£160.00
			B Green back		£4.50	£225.00
A	C	50	Boy Scouts, 3rd series (1912):	H.62/OG.43		
			A Blue back		£3.20	£160.00
			B Green back		£4.50	£225.00
A	C	50	Boy Scouts, 4th series, green back (1913)		£3.20	£160.00
A	C	25	Boy Scouts, 5th series, green back (1914)		£3.20	£80.00
A	C	50	Boy Scouts (1929)	OG.46	£2.50	£125.00
A	C	50	British Birds:	H.229/OG.47		
			A White back (1905)		£2.00	£100.00
			B Toned back (1906)		£1.80	£90.00
A	C	50	British Birds, Second Series (1908)		£2.20	£110.00
A	C	50	British Birds (Cut-Outs) (1923)	OG.49	£1.00	£50.00
A	C	50	British Birds and Their Eggs (1939)	H.571-3	£2.60	£130.00
A	C	50	British Costumes from 100 BC to 1904 (1905)	OG.51	£6.00	£300.00
A	U	50	Broadcasting (1935)	H.571-4	£1.70	£85.00
A	C	50	By the Roadside (1932)		£1.10	£55.00
A	C	44	Captains of Association Football Clubs and Colours (1926)		£3.00	£130.00

Size	*Print-ing*	*Number in set*		*Handbook reference*	*Price per card*	*Complete set*

OGDENS LTD, Liverpool *(continued)*

A	U	50	Cathedrals and Abbeys (1936):			
			A Cream card		£1.10	£55.00
			B White card		£1.10	£55.00
A	C	50	Champions of 1936 (1937)	H.571-5	£1.80	£90.00
A	C	50	Children of All Nations (cut-outs) (1923)	H.656/OG.58	£1.00	£50.00
A	C	50	Club Badges (1914)		£5.00	£250.00
A	C	50	Colour in Nature (1932)		£1.00	£50.00
—	C	? 27	*Comic Pictures (1890-95) (size varies)	OG.62	£350.00	—
A	C	50	Construction of Railway Trains (1930)		£2.50	£125.00
A	C	50	Coronation Procession (sectional) (1937)	H.571-6	£1.60	£80.00
A	U	50	Cricket, 1926		£2.60	£130.00
A2	C	12	*Cricket and Football Terms — Women (c1896)	OG.69	£400.00	—
D2	U	50	*Cricketers and Sportsmen (c1898)	OG.70	£90.00	—
A	C	25	Derby Entrants, 1926		£2.60	£65.00
A	C	50	Derby Entrants, 1928		£2.20	£110.00
A	U	50	Derby Entrants, 1929		£2.40	£120.00
A	C	50	Dogs (1936)	H.571-7	£2.40	£120.00
A	U	28	*Dominoes — Actresses — 'FROGA A' back (c1900):	H.20/OG.75		
			A Mitred corners (7 backs)		£25.00	—
			B Unmitred corners (7 backs)		£25.00	—
A	U	56	*Dominoes — Beauties — 'MOM' back (c1900)	H.277/OG.77	£25.00	—
A2	BW	55	*Dominoes — black back (1909)		£1.50	£80.00
A	C	25	Famous Dirt-Track Riders (1929)		£5.00	£125.00
A	C	50	Famous Footballers (1908)		£4.00	£200.00
A	U	50	Famous Rugby Players (1926-27)		£2.40	£120.00
A	C	50	Flags and Funnels of Leading Steamship Lines (1906)	H.67/OG.81	£4.00	£200.00
A	C	50	Football Caricatures (1935)	H.571-8	£2.60	£130.00
—	C	43	*Football Club Badges (shaped for buttonhole) (c1910)	OG.85	£7.50	—
A	C	50	Football Club Captains (1935)	H.571-9	£2.50	£125.00
A	C	51	Football Club Colours (1906):	H.68/OG.86		
			Nos. 1-50		£3.80	£190.00
			No. 51		—	£5.00
A	C	50	Foreign Birds (1924)		90p	£45.00
A	C	50	Fowls, Pigeons and Dogs (1904)	H.64/OG.88	£3.20	£160.00
A	U	25	Greyhound Racing — '1st Series ...' (1927)		£4.00	£100.00
A	U	25	Greyhound Racing — '2nd Series ...' (1928)		£4.00	£100.00
—	C	1	*History of the Union Jack (threefold card) (51 × 37mm closed) (1901)	OG.102	—	£225.00
A	C	50	How to Swim (1935)	H.571-10	£1.00	£50.00
A	BW	50	Infantry Training (1915)	OG.105	£2.80	£140.00
A	C	50	Jockeys, and Owners' Colours (1927)		£2.50	£125.00
A	C	50	Jockeys 1930 (1930)		£2.50	£125.00
A	C	50	Leaders of Men (1924)		£1.80	£90.00
A	C	25	Marvels of Motion (1928)		£2.20	£55.00
K2	C	52	*Miniature Playing Cards — Actresses and Beauties back (c1900):	OG.115		
			I Unnamed, no numeral (76 backs known)		£5.00	—
			II Unnamed, 'numeral 40' (26 backs known)		£5.00	—
			III Named, 'numeral 46' (26 backs known)		£5.00	—
			IV Named, no numeral (26 backs known)		£5.00	—
K2	C	52	*Miniature Playing Cards, blue Tabs 'Shield and Flower' design back (1909)	OG.118	£3.00	—
K2	C	52	*Miniature Playing Cards, yellow 'Coolie Cut Plug' design back:	OG.116		
			A Yellow back (1904)		£3.00	—
			B Yellow back with white border (1904)		£4.00	—
A	C	50	Modern British Pottery (1925)		£1.00	£50.00

Size	Printing	Number in set		Handbook reference	Price per card	Complete set

OGDENS LTD, Liverpool *(continued)*

Size	Printing	Number in set		Handbook reference	Price per card	Complete set
A	C	50	Modern Railways (1936)	H.571-11	£2.20	£110.00
A	BW	50	Modern War Weapons (1915):	OG.122		
			A Original numbering		£3.20	£160.00
			B Numbering re-arranged		£11.00	—
A	C	25	Modes of Conveyance (1927)		£2.40	£60.00
A	C	50	Motor Races 1931 (1931)		£2.60	£130.00
A	C	50	Ocean Greyhounds (1938)	H.571-12	£1.20	£60.00
A	C	25	Optical Illusions (1923)	H.560/OG.127	£3.00	£75.00
A	C	50	Orders of Chivalry (1907)		£3.50	£175.00
A	C	25	Owners, Racing Colours and Jockeys (1914)		£4.00	£100.00
A	C	50	Owners, Racing Colours and Jockeys (1906)		£3.20	£160.00
A	C	25	Picturesque People of the Empire (1927)		£1.40	£35.00
A	U	50	Picturesque Villages (1936)		£1.40	£70.00
A	C	25	Poultry (1915):			
			A 'Ogden's Cigarettes' on front		£5.40	£135.00
			B Without 'Ogden's Cigarettes' on front		£5.40	£135.00
A	C	25	Poultry, 2nd series, as 'B' above (1916)		£5.40	£135.00
A	C	25	Poultry Alphabet (1924)		£4.40	£110.00
A	C	25	Poultry Rearing and Management — '1st Series ...' (1922)		£3.00	£75.00
A	C	25	Poultry Rearing and Management — '2nd Series ...' (1923)		£3.00	£75.00
A	U	50	Prominent Cricketers of 1938 (1938)	H.571-13	£2.50	£125.00
A	C	50	Prominent Racehorses of 1933 (1934)	H.571-l4	£2.00	£100.00
A	C	25	Pugilists and Wrestlers, Nd. 1-25 (1908)		£5.60	£140.00
A	C	25	Pugilists and Wrestlers, Nd.26-50:			
			A White back (1909)		£5.60	£140.00
			B Toned back (1908)		£5.60	£140.00
A	C	25	Pugilists and Wrestlers, 2nd series, Nd. 51-75 (1909)		£6.00	£150.00
A	U	50	Pugilists in Action (1928)		£3.50	£175.00
A	C	50	Racehorses (1907)		£3.50	£175.00
A	C	50	Racing Pigeons (1931)		£4.00	£200.00
A	C	25	Records of the World (1908)		£3.00	£75.00
A	C	50	Royal Mail (1909)	H.82/OG.147	£4.20	£210.00
A	C	50	Sea Adventure (1939)	H.571-15	50p	£25.00
A	C	50	Sectional Cycling Map (1910)	H.74/OG.150	£3.20	£160.00
A	C	50	*Shakespeare Series (c1903):	OG.151		
			A Unnumbered		£13.00	£650.00
			B Numbered		£13.00	£650.00
A	C	50	Shots from the Films (1936)	H.571-16	£2.00	£100.00
A	U	25	Sights of London (1923)		£1.60	£40.00
A	C	50	Smugglers and Smuggling (1932)		£2.20	£110.00
A	C		Soldiers of the King (1909):	OG.156		
		50	A Grey printing on front		£5.00	£250.00
		25	B Brown printing on front		£6.00	—
A	U	50	Steeplechase Celebrities (1931)		£2.00	£100.00
A	C	50	Steeplechase Trainers, and Owners' Colours (1927)		£2.00	£100.00
A	C	50	The Story of Sand (1934)		90p	£45.00
A	C	50	Swimming, Diving and Life-Saving (1931)	H.523/OG.161	£1.40	£70.00
D	C	25	*Swiss Views, Nd. 1-25 (c1905)		£4.00	£100.00
D	C	25	*Swiss Views, Nd. 26-50 (c1905)		£5.00	£125.00
A	C	25	Trainers, and Owners' Colours — '1st Series ...' (1925)		£2.40	£60.00
A	C	25	Trainers, and Owners' Colours — '2nd Series ...' (1926)		£3.00	£75.00
A	C	50	Trick Billiards (1934)	H.571-17	£1.60	£80.00
A	C	50	Turf Personalities (1929)		£2.40	£120.00
D	C	48	Victoria Cross Heroes (1901)	OG.168	£15.00	£750.00

Size	Print-ing	Number in set		Handbook reference	Price per card	Complete set

OGDENS LTD, Liverpool *(continued)*

Size	Print-ing	Number in set		Handbook reference	Price per card	Complete set
A	C	25	Whaling (1927)		£2.60	£65.00
A	C	50	Yachts and Motor Boats (1930)		£2.50	£125.00
A	C	50	Zoo Studies (1937)	H.571-18	50p	£25.00
'GUINEA GOLD' SERIES						
			(The Set ...S and X numbers represent the reference numbers quoted in the original Ogden's Reference Book).			
D	P	1148	1-1148 Series (c1901):	OG.330S		
			Nos. 1-200		60p	£120.00
			Nos. 201-500		£1.50	—
			Nos. 501-900, excl. 523 and 765		£1.20	—
			Nos. 901-1000, excl. 940, 943, 947 and 1000		£1.80	—
			Nos. 1001-1148, excl. 1003, 1006-8, 1024, 1030, 1033, 1034, 1037, 1040, 1042, 1048, 1066, 1081, 1082, 1088		£1.80	—
			Scarce Nos: 523, 940, 943, 947, 1000, 1003, 1007, 1008, 1024, 1030, 1033, 1034, 1037, 1040, 1042, 1048, 1066, 1088		£60.00	—
			Very scarce Nos. 765, 1006, 1081, 1082		—	—
D	CP	?	Selected numbers from 1-1148 Series (c1900)		£5.00	—
D	P		400 New Series I (c1902)		£1.25	£500.00
D	P		400 New Series B (c1902)		£1.50	£600.00
D	P		300 New Series C (c1902)		£1.20	£360.00
D	P	? 323	Set 73S Base B Actresses (c1900)	OG.340S	£3.00	—
			Set 75S Base D (c1900):	OG.350S		
D	P	? 318	List DA — White Panel Group		£1.20	—
D	P	? 58	List DB — The Denumbered Group		£2.75	—
D	P	? 62	List DC — The Political Group		£1.20	—
D	P	? 193	List DD — Boer War etc		£1.00	—
D	P	? 46	List DE — Pantomime and Theatre Group		£4.00	—
D	P	? 376	List DF — Actors and Actresses		£1.50	—
D	P	? 40	Set 76S Base E Actors and Actresses (c1900)	OG.355S	£3.75	—
D	P	? 59	Set 77S Base F Boer War etc (c1901)	OG.360S	£1.00	—
			Set 78S Base I (c1900):	OG.365S		
			List IA — The small Machette Group:			
D	P	83	I Actors and Actresses		£1.30	—
D	P	14	II London Street Scenes		£3.50	—
D	P	32	III Turner Pictures		£2.00	—
D	P	11	IV Cricketers		£13.00	—
D	P	18	V Golf		£25.00	—
D	P	10	VI Views and Scenes Abroad		£1.75	—
D	P	30	VII Miscellaneous		£1.30	—
D	P	639	List IB — The Large Machette Group		£1.20	—
D	P	5	List IC — The White Panel Group		£5.00	—
D	P	30	Set 79S Base J Actresses (c1900)	OG.370S	£4.00	—
D	P	238	Set 80S Base K Actors and Actresses (c1900)	OG.375S	£3.00	—
D	P	216	Set 81S Base L Actors and Actresses (c1900)	OG.380S	£2.50	—
			Set 82S Base M (c1901):	OG.385S		
D	P	3	List Ma Royalty		£3.00	£9.00
D	P	77	List Mb Cricketers		£25.00	—
D	P	50	List Mc Cyclists		£6.00	—
D	P	150	List Md Footballers		£20.00	—
D	P	50	List Me Pantomime and Theatre Group		£6.50	—
D	P	33	List Mf Footballers and Cyclists		£15.00	—
D	P	27	List Mg Boer War and Miscellaneous		£1.10	—
D	P	? 2951	List Mh Actors and Actresses		£1.20	—
Guinea Gold Series, Large and Medium						
H	P	77	Set 73X Actresses Base B (c1900)	OG.340X	£18.00	—

Size	*Print-ing*	*Number in set*		*Handbook reference*	*Price per card*	*Complete set*

OGDENS LTD, Liverpool *(continued)*

H2	P	1	Set 74X Actress Base C (c1900)	OG.345X	—	£50.00
—	P	55	Set 75X Base D List DX1 medium size (73 × 55mm) (c1901)	OG.350X	£15.00	—
			Set 75X Base D large size (c1901):	OG.350X		
H	P	50	List DB – The Denumbered Group		£2.00	—
H	P	58	List DD – Boer War etc.		£2.00	—
H	P	45	List DE – Pantomime and Theatre Group		£6.00	—
H	P	270	List DX2 – Actors and Actresses		£2.00	—
H	P	24	Set 78X Actresses Base I (c1900)	OG.365X	£40.00	—
H	P	406	Set 82X Actors, Actresses, Boer War Etc Base M (c1901)	OG.385X	£2.00	—

'TABS' SERIES

(The listing includes both home and overseas 'Tabs' issues.)

D	BW	200	*Actresses (c1900)	OG.7	£2.50	—
D	BW	200	*Actresses and Foreign Views (c1900)	OG.14	£2.20	—
D	BW	? 331	*Composite Tabs Series, with 'Labour Clause' (1901)	OG.63		
			1 General de Wet		—	£5.00
			1 General Interest		—	£6.00
			17 Heroes of the Ring		£7.50	—
			1 HM the Queen		—	£5.00
			2 HRH the Prince of Wales		£4.00	£8.00
			14 Imperial Interest		£1.00	£14.00
			106 Imperial or International Interest		£1.00	—
			3 International Interest		£2.00	£6.00
			14 International Interest or a Prominent British Officer		£1.00	£14.00
			22 Leading Athletes		£2.70	—
			15 Leading Favourites of the Turf		£4.00	—
			54 Leading Generals at the War		£1.00	£54.00
			2 Members of Parliament		£3.50	£7.00
			11 Notable Coursing Dogs		£7.50	—
			12 Our Leading Cricketers		£15.00	—
			17 Our Leading Footballers		£9.00	—
			37 Prominent British Officers		£1.00	£37.00
			1 The Yacht 'Columbia'		—	£6.00
			1 The Yacht 'Shamrock'		—	£6.00
D	BW	? 71	*Composite Tabs Series, without 'Labour Clause' (c1900):	OG.64		
			40 General Interest		£26.00	—
			31 Leading Artists of the Day		£22.00	—
D	BW	? 114	*Composite Tabs Series, Sydney issue (c1900):	OG.65		
			1 Christian de Wet		£10.00	—
			1 Corporal G. E. Nurse, VC		£10.00	—
			15 English Cricketer Series		£60.00	—
			1 Imperial Interest		£10.00	—
			29 Imperial or International Interest		£8.00	—
			6 International Interest		£8.00	—
			1 Lady Sarah Wilson		£10.00	—
			41 Leading Generals at the War		£8.00	—
			13 Prominent British Officers		£8.00	—
D	BW	150	General Interest, Series 'A' (1901)	OG.89	£1.10	—
D	BW	200	General Interest, Series 'B' (1902)	OG.90	£1.00	£200.00
D	BW	470	General Interest, Series 'C' (1902):			
			C.1-200	OG.91	£1.00	£200.00
			C.201-300		£2.20	—
			C.301-350		£1.20	£60.00
			No Letter, Nd 1-120		£1.20	—
D	BW	200	General Interest, Series 'D' (1902)	OG.92	£1.00	£200.00

Size	Printing	Number in set		Handbook reference	Price per card	Complete set
OGDENS LTD, Liverpool *(continued)*						
D	BW	120	General Interest, Series 'E' (1902)	OG.93	£1.20	—
D	BW	420	General Interest, Series 'F' (1902):	OG.94		
			F.1-200		£1.20	—
			F.201-320		£1.20	—
			F.321-420		£2.70	—
D	BW	? 400	General Interest, Sydney issue (c1902):	OG.99		
			Nd 1-100 on front		£2.75	—
			Nd 101-400 on back		£2.75	—
		? 106	Unnumbered, mostly similar numbered cards 101-200		£5.00	—
D	BW	196	*General Interest, unnumbered, similar style C.201-300 (1902):	OG.95		
			76 Stage Artistes		£1.00	—
			41 Celebrities		£1.00	—
			56 Footballers		£2.50	—
			23 Miscellaneous		£1.00	—
D	BW	100	*General Interest, unnumbered, similar style C.301-350 (1902):	OG.96		
			28 Actresses		£1.00	—
			40 Castles		£1.00	—
			12 Dogs		£1.25	—
			20 Miscellaneous		£2.00	—
D	BW	300	*General Interest, unnumbered, similar style F.321-420 (1903):	OG.97		
			A 100 with full stop after caption		£1.30	£130.00
			B Without full stop after caption:			
			79 I Stage Artistes		£1.00	£80.00
			21 II Cricketers		£10.00	—
			25 III Football		£6.00	—
			15 IV Golf		£22.00	—
			10 V Cyclists		£5.00	—
			9 VI Fire Brigades		£5.00	—
			5 VII Aldershot Gymnasium		£3.00	£15.00
			36 VIII Miscellaneous		£1.00	—
D	BW	? 111	*General Interest, 'oblong' back (c1900)	OG.98	£15.00	—
D	BW	? 75	*Leading Artistes of the Day, numbered 126-200, plain backs (c1900)	H.1/OG.109	£14.00	—
D	BW	? 71	Leading Artistes of the Day with 'Labour Clause' (c1900):	OG.110		
			A Type-set back		£1.20	—
			B Plain back		£20.00	—
D	BW	? 25	Leading Artistes of the Day, without 'Labour Clause' (c1900):	OG.111-1		
			A With caption, type-set back		£15.00	—
			B With caption, plain back		£15.00	—
			C Without caption, type-set back		£15.00	—
D	BW	? 91	Leading Artistes of the Day, without 'Labour Clause' (c1900):	OG.111-2		
			A Type-set back		£11.00	—
			B Plain back		£11.00	—
D	BW	25	Leading Generals at the War, with descriptive text (c1900):	OG.112		
			A 'Ogden's Cigarettes' back		£2.00	—
			B 'Ogden's Tab Cigarettes' back		£1.40	£35.00
D	BW		Leading Generals at the War, without descriptive text (c1900):	OG.113		
		? 47	A 'Ogden's Tab Cigarettes' back (47 known)		£1.00	—
		? 25	B 'Ogden's Lucky Star' back (25 known)		£6.00	—

Size	Printing	Number in set		Handbook reference	Price per card	Complete set

OGDENS LTD, Liverpool *(continued)*

D	BW	50	*Stage Artistes and Celebrities (c1900)	OG.157	£2.80	£140.00
OVERSEAS ISSUES						
D2	BW	51	Actresses, black and white Polo issue (1906)	OG.10	£3.20	—
D	U	30	Actresses, unicoloured Polo issue (1908):	OG.11		
			A Tin foil at back white		£3.00	£90.00
			B Tin foil at back shaded		£3.40	£100.00
D2	C	17	Animals Polo issue (1916)	OG.18	£12.00	—
A1	C	60	Animals — cut-outs:	OG.17		
			A Ruler issue (1912)		£3.00	—
			B Tabs issue (1913):			
			i With captions		£3.00	—
			ii Without captions		£4.50	—
D2	C	50	Aviation series Tabs issue (1912):	OG.22		
			A Ogdens at base		£7.00	—
			B Ogdens England at base		£8.00	—
			Beauties green net design back 1901:	OG.27		
D	BW	? 66	A Front black & white		£15.00	—
D	C	? 98	B Front coloured		£28.00	—
D2	C	45	Beauties Picture Hats Polo issue (1911)	OG.28	£6.50	—
D	C	50	Best Dogs of Their Breed Polo issue (1916):	OG.32		
			A Back in red		£8.00	—
			B Back in blue with Eastern characters		£8.00	—
			C Back in blue without Eastern characters		£8.00	—
D	C	52	Birds of Brilliant Plumage Ruler issue (1914):	OG.36		
			A Fronts with framelines		£3.20	—
			B Fronts without framelines		£3.20	—
A	C	25	British Trees and Their Uses, Guinea Gold issue (1927)	OG.52	£2.00	£50.00
D	C	25	China's Famous Warriors, Ruler issue (1913)	OG.59	£6.00	—
A	C	25	Famous Railway Trains, Guinea Gold issue (1928)	OG.79	£2.80	£70.00
D2	C	20	Flowers, Polo issue (1915):	OG.82		
			A Without Eastern inscription		£5.50	—
			B With Eastern inscription		£5.50	—
D2	U	25	Indian Women, Polo issue (1919):	OG.104		
			A Framework in light apple green		£6.00	—
			B Framework in dark emerald green		£6.00	—
—	C	52	Miniature Playing Cards, Polo issue (56 × 38mm) (c1910)	OG.117	£13.00	—
D2	BW		Music Hall Celebrities (1911):	OG.125		
		30	A Polo issue		£6.00	—
		50	B Tabs issue		£6.00	—
A	C	50	Riders of the World, Polo issue (1911)	OG.146	£4.00	—
D2	U	50	Russo-Japanese series (1905)	OG.148	£22.00	—
D2	C	36	Ships and Their Pennants, Polo issue (1911)	OG.153	£6.50	—
D2	C	32	Transport of the World, Polo issue (1917)	OG.165	£6.00	—

THE ORLANDO CIGARETTE & CIGAR CO., London

A	C	40	*Home & Colonial Regiments (c1901)	H.69	£600.00	—

OSBORNE TOBACCO CO. LTD, Portsmouth & London

A	U	50	Modern Aircraft (1953):	H.895		
			A Dark Blue back:			
			i Firm's name in one line		50p	£25.00
			ii Firm's name in two lines		£2.00	—
			B Light Blue back		£1.00	£50.00
			C Brown back		50p	£25.00

Size	*Print-ing*	*Number in set*		*Handbook reference*	*Price per card*	*Complete set*

W.T. OSBORNE & CO., London

D	C	40	*Naval and Military Phrases (c1904):	H.14		
			A White Border		£45.00	—
			B No Border		£45.00	—

PALMER & CO., Bedford

—	U	12	'Manikin' Cards (79 × 51mm) (c1920)	H.481	£120.00	—

J.A. PATTREIOUEX, Manchester

	P		Beautiful Scotland (1939):	H.564-1		
D		28	A Small size		£1.10	£30.00
—		48	B Medium size (77 × 52mm)		30p	£15.00
—	P	48	The Bridges of Britain (77 × 52mm) (1938)		30p	£15.00
—	P	48	Britain from the Air (77 × 52mm) (1939)		30p	£15.00
A	C	50	British Empire Exhibition Series (c1928)		£2.50	£125.00
—	P	48	British Railways (77 × 52mm) (1938)		70p	£35.00
A	C	50	Builders of the British Empire (c1929)		£3.00	£150.00
—	C	24	Cadet's Jackpot Jigsaws (90 × 65mm) (1969)		£1.50	—
A	C	50	Celebrities in Sport (c1930)		£5.00	£250.00
	P		Coastwise (1939):	H.564-2		
D		28	A Small size		£1.25	£35.00
—		48	B Medium size (77 × 52mm)		30p	£15.00
A	C	75	Cricketers Series (1926)	H.665	£11.00	—
A	C	50	Dirt Track Riders (1929)		£11.00	—
D	P	54	Dirt Track Riders (1930):			
			A Descriptive back		£12.00	—
			* B Non-descriptive back		£25.00	—
—	P	48	Dogs (76 × 51mm) (1939)		50p	£25.00
A	C	30	Drawing Made Easy (c1930)		£2.50	£75.00
A	C	52	The English and Welsh Counties (c1928)		£2.00	£105.00
	P		Flying (1938):	H.564-3		
D		28	A Small size		£1.80	—
		48	B Medium size (77 × 52mm)		50p	£24.00
A2	P	78	Footballers in Action (1934)		£4.00	—
A	C		Footballers Series (1927):			
		50	A Captions in blue		£9.00	—
		100	B Captions in brown		£9.00	—
—	P	48	Holiday Haunts by the Sea (77 × 52mm) (1937)		30p	£15.00
A	C	25	'King Lud' Problems (c1935)	H.638	£18.00	—
A	C	26	Maritime Flags (c1932)		£10.00	—
—	P	48	The Navy (1937):			
			A Large captions on back 2mm high		60p	£30.00
			B Smaller captions on back 1mm high		70p	£35.00
	P		Our Countryside (1938):	H.564-4		
D		28	A Small size		£1.50	£42.00
		48	B Medium size (77 × 52mm)		30p	£15.00
A	U	25	Photos of Football Stars (c1930)	H.666	£32.00	—
D	C	50	Railway Posters by Famous Artists (c1930)		£8.00	—
A2	P	54	Real Photographs of London (1936)		£2.50	—
D	P	28	Shots from the Films (1938)	H.566	£2.75	—
—	P	48	Sights of Britain — 'Series of 48' (76 × 51 mm) (1936)		50p	£25.00
—	P	48	Sights of Britain — 'Second Series ...' (76 × 51mm) (1936):			
			A Large captions on back 2mm high		30p	£15.00
			B Smaller captions on back 1mm high		35p	£17.50
—	P	48	Sights of Britain — 'Third Series ...' (76 × 51mm) (1937)		40p	£20.00

Size	Print-ing	Number in set		Handbook reference	Price per card	Complete set

J.A. PATTREIOUEX, Manchester *(continued)*

Size	Print-ing	Number in set		Handbook reference	Price per card	Complete set
—	P	48	Sights of London — 'First Series ...' (76 × 51mm) (1935)		£1.25	£60.00
—	P	12	Sights of London — 'Supplementary Series of 12 Jubilee Pictures' (76 × 51mm) (1935)		£1.00	£12.00
A2	P	54	Sporting Celebrities (1935)		£4.25	—
—	P	96	Sporting Events and Stars (76 × 50mm) (1935)		£2.00	£200.00
A	C	50	Sports Trophies (c1931)		£3.00	£150.00
—	C	24	Treasure Island (65 × 45mm) (1968)		£1.50	—
A2	CP	51	*Views (c1930)	H.597	£1.10	£55.00
A2	P	54	Views of Britain (1937)		£1.60	—
—	P	48	Winter Scenes (76 × 52mm) (1937)		30p	£15.00

1920s PHOTOGRAPHIC SERIES. Listed in order of letters and/or numbers quoted on cards.

Size	Print-ing	Number in set		Handbook reference	Price per card	Complete set
H2	P	50	*Animals and Scenes — unnumbered 'Junior Member' back (c1925)	H.595-1	£1.50	—
H2	P	50	Animals and Scenes, Nd 1-50 (c1925)		£1.20	—
H2	P	50	*Scenes, Nd 201-250 'Junior Member' back (c1925)		£1.20	—
C	P	96	Animals and Scenes, Nd 250-345 (c1925):	H.595-2B		
			A 'Casket/Critic' back (i) grey		£1.20	—
			(ii) brown		£1.20	—
			* B 'Junior Member' back		£1.20	—
C	P	96	Animals and Scenes, Nd 346-441 (c1925):			
			A 'Casket/Critic' back		£1.20	—
			B 'Club Member' back		£1.20	—
			* C 'Junior Member' back		£1.20	—
H	P	50	*Animal Studies, Nd A42-A91 'Junior Member' back (c1925)		£1.20	—
H	P	50	*Animal Studies, Nd A92-A141 'Junior Member' back (c1925)		£1.20	—
H	P	50	*Animal Studies, Nd A151-A200 'Junior Member' back (c1925)		£1.20	—
C	P		*Natives and Scenes (c1925):	H.595-2G		
		36	A 'Series 1/36 B' on front, Nd 1-36 'Junior Member' back		£1.50	—
		96	B 'Series 1/96 B' on front, Nd 1-96 'Junior/Club Member' back		£1.50	—
C	P	96	*Foreign Scenes, Nd 1/96C-96/96C (c1925)		£1.20	—
C	P	96	Cricketers, Nd C1-C96, 'Casket Cigarettes' on front (c1925):	H.595-2C		
			A Printed back		£50.00	—
			* B Plain back		£50.00	—
C	P	96	*Animals — 'Series Nos CA1 to 96'. Back 7 (c1925)	H.595-2A	£1.20	—
C	P	96	*Natives and Scenes (c1925):			
			A 'C.B.1 to 96' on front. 'Club/Critic Member' back:			
			1 Nd 1-96		£1.20	—
			2 Nd C.B.1-C.B.96		£1.20	—
			B 'J.S. 1 to 96' on front. 'Junior Member' back		£1.20	—
C	P	96	*Animals and Scenes — 'CC1 to 96' on front (c1925)		£1.20	—
H2	P	50	*British Scenes — 'Series C.M.1-50.A' on front (c1925)		£1.20	—
H2	P	50	*Foreign Scenes (c1925):			
			A 'Series CM. 1/50 B' on front		£1.20	—
			B 'J.M. Series 1/50' on front		£1.20	—
H2	P	50	*Foreign Scenes (c1925):	H.595-2H		
			A 'Series C.M. 101-150.S' on front		£1.20	—
			B Nd S.101-S.150 on front		£1.20	—
C	P	96	*Foreign Scenes, Nd 1/96D-96/96D (c1925)		£1.50	—
H2	P	50	*Foreign Scenes, Nd 1/50E-50/50E (c1925)		£1.20	—

Size	*Print-ing*	*Number in set*		*Handbook reference*	*Price per card*	*Complete set*

J.A. PATTREIOUEX, Manchester *(continued)*

H2	P	50	*Foreign Scenes, Nd 1/50F-50/50F (c1925)		£1.20	—
C	P	96	Footballers, Nd F.1-F.96. 'Casket' and 'Critic' back (c1925)		£11.00	—
C	P	95	Footballers, Nd F.97-F.191. 'Casket' and 'Critic' back styles (c1925)		£11.00	—
H	P	50	Football Teams, Nd F.192-F.241. ('Casket' and 'Critic') (1922)	H.595-2F	£50.00	—
C	P	96	*Footballers — 'Series F.A. 1/96' on front (c1922)		£9.00	—
C	P	96	*Footballers — 'Series F.B. 1/96' on front (1922)	H.595-2D	£9.00	—
C	P	96	*Footballers — 'Series F.C. 1/96' on front (c1922)	H.595-2E	£9.00	—
H2	P	50	*Scenes — 'G. 1/50' on front (c1925)		£1.50	—
H2	P	50	*Scenes — '1/50. H' on front (c1925)	H.595-2J	£1.50	—
H2	P	50	*Animals and Scenes, Nd I.1-I.50 (c1925)		£1.50	—
H2	P	50	Famous Statues — 'J.C.M. 1 to 50 C' on front (c1925)		£2.00	—
H2	P	50	*Scenes, Nd JCM 1/50D-JCM 50/50D (c1925):			
			A 'Junior/Club Member' back		£1.30	—
			B 'Junior Member' back		£1.30	—
B1	P	30	Child Studies, Nd J.M. No. 1-J.M. No. 30 (c1925)		£4.00	—
B1	P	30	*Beauties, Nd J.M.1-J.M.30 (c1925)		£3.00	—
H2	P	50	*Foreign Scenes — 'J.M. 1 to 50 A' on front (c1925)	H.595-2I	£1.20	—
H2	P	50	British Empire Exhibition 'J.M. 1 to 50 B' on front (c1925)		£2.00	—
C	P	96	*Animals and Scenes — 'J.S. 1/96A'on front (c1925)		£1.00	—
H2	P	50	*Scenes, Nd S.1-S.50.' Junior Member' back (c1925)		£1.20	—
H2	P	50	*Scenes, Nd S.5l-S.100.' Junior Member' back (c1925)		£1.20	—
B1	P	50	**Cathedrals and Abbeys, Nd S.J. 1-S.J. 50. Plain back (c1925)*		£2.50	—
B1	P	50	**British Castles. Nd S.J. 51-S.J. 100. Plain back (c1925)*		£2.50	—
H2	P	4	*Scenes, Nd V.1-V.4. 'Junior Member' back (c1925)	H.595-1	£5.00	—

W. PEPPERDY

A	C	30	*Army Pictures, Cartoons, etc (c1916)	H.12	£120.00	—

M. PEZARO & SON, London

D	C	25	*Armies of the World (c1900):	H.43		
			A Cake Walk Cigarettes		£130.00	—
			B Nestor Virginia Cigarettes		£130.00	—
D	C	? 19	Song Titles Illustrated (c1900)	H.323	£300.00	—

GODFREY PHILLIPS LTD, London

40 page Godfrey Phillips reference book — £4.50
The Card Issues of Godfrey Phillips & Associated Companies (2009 Edition) reference book, 256 pages — £28.00

D1	C	25	*Actresses 'C' Series, Nd 101-125 (c1900):	GP.1		
			A Blue Horseshoe design back		£35.00	—
			B Green back, 'Carriage' Cigarettes		£30.00	—
			C Blue back, 'Teapot' Cigarettes		£85.00	—
			D Blue back, 'Volunteer' Cigarettes		£85.00	—
			E Blue back, 'Derby' Cigarettes		£85.00	—
			F Blue back 'Ball of Beauty' Cigarettes		£85.00	—
—	C	50	*Actresses — oval card (38 × 62mm) (1916):	GP.2		
			A With name		£7.00	—
			B *Without Maker's and Actress's Name*		£5.00	£250.00
A2	C	1	*Advertisement Card — 'Grand Cut' (1934)	GP.2	—	£15.00
A2	C	1	*Advertisement Card — 'La Galbana Fours' (1934)	GP.2	—	£15.00

Size	Print-ing	Number in set		Handbook reference	Price per card	Complete set

GODFREY PHILLIPS LTD, London *(continued)*

Size	Print-ing	Number in set		Handbook reference	Price per card	Complete set
A	C	50	Aircraft (1938)	GP.5	£2.00	£100.00
A2	C	54	Aircraft — Series No. 1 (1938):	GP.4		
			A Millhoff and Philips names at base		£4.00	—
			B Phillips and Associated Companies at base:			
			1 Front varnished		£3.00	£160.00
			2 Front matt		50p	£27.00
D	C	40	Animal Series (c1905)		£6.50	£260.00
—	C	30	Animal Studies (61 × 53mm) (1936)		30p	£9.00
A2	C	50	Annuals (1939):	GP.9		
			A Home issue		25p	£12.50
			B New Zealand issue (dates for planting 4-6 months later). See Overseas Issues			
B	C	25	Arms of the English Sees (1924)		£4.40	£110.00
A	BW		B.D.V. Package Issues (1932-34):			
		17	Boxers	GP.161	£7.00	—
		55	Cricketers	GP.162	£8.00	—
		68	Film Stars	GP.168	£2.50	—
		136	Footballers	GP.163	£6.00	—
		19	Jockeys	GP.164	£4.50	—
		21	Speedway Riders	GP.165	£9.00	—
		28	Sportsmen	GP.166	£4.50	—
D1	C	25	*Beauties, Nd B.801-825 (c1902)	GP.12	£12.00	£300.00
A1	U	24	*Beauties, collotype — 'HUMPS' (c1895):	H.222/GP.24		
			A 'Awarded 7 Gold Medals 1895' on front		£85.00	—
			B 'PLUMS' on front		£600.00	—
A	C	30	*Beauties, 'Nymphs' (c1896)	GP.14	£90.00	—
D			*Beauties — 'PLUMS' (1897):	H.186/GP.16		
	BW	? 60	A Front in black and white		£175.00	—
	C	50	B Plum-coloured background		£70.00	—
	C	50	C Green background		£70.00	—
DA	C	44	Beauties of Today, small — 'A Series of 44 ...' (1937)		£1.50	—
A	C	50	Beauties of Today, small — 'A Series of 50 ...' (1938)	GP.20	£1.00	£50.00
A2	P	54	Beauties of Today, small — 'A Series of Real Photographs ...' (1939)		£1.40	£75.00
A	C	36	Beauties of Today, small — 'A Series of 36 ... Second Series' (1940)		£1.10	£40.00
—	P		Beauties of Today, large (83 × 66mm) (c1938)	GP.24		
		36	First arrangement, known as 'Series A'		£3.50	—
		36	Second arrangement, known as 'Series B'		£6.00	—
J2	P	36	Beauties of Today, extra-large, unnumbered (1937)	GP.25	£1.50	£55.00
J2	P	36	Beauties of Today, extra-large — 'Second Series' (1938)		£1.25	£45.00
J2	P	36	Beauties of Today, extra-large — 'Third Series' (1938)		£1.10	£40.00
J2	P	36	Beauties of Today, extra-large — 'Fourth Series' (1938)		£1.10	£40.00
J2	P	36	Beauties of Today, extra-large — 'Fifth Series' (1938)		£1.00	£36.00
J2	P	36	Beauties of Today, extra-large — 'Sixth Series' (1939)		£1.00	£36.00
J2	P	36	Beauties of Today, extra-large — Unmarked (1939):	GP.31		
			A Back 'Godfrey Phillips Ltd'		£1.00	£36.00
			B Back 'Issued with B.D.V. Medium Cigarettes ...'		50p	£18.00
A2	BW	36	Beauties of the World — Stage, Cinema, Dancing Celebrities (1931)		£1.50	£55.00
A2	C	36	Beauties of the World — Series No. 2 — Stars of Stage and Screen (1933)		£1.65	£60.00
A1	C	50	Beautiful Women (c1905):	H.284/GP.32		
			A Inscribed 'W.I. Series'		£11.00	—
			B Inscribed 'I.F. Series'		£11.00	—

GODFREY PHILLIPS LTD, London *(continued)*

Size	*Printing*	*Number in set*		*Handbook reference*	*Price per card*	*Complete set*
—	C	50	Beautiful Women, Nd W.501-550 (55 × 75mm) (c1905)	H.284/GP.32	£24.00	—
—	C	30	Beauty Spots of the Homeland (126 × 89mm) (1938)		50p	£15.00
A	C	50	Bird Painting (1938)		90p	£45.00
D1	C	25	*Boxer Rebellion — Sketches (1904)	H.46/GP.35	£32.00	—
—	C	30	**British Beauties — Oval Card* (36 × 60mm) *Plain back (c1910)*	H.244/GP.15	£3.00	£90.00
D	U	50	'British Beauties' photogravure (c1916)	GP.38	£8.00	£400.00
—	PC	76	British Beauties (37 × 51mm) (c1916)		£3.20	£245.00
A	C	54	British Beauties Nd 1-54 (1914):	GP.36		
			(a) Blue back, grey-black, glossy front		£2.50	£135.00
			(b) *Plain back, grey-black, glossy front*		£3.50	—
			(c) *Plain back, sepia, matt front*		£3.50	—
A	C	54	British Beauties Nd 55-108 (1914):	GP.37		
			A Blue back, grey-black, semi-glossy front		£2.50	£135.00
			B Blue back, grey-black matt front		£2.50	£135.00
			C *Plain back, grey-black matt front*		£3.50	—
A	C	50	British Birds and Their Eggs (1936)		£1.10	£55.00
D1	C	30	British Butterflies, No. 1 issue (1911)		£4.50	£135.00
A	C	25	British Butterflies:	GP.42		
			A Back in pale blue (1923)		£1.40	£35.00
			B Back in dark blue (1927)		£1.00	£25.00
			C 'Permacal' transfers (1936)		80p	£20.00
A2	C	25	British Orders of Chivalry and Valour (1939):	GP.43		
			A Back 'Godfrey Phillips Ltd'		£2.80	£70.00
			B Back 'De Reszke Cigarettes' (no maker's name)		£2.80	£70.00
D1	U	25	British Warships, green photo style (1915)		£9.00	£225.00
L	U	25	British Warships, green photo style (1915)		£40.00	—
A1	P	80	British Warships, 'real photographic' (c1916)	GP.45	£16.00	—
D1	C	50	*Busts of Famous People (1906):			
			A Pale green back, caption in black		£30.00	—
			B Brown back, caption in black		£50.00	—
			C Green back, caption in white		£7.00	£350.00
—	C	36	Characters Come to Life (61 × 53mm) (1938)		£1.00	£36.00
D1	C	25	*Chinese Series (c1910):	GP.48		
			A Back in English		£8.00	£200.00
			B 'Volunteer' Cigarettes back		£10.00	£250.00
—	P	25	*Cinema Stars — Circular (57mm diam.) (1924)	GP.49	£3.40	—
A	P	52	Cinema Stars — Set 1 (1929)	GP.50	£2.75	—
A2	U	30	Cinema Stars — Set 2 (1924)	GP.51	£2.75	—
A2	BW	30	Cinema Stars — Set 3 (1931)	GP.52	£1.50	£45.00
A2	C	32	Cinema Stars — Set 4 (1934)	GP.53	£1.50	£48.00
A2	BW	32	Cinema Stars — Set 5 (1934)	GP.54	£1.75	£55.00
A	C	50	*Colonial Troops (1904)	H.40/GP.56	£27.00	—
			Come to Life Series — see 'Zoo Studies'			
	C		Coronation of Their Majesties (1937):	GP.57		
A2		50	A Small size		25p	£12.50
—		36	B Medium size (61 × 53mm)		25p	£9.00
—		24	C Postcard size (127 × 89mm):			
			i Back with postcard format		£1.40	£35.00
			ii Back without postcard format		£4.00	—
	P		Cricketers (1924):	GP.58		
K2		198	*A Miniature size, 'Pinnace' photos (Nd 16c-225c)		£9.00	—
D		192	B Small size, brown back (selected Nos)		£9.00	—
B1		? 157	*C Large size, 'Pinnace' photos		£40.00	—
B1		25	D Large size, brown back (selected Nos)		£24.00	—
—		? 180	*E *Cabinet size*		£40.00	—

Size	*Print-ing*	*Number in set*		*Handbook reference*	*Price per card*	*Complete set*

GODFREY PHILLIPS LTD, London *(continued)*

D	BW	1	Cricket Fixture Card (Radio Luxembourg) (1936)		—	£7.00
D	C	25	Derby Winners and Jockeys (1923)		£4.00	£100.00
D1	C	30	Eggs, Nests and Birds, No. 1 issue (1912):			
			A Unnumbered	GP.60	£6.00	£180.00
			B Numbered		£6.00	£180.00
D1	C	25	Empire Industries (1927)	GP.61	£1.40	£35.00
A2	C	50	*Evolution of the British Navy* (1930)		—	£90.00
			49 different (minus No 40)		£1.00	£50.00
D	C	25	Famous Boys (1924)		£2.60	£65.00
D	C	32	Famous Cricketers (1926)		£5.50	—
A	C	25	Famous Crowns (1938)		40p	£10.00
A2	C	50	Famous Footballers (1936)	GP.66	£2.20	£110.00
—	C	36	Famous Love Scenes (60 × 53mm) (1939)		70p	£25.00
A2	C	50	Famous Minors (1936)		30p	£15.00
—	C	26	Famous Paintings (128 × 89mm) (1938)	GP.69	£1.30	£35.00
D	C	25	Feathered Friends (1928)	GP.70	£1.60	£40.00
A2	C	50	Film Favourites (1934)	GP.71	70p	£35.00
A2	C	50	Film Stars (1934)	GP.73	80p	£40.00
—	C	24	*Film Stars — '... No. ... of a series of 24 cards ...' (128 × 89mm) (1934):	GP.74		
			A Postcard format back		£3.00	£75.00
			B Back without postcard format		£4.00	£100.00
—	C	24	*Film Stars — '... No. ... of a series of cards', Nd 25-48 (128 × 89mm) (1935):	GP.75		
			A Postcard format back		£3.00	—
			B Back without postcard format		£6.00	—
—	C	24	*Film Stars '... No. ... of a series of cards', vivid backgrounds (128 × 89mm) (1936):	GP.76		
			A Postcard format back		£2.00	—
			B Back without postcard format		£3.00	—
D	C	25	First Aid Series, green back (1914)	GP.78	£7.00	£175.00
D	C	50	First Aid, black back (1923)	GP.77	£1.50	£75.00
D	C	25	*Fish (1924)		£2.60	£65.00
	C	30	Flower Studies (1937):			
—			A Medium size (61 × 53mm)		25p	£7.50
—			*B Postcard size (128 × 89mm)		70p	£21.00
	P	2462	Footballers — 'Pinnace' photos (1922-24):			
K2			A Miniature size: (Prices shown apply to numbers 1 to 940, for numbers above 940 prices are doubled)	GP.155		
		112	1a 'Oval' design back, in brown		£4.00	—
		400	1b 'Oval' design back, in black		£2.00	—
		? 388	2 Double-lined oblong back		£2.00	—
		? 890	3 Single-lined oblong back, address 'Photo'		£1.30	—
		? 2350	4 Single-lined oblong back, address 'Pinnace' photos		£1.30	—
—			B Large size (83 × 59mm):	GP.156		
		? 400	1 'Oval' design back		£3.50	—
			2 Double-lined oblong back:			
		? 63	a Address 'Photo'		£10.00	—
		? 2462	b Address 'Pinnace' photos		£3.50	—
—		? 2462	C Cabinet size (153 × 111mm)	GP.157	£10.00	—
—		? 24	D Football Teams (153 × 111mm)	GP.157	£500.00	—
—	C	30	Garden Studies (128 × 89mm) (1938)		50p	£15.00
A	C	13	*General Interest (c1895)	GP.83	£45.00	£600.00
—	BW	100	*Guinea Gold Series, unnumbered (64 × 38mm) Inscribed 'Phillips' Guinea Gold', matt (1899)	GP.87	£6.50	—

Size	*Print-ing*	*Number in set*		*Handbook reference*	*Price per card*	*Complete set*

GODFREY PHILLIPS LTD, London *(continued)*

—	BW	90	*Guinea Gold Series, numbered 101-190 (68 × 41mm).			
			Inscribed 'Smoke Phillips ...' (1902):	GP.88		
			A Glossy		£5.00	—
			B Matt		£5.00	—
			*Guinea Gold Series, unnumbered (63 × 41mm) (c1900)	GP.89		
			Actresses:			
	BW	135	A Black front		£5.00	—
	U	100	B Brown front		£10.00	—
	BW	26	Celebrities, Boer War		£5.00	—
A2	C	25	Home Pets (1924)	GP.90	£2.20	£55.00
A2	U	25	How to Build a Two Valve Set (1929)		£2.60	£65.00
D1	C	25	How to Do It Series (1913)		£7.00	£175.00
D	C	25	How to Make a Valve Amplifier ..., Nd 26-50 (1924)		£3.20	£80.00
A	C	25	How to Make Your Own Wireless Set (1923)		£2.60	£65.00
D	C	25	Indian Series (1908)		£14.00	£350.00
A2	C	54	In the Public Eye (1935)		50p	£27.00
A2	C	50	International Caps (1936)	GP.66	£2.00	£100.00
A2	C	37	Kings and Queens of England (1925):			
			Nos 1 and 4		£30.00	—
			Other numbers		£2.00	£70.00
A2	U	25	Lawn Tennis (1930)		£3.00	£75.00
K1	C	52	*Miniature Playing Cards (c1905)	GP.99	£120.00	—
K2	C	53	*Miniature Playing Cards (1932-34):	GP.100		
			A Back with exchange scheme:			
			1 Buff. Offer for 'pack of playing cards'		60p	—
			2 Buff. Offer for 'playing cards, dominoes or chess'		60p	£30.00
			3 Buff. Offer for 'playing cards, dominoes or draughts'		60p	£30.00
			4 Lemon		60p	—
			5 White, with red over-printing		60p	—
			B *Blue scroll back*		60p	£30.00
A2	C	25	Model Railways (1927)	GP.101	£3.20	£80.00
D1	C	30	Morse and Semaphore Signalling (1916):	GP.102		
			'Morse Signalling' back		£10.00	£300.00
			'Semaphore Signalling' back		£10.00	£300.00
D	C	50	Motor Cars at a Glance (1924)		£4.00	£200.00
D	C	20	Novelty Series (1924)		£12.00	—
A2	C	48	The 'Old Country' (1935)		80p	£40.00
A	C	25	Old Favourites (1924)	GP.107	£1.80	£45.00
—	C	36	Old Masters (60 × 53mm) (1939)		50p	£18.00
A	U	36	Olympic Champions Amsterdam, 1928		£2.50	£90.00
A	C	25	Optical Illusions (1927)		£2.60	£65.00
	C		'Our Dogs' (1939):	GP.110		
A2		36	A Small size (export)		£1.60	£60.00
—		30	B Medium size (60 × 53mm)		60p	£18.00
—		30	*C Postcard size (128 × 89mm)		£3.40	—
—	BW	48	'Our Favourites' (60 × 53mm) (1935)		25p	£12.50
—	C	30	Our Glorious Empire (128 × 89mm) (1939)		70p	£21.00
	C	30	'Our Puppies' (1936):	GP.113		
—			A Medium size (60 × 53mm)		£1.65	£50.00
—			*B Postcard size (128 × 89mm)		£1.80	£55.00
A2	C	25	Personalities of Today (Caricatures) (1932)		£2.00	£50.00
A2	C	25	Popular Superstitions (1930)		£1.60	£40.00
J2		20	'Private Seal' Wrestling Holds (export) (c1920)		£35.00	—
A	C	25	Prizes for Needlework (1925)	GP.116	£2.20	£55.00
D	C	25	Railway Engines (1924)		£3.20	£80.00

GODFREY PHILLIPS LTD, London *(continued)*

Size	*Print-ing*	*Number in set*		*Handbook reference*	*Price per card*	*Complete set*
—	P	27	Real Photo Series — Admirals and Generals of the Great War. Cut-outs for buttonhole (28 × 40mm) (c1915)	GP.118	£7.50	—
D	C	25	Red Indians (1927)	GP.119	£3.60	£90.00
A	C	20	Russo-Japanese War Series (1904)	H.100/GP.120	£300.00	—
A	C	25	School Badges (1927)	GP.121	£1.10	£27.50
A	C		Screen Stars (1936):			
		48	First arrangement, known as 'Series A':	GP.122		
			i Frame embossed		£1.20	£60.00
			ii Frame not embossed		£1.60	£80.00
		48	Second arrangement, known as 'Series B'	GP.123	£1.00	£50.00
A2	C		A Selection of B.D.V. Wonderful Gifts:			
		48	'... based on 1930 Budget' (1930)	GP.84	£1.20	—
		48	'... based on 1931 Budget' (1931)	GP.85	£1.20	—
		48	'... based on 1932 Budget' (1932)	GP.86	£1.00	£50.00
		30	Semaphore Signalling — see 'Morse and Semaphore Signalling'			
D	C	25	Ships and Their Flags (1924)	GP.124	£3.00	£75.00
—	C	36	Ships that have Made History (60 × 53mm) (1938)		60p	£22.00
—	C	48	Shots from the Films (60 × 53mm) (1934)	GP.126	80p	£40.00
A2	C	50	Soccer Stars (1936)	GP.66	£1.80	£90.00
A2	C	36	Soldiers of the King (1939):	GP.127		
			A Inscribed 'This surface is adhesive'		£1.60	—
			B Without the above:			
			1 Thin card		70p	£25.00
			2 Thick card		70p	£25.00
	C		Special Jubilee Year Series (1935):	GP.128		
—		20	A Medium size (60 × 53mm)		40p	£8.00
—		12	B Postcard size (128 × 89mm)		£2.00	£24.00
A2	U	30	Speed Champions (1930)		£2.00	£60.00
A2	U	36	Sporting Champions (1929)		£2.75	£100.00
D1	C	25	Sporting Series (c1910)	GP.131	£18.00	—
D	C	25	Sports (1923):	GP.131		
			A White card		£4.00	—
			B Grey card		£4.00	—
A2	C	50	*Sportsmen — 'Spot the Winner' (1937):			
			A Inverted back		£1.10	£55.00
			B Normal back		£1.50	£75.00
A	BW		Sports Package Issues:			
		25	Cricketers (1948)	GP.171	£9.00	—
		25	Cricketers (1951)	GP.177	£9.00	—
		25	Footballers (1948)	GP.172	£8.00	—
		50	Footballers (1950)	GP.176	£8.00	—
		25	Footballers (1951)	GP.178	£8.00	—
		25	Football & Rugby Players (1952)	GP.180	£7.00	—
		25	Jockeys (1952)	GP.179	£5.00	—
		25	Radio Stars (1949)	GP.175	£3.00	—
		50	Sportsmen (1948)	GP.173	£5.00	—
		25	Sportsmen (1949)	GP.174	£5.00	—
		25	Sportsmen (1953)	GP.181	£5.00	—
		25	Sportsmen (1954)	GP.182	£5.00	—
A2	C		Stage and Cinema Beauties (1933):	H.572		
		35	First arrangement — known as 'Series A'	GP.133	£1.15	£40.00
		35	Second arrangement — known as 'Series B'	GP.134	£1.15	£40.00
A2	C	50	Stage and Cinema Beauties (1935)	GP.135	£1.20	£60.00
A	U	?	Stamp Cards (four colours, several wordings) (c1930)	GP.287	£2.50	—
A2	CP	54	Stars of the Screen — 'A Series of 54' (1934)		£1.20	£65.00

Size	Printing	Number in set		Handbook reference	Price per card	Complete set

GODFREY PHILLIPS LTD, London *(continued)*

Size	Printing	Number in set		Handbook reference	Price per card	Complete set
A2	C	48	Stars of the Screen — 'A Series of 48' (1936):			
			A Frame not embossed		90p	£45.00
			B Frame embossed		90p	£45.00
			C In strips of three, per strip		£2.50	£40.00
D1	C	25	*Statues and Monuments (cut-outs) (1907):	GP.139		
			A Provisional Patent No. 20736		£8.00	£200.00
			B Patent No. 20736		£8.00	£200.00
D	C	25	*Territorial Series (Nd 51-75) (1908)		£25.00	—
A	U	25	The 1924 Cabinet (1924)		£2.00	£50.00
A	C	50	This Mechanized Age — First Series (1936):			
			A Inscribed 'This surface is adhesive'		30p	£15.00
			B Without the above		36p	£18.00
A	C	50	This Mechanized Age — Second Series (1937)		40p	£20.00
A1	C	25	*Types of British and Colonial Troops (1899)	H.76/GP.145	£45.00	—
D1	C	25	*Types of British Soldiers (Nd M.651-75) (1900)	H.144/GP.146	£25.00	£625.00
A	C	63	*War Photos (1916)	GP.149	£9.00	—
—	C	30	Zoo Studies — Come to Life Series (101 × 76mm) (1939)		£1.30	£40.00
			Spectacles for use with the above		—	£8.00

SILKS. Known as 'the B.D.V. Silks'. All unbacked. Inscribed 'B.D.V. Cigarettes' or 'G.P.' (Godfrey Phillips), or anonymous. Issued about 1910-25. 'Ha' prefix refers to original Handbook Part II. Nos 201 to 253 refer to new Godfrey Phillips Reference Book.

Size	Printing	Number in set		Handbook reference	Price per card	Complete set
—	C	62	**Arms of Countries and Territories (73 × 50mm) — Anonymous*	201	£4.00	—
—	C	32	*Beauties — Modern Paintings (B.D.V.):	Ha.505-13/202		
			A Small size (70 × 46mm)		£12.00	—
			B Extra-large size (143 × 100mm)		£40.00	—
—	C	100	*Birds II (68 × 42mm) — B.D.V	Ha.505-2/203	£3.00	—
—	C	12	*Birds of the Tropics III — B.D.V.:	Ha.505-3/204		
			A Small size (71 × 47mm)		£11.00	—
			B Medium size (71 × 63mm)		£13.00	—
			C Extra-large size (150 × 100mm)		£17.00	—
—	U	24	**British Admirals (83 × 76mm) — Anonymous*	Ha.504-5/205	£6.50	—
—	C		**British Butterflies and Moths II — Anonymous:*	Ha.505-6/206		
		40	*Nos 1-40. Large size, 76 × 61mm*		£6.00	—
		10	*Nos 41-50. Medium size. 70 × 51mm*		£6.00	—
—	C	108	*British Naval Crests II:	Ha.504-4/207		
			A B.D.V., size 70 × 47mm		£2.00	—
			B *Anonymous, size 70 × 51mm*		£2.00	—
—	C	25	**Butterflies I (70 × 48mm) — Anonymous*	Ha.505-5/208	£10.00	—
—	C	47	Ceramic Art — B.D.V.:	Ha.505-16/209		
			A Small size (70 × 43mm)		£1.00	£47.00
			B Small size (70 × 48mm)		£1.00	—
			C Medium size (70 × 61mm)		£1.75	—
—	C		*Clan Tartans:			
			A Small size (71 × 48mm):	Ha.505-15/210		
		49	1 *Anonymous*		£1.10	£55.00
		65	2 B.D.V		£1.10	£70.00
		56	B Medium size (70 × 60mm) — B.D.V		£3.00	—
		12	C Extra-large size (150 × 100mm) B.D.V. (selected Nos.)		£5.50	—
—	C	108	**Colonial Army Badges (71 × 50mm) — Anonymous*	Ha.502-3/211	£2.80	—
—	C	17	County Cricket Badges (69 × 48mm):	Ha.505-8/212		
			A *Anonymous*		£18.00	—
			B B.D.V		£18.00	—

Size	Print-ing	Number in set		Handbook reference	Price per card	Complete set

GODFREY PHILLIPS LTD, London *(continued)*

Size	Print-ing	Number in set		Handbook reference	Price per card	Complete set
—	C	108	*Crests and Badges of the British Army II:	H.502-2/213		
			A1 *Small size* (70 × 48mm) Anonymous:			
			(a) *Numbered*		£1.30	£140.00
			(b) *Unnumbered*		£1.30	£140.00
			A2 Small size (70 × 48mm) — B.D.V		£1.30	£140.00
			A3 Medium size (70 × 60mm):			
			(a) *Anonymous*		£1.50	—
			(b) B.D.V		£1.50	—
—	C		**Flags — Set 4 — Anonymous:*	Ha.501-4/214		
		? 143	*A 'Long' size (82 × 53mm)*		£1.70	—
			B 'Short' size (70 × 48mm):			
		? 143	*1 First numbering arrangement (as A)*		£1.40	—
		? 108	*2 Second numbering arrangement*		£1.00	—
		? 113	*3 Third numbering arrangement*		£1.00	—
—	C		**Flags — Set 5 — Anonymous:*	Ha.501-5/215		
			A Small size (70 × 50mm):			
		20	*1 With caption*		£1.00	—
		6	*2 Without caption, flag 40 × 29mm*		£1.20	—
		? 6	*3 Without caption, flag 60 × 41mm*		£1.20	—
		? 8	*B Extra-large size (155 × 108mm)*		£14.00	—
—	C	18	**Flags — Set 6 — Anonymous:*	Ha.501-6/216		
			A Size 69 × 47mm		£1.00	£18.00
			B Size 71 × 51mm		£1.00	£18.00
—	C	20	**Flags — Set 7 (70 × 50mm) — Anonymous*	Ha.501-7/217	£1.00	—
—	C	50	**Flags — Set 9 — ('5th Series') (70 × 48mm) — Anonymous*	Ha.501-9/218	£1.80	£90.00
—	C		*Flags — Set 10:	Ha.501-10/219		
		120	*'7th Series' (70 × 48mm) — Anonymous*		90p	—
		120	*'10th Series' (70 × 62mm) — Anonymous*		£1.00	—
		120	*'12th Series' (70 × 48mm) — Anonymous*		90p	—
		65	'15th Series' (70 × 62mm) (selected Nos.) — B.D.V.		£1.20	—
		65	'16th Series' (70 × 62mm) (selected Nos.) — B.D.V.		£1.20	—
			'20th Series' (70 × 48 mm) — B.D.V.:			
		132	A B.D.V. in brown		£1.00	—
		48	B B.D.V. in orange		£2.50	—
		126	'25th Series' (70 × 48mm) — B.D.V.		90p	—
		62	'25th Series' '(70 × 62mm) (selected Nos.) — B.D.V.		£3.00	—
			'26th Series' (70 × 48mm) — B.D.V.:			
		112	A 26th Series in brown		£1.00	—
		55	B 26th Series in blue		£4.00	—
		70	'28th Series' (70 × 48mm) (selected Nos.) — B.D.V.		£1.00	—
—	C		*Flags — Set 12:	Ha.501-12/220		
		1	*A 'Let 'em all come' (70 × 46mm) — Anonymous*		—	£11.00
			B Allied Flags (grouped):			
		1	*Four Flags — Anonymous:*			
			1 Small size (70 × 46mm)		—	£9.00
			2 Extra-large size (163 × 120mm)		—	£40.00
		1	Seven Flags (165 × 116mm):			
			1 Anonymous		—	£9.00
			2 B.D.V. in brown or orange		—	£9.00
		1	Eight Flags (165 × 116mm) — B.D.V.		—	£40.00
—	C		*Flags — Set 13:	Ha.501-13/221		
		? 23	*A Size 163 × 114mm — Anonymous*		£2.25	—
		? 27	B Size 163 × 114mm — B.D.V. in brown, orange, blue, green or black		£2.25	—
		? 23	C Size 150 × 100mm — B.D.V.		£2.25	—

Size	*Print-ing*	*Number in set*		*Handbook reference*	*Price per card*	*Complete set*

GODFREY PHILLIPS LTD, London *(continued)*

—	C	26	**Flags — Set 14 ('House Flags') (68 × 47mm) — Anonymous*	Ha.501-14/229	£8.50	—
—	C	25	*Flags — Set 15 (Pilot and Signal Flags) (70 × 50mm):	Ha.501-15/244		
			A Numbered 601-625 — Anonymous		£3.60	£85.00
			B Inscribed 'Series II' — B.D.V.		£2.40	£60.00
—	C		*Football Colours:	Ha.505-9/222		
		? 21	*A Anonymous. size 68 × 49mm*		£8.00	—
		? 86	B B.D.V., size 68 × 49mm		£6.00	—
		? 78	C B.D.V., size 150 × 100mm		£6.00	—
—	C	126	G.P. Territorial Badges (70 × 48mm)	Ha.502-12/223	£2.20	—
—	U	25	**Great War Leaders II (81 × 68mm) — Anonymous*	Ha.504-7/224	£6.40	—
—	U	50	**Great War Leaders III and Warships, sepia, black or blue on white or pink material (70 × 50mm) — Anonymous*	Ha.504-10/225	£6.40	—
—	C		*Great War Leaders IV and Celebrities:	Ha.504-11/226		
		3	*A Small size (70 × 48mm) — Anonymous*		£6.00	—
		4	B Small size (70 × 48mm) — B.D.V.		£6.50	—
		3	*C Medium size (70 × 63mm) — Anonymous*		£6.00	—
		2	D Medium size (70 × 63mm) — B. D.V.		£6.00	—
		? 18	E Extra-large size (150 × 100mm) — B.D.V.		£6.00	—
		? 4	*F Extra-large size (150 × 110mm) — Anonymous*		£6.00	£24.00
		? 1	G Extra-large size (150 × 110mm) — B.D.V.		—	£15.00
		? 25	*H Extra-large size (163 × 117mm) — Anonymous*		£6.00	—
		? 44	I Extra-large size (163 × 117mm) — B.D.V.		£6.00	—
—	C		Heraldic Series — B.D.V.:	Ha.504-17/228		
		25	A Small size (68 × 47mm)		£1.20	£30.00
		25	B Small size (68 × 43mm)		£1.20	£30.00
		25	C Medium size (68 × 60mm)		£3.00	—
		12	D Extra-large size (150 × 100mm) (selected Nos)		£5.50	£65.00
—	C	10	**Irish Patriots — Anonymous:*	Ha.505-11/230		
			A Small size (67 × 50mm)		£12.00	—
			B Large size (83 × 76mm)		£12.00	—
			C Extra-large size (152 × 110mm)		£17.00	—
—	C	1	*Irish Republican Stamp (70 × 50mm)	Ha.505-12/231	—	£2.00
—	C	10	Miniature Rugs (89 × 55mm) (c1920)	GP.232	£9.00	—
—	C	54	**Naval Badges of Rank and Military Headdress (70 × 47mm) — Anonymous*	Ha.504-9/233	£6.00	—
—	C	40	*Old Masters — Set 1 (155 × 115mm) — B.D.V.	Ha.503-1/235	£32.00	—
—	C	20	*Old Masters — Set 2 (150 × 105mm):	Ha.503-2/236		
			A *Anonymous*		£4.00	—
			B B.D.V. wording above picture		£4.00	—
			C B.D.V. wording below picture		£6.00	—
—	C		*Old Masters — Set 3A (70 × 50mm):	Ha.503-3A/237		
		40	A B.D.V.		£3.00	—
		55	B *Anonymous*		£2.50	—
—	C	30	**Old Masters — Set 3B (70 × 50mm) — Anonymous*	Ha.503-3B/237	£2.50	—
—	C	120	**Old Masters — Set 4 (70 × 50mm) — Anonymous*	Ha.503-4/238	£2.00	—
—	C		*Old Masters — Set 5 (70 × 50mm):	Ha.503-5/239		
		20	A *Unnumbered — Anonymous*		£3.00	—
		60	B Nd. 1-60 — B.D.V		£1.20	£72.00
		20	*C Nd. 101-120 — Anonymous:*			
			1 Numerals normal size		£2.00	—
			2 Numerals very small size		£2.00	£40.00
		20	D Nd. 101-120 — B.D.V.		£1.80	£36.00
—	C	50	*Old Masters — Set 6 (67 × 42mm) — B.D.V.	Ha.503-6/240	£1.20	£60.00
—	C	50	**Old Masters — Set 7, Nd. 301-350 (67 × 47mm) — Anonymous*	Ha.503-7/241	£2.50	—

Size	Printing	Number in set		Handbook reference	Price per card	Complete set

GODFREY PHILLIPS LTD, London *(continued)*

—	C	50	**Orders of Chivalry I (70 × 48mm) — Anonymous*	Ha.504-14/242	£2.20	—
—	C	24	*Orders of Chivalry — Series 10 (70 × 50mm):	Ha.504-16/243		
			A Nd. 1-24 — B.D.V.		£1.80	£45.00
			B Nd. 401-424 — G.P		£2.00	£50.00
—	C	72	**Regimental Colours II (76 × 70mm) — Anonymous*	Ha.502-7/245	£4.50	—
—	C		*Regimental Colours and Crests III:	Ha.502-8/246		
			A Small size (70 × 51mm):			
		40	*1 Colours with faint backgrounds — Anonymous*		£1.60	—
		120	*2 Colours without backgrounds — Anonymous*		£1.75	—
		120	3 Colours without backgrounds — B.D.V.		£1.75	—
		120	B Extra-large size (165 × 120mm):			
			1 Anonymous — unnumbered		£6.50	—
			2 B.D.V. — numbered		£6.00	—
—	C	50	*Regimental Colours — Series 12 (70 × 50mm) — B.D.V.	Ha.502-11/247	£2.00	£100.00
—	C	10	**Religious Pictures — Anonymous:*	Ha.505-10/248		
			A Small size (67 × 50mm)		£18.00	—
			B Large size (83 × 76 mm)		£20.00	—
			C Extra-large size (155 × 110mm)		£27.00	—
—	C	75	*Town and City Arms — Series 30 (48 unnumbered, 27 numbered 49-75) — B.D.V.:	Ha.504-13/250		
			A Small size (70 × 50mm)		£2.00	—
			B Medium size (70 × 65mm)		£3.00	—
—	C	25	**Victoria Cross Heroes I (70 × 50mm) — Anonymous*	Ha.504-1/251	£12.00	—
—	C	? 25	**Victoria Cross Heroes II (70 × 50mm) — Anonymous*	Ha.504-2/252	£12.00	—
—	C	90	**War Pictures (70 × 48mm) — Anonymous*	Ha.504-8/253	£6.00	—

OVERSEAS ISSUES (AUSTRALIA AND NEW ZEALAND)

A2	U	50	*Animal Studies (c1930)	GP.7	£2.00	—
A2	C	50	Annuals (1939) (New Zealand issue)	GP.9	£1.50	£75.00
D	BW	50	Australian Sporting Celebrities (1932)		£3.00	—
D	BW	50	Film Stars (1934)		£2.00	—
D	C	50	Stars of British Films (1934):			
			A Back 'B.D.V. Cigarettes'		£1.80	—
			B Back 'Grey's Cigarettes ...'		£1.80	—
			C Back 'De Reszke Cigarettes'		£1.80	—
			D Back 'Godfrey Phillips (Aust)'		£1.80	—
D	BW	38	Test Cricketers, 1932-1933:			
			A 'Issued with Grey's Cigarettes'		£3.50	—
			B 'Issued with B.D.V. Cigarettes'		£3.50	—
			C Back 'Godfrey Phillips (Aust.)'		£3.50	—
D2	C		Victorian Footballers (1933):			
		50	1 'Series of 50':			
			A 'Godfrey Phillips (Aust.)'		£4.00	—
			B 'B.D.V. Cigarettes ...'		£4.00	—
			C 'Grey's Cigarettes'		£4.00	—
		75	2 'Series of 75':			
			D 'B.D.V. Cigarettes ...'		£5.00	—
D	BW	50	Victorian League and Association Footballers (1934)		£5.00	—
A2	C	100	*Who's Who in Australian Sport (1933)	GP.150	£3.50	—

JOHN PLAYER & SONS, Nottingham

44 page reference book — £4.50

A	C	25	*Actors and Actresses (1898)	H.337	£25.00	£625.00
A1	BW	50	*Actresses (c1897)	H.339	£25.00	—

Size	*Print-ing*	*Number in set*		*Handbook reference*	*Price per card*	*Complete set*

JOHN PLAYER & SONS, Nottingham *(continued)*

A	C	8	*Advertisement Cards (1893-94) multi-backed	H.338	From £300.00	—
	C	1	*Advertisement Card (Sailor) (c1930):			
A			A Small size		—	£5.00
B			B Large size		—	£20.00
B	BW	1	Advertisement Card — Wants List (1936)		—	£1.00
A	C	50	Aeroplanes (1935):			
			A Home issue — titled 'Aeroplanes (Civil)'		£1.10	£55.00
			B Irish issue — titled 'Aeroplanes'		£1.50	£75.00
A	C	50	Aircraft of the Royal Air Force (1938):			
			A Home issue — with I.T.C. clause		£1.00	£50.00
			B Channel Islands issue — without I.T.C. clause		£1.50	£75.00
J	C	10	Allied Cavalry or Regimental Uniforms:	H.340		
			Allied Cavalry (1914)		£10.00	£100.00
			Regimental Uniforms (1914)		£9.00	£90.00
A	C	50	Animals of the Countryside (1939):			
			A Home issue — adhesive, with I.T.C. clause		25p	£12.50
			B Irish issue — non-adhesive, green numerals overprinted		£1.00	—
			C Channel Islands issue — adhesive, without I.T.C. clause		70p	£35.00
B	C	25	Aquarium Studies (1932)		£1.80	£45.00
B	C	25	Architectural Beauties (1927)		£2.20	£55.00
A	C	50	Arms and Armour (1909):	H.273		
			A Home issue — with I.T.C. clause		£2.50	£125.00
			B Overseas issue — without I.T.C. clause — see Overseas section			
A	C	50	Army Corps and Divisional Signs, 1914-1918 (1924)		60p	£30.00
A	C	100	Army Corps and Divisional Signs, 1914-1918, '2nd Series' (1925):			
			Nos. 51-100		70p	£35.00
			Nos. 101-150		70p	£35.00
A	C	25	Army Life (1910)	H.78	£2.00	£50.00
J	C	12	Artillery in Action (1917)		£5.00	£60.00
A	U	50	Association Cup Winners (1930)	H.667	£1.80	£90.00
	C		Aviary and Cage Birds:			
A		50	A Small size (1933):			
			1 Cards		£1.00	£50.00
			2 Transfers		40p	£20.00
B		25	B Large size (1935)		£3.60	£90.00
A	C	50	Badges and Flags of British Regiments (1904):	H.341		
			A Brown back, unnumbered		£2.50	£125.00
			B Brown back, numbered		£2.50	£125.00
A	C	50	Badges and Flags of British Regiments (1903):			
			A Green back, thick card		£2.50	£125.00
			B Green back, thin card		£2.50	£125.00
A	C	50	Birds and Their Young (1937):			
			A Home issue — adhesive, with I.T.C. clause		25p	£12.50
			B Irish issue:			
			1 Adhesive, with large green numerals		£1.00	—
			2 Non-adhesive, with large green numerals		£1.00	—
			C Channel Islands issue — adhesive, without I.T.C. clause		70p	£35.00
A	C	25	Birds and Their Young, 1st series (unissued) (1955)		24p	£6.00
A	C	25	Birds and Their Young, 2nd series (unissued) (1955)		20p	£4.00
—	P	10	*Bookmarks — Authors (139 × 51mm) (1905)		£65.00	—
A	C	25	Boxing (1934)		£6.00	—

Size	Printing	Number in set		Handbook reference	Price per card	Complete set

JOHN PLAYER & SONS, Nottingham *(continued)*

Size	Printing	Number in set		Handbook reference	Price per card	Complete set
A	C	50	Boy Scout and Girl Guide Patrol Signs and Emblems (1933):			
			A Cards		40p	£20.00
			B Transfers		40p	£20.00
B	C	25	British Butterflies (1934)		£4.40	£110.00
A	C	50	British Empire Series (1904):	H.343		
			A Grey-white card, matt		£1.30	£65.00
			B White card, semi-glossy		£1.50	£75.00
	C	25	British Livestock:			
A			A Small card (1915)		£3.00	£75.00
			B Medium card — see Overseas section			
J			C Extra-large card, brown back (1916)		£4.00	£100.00
J			D Extra-large card, blue back (1923)		£3.60	£90.00
B	C	25	British Naval Craft (1939)		£1.00	£25.00
J	C	20	British Pedigree Stock (1925)		£4.00	£80.00
B	C	25	British Regalia (1937)		£1.20	£30.00
A	C	50	Butterflies (1932):			
			A Cards		£1.30	£65.00
			B Transfers		40p	£20.00
A	C	50	Butterflies and Moths (1904)	H.80	£1.90	£95.00
	C		Bygone Beauties:			
A		25	A Small card (1914)		£1.60	£40.00
J		10	B Extra-large card (1916)		£4.50	£45.00
—	U	? 32	*Cabinet Size Pictures, 1898-1900 (220 × 140mm):	H.476		
			A Plain back		£90.00	—
			B Printed back		£90.00	—
A	C	1	Card Scheme — Joker Card (c1935)		—	£5.00
A	C	20	Castles, Abbeys etc (c1894):	H.345		
			A Without border		£28.00	£560.00
			B White border		£28.00	£560.00
B	C	24	Cats (1936)		£7.00	—
A	C	50	Celebrated Bridges (1903)	H.346	£3.00	£150.00
A	C		Celebrated Gateways (1909):	H.347		
		50	A Thick card		£1.50	£75.00
		25	B Thinner card (26-50 only)		£1.80	—
A	C	25	Ceremonial and Court Dress (1911)	H.145	£1.80	£45.00
B	C	25	Championship Golf Courses (1936)		£8.00	£200.00
	C		Characters from Dickens:	H.348		
A		25	Small card, lst series (1912)		£2.40	£60.00
J		10	Extra-large card (1912)..		£6.00	£60.00
A	C	25	Characters from Dickens, 2nd series (1914)	H.348	£2.40	£60.00
A	C	50	Characters from Dickens (1st & 2nd series combined) (1923)	H.348	£1.40	£70.00
B	C	25	Characters from Fiction (1933)		£3.80	£95.00
A	C	25	Characters from Thackeray (1913)		£1.60	£40.00
A	C	50	Cities of the World (1900):			
			A Grey-mauve on white back		£4.00	—
			B Grey-mauve on toned back		£4.00	—
			C Bright mauve on white back		£4.00	—
B	C	20	Clocks — Old and New (1928)		£5.00	£100.00
A	C	25	Colonial and Indian Army Badges (1916)		£1.40	£35.00
A	C	50	Coronation Series Ceremonial Dress (1937):			
			A Home issue — with I.T.C. clause		30p	£15.00
			B Channel Islands issue — without I.T.C. clause		£1.00	£50.00
A	C	25	*Counties and Their Industries:	H.349		
			A Unnumbered (c1910)		£2.40	£60.00
			B Numbered (1914)		£2.40	£60.00

Size	Printing	Number in set		Handbook reference	Price per card	Complete set

JOHN PLAYER & SONS, Nottingham *(continued)*

A	C	50	*Countries — Arms and Flags:			
			A Thick card (1905)		90p	£45.00
			B Thin Card (1912)		£1.10	£55.00
A	C	50	*Country Seats and Arms (1906)		90p	£45.00
A	C		*Country Seats and Arms, 2nd series (1907):			
		25	A Nd. 51-75 First printing		£1.60	£40.00
		50	B Nd. 51-100 Second printing		90p	£45.00
A	C	50	*Country Seats and Arms, 3rd series (1907)		90p	£45.00
B	C	25	Country Sports (1930)		£5.60	£140.00
A	C	50	Cricketers, 1930 (1930)		£1.50	£75.00
A	C	50	Cricketers, 1934 (1934)		£1.20	£60.00
A	C	50	Cricketers, 1938 (1938):			
			A Home issue — with I.T.C. clause		£1.00	£50.00
			B Channel Islands issue — without I.T.C. clause		£1.80	£90.00
A	C	50	Cricketers, Caricatures by 'Rip' (1926)		£1.80	£90.00
	C		Cries of London:	H.350		
A		25	Small cards, 1st series (1913)		£2.00	£50.00
J		10	Extra-large cards, 1st series (1912)		£4.50	£45.00
J		10	Extra-large cards, 2nd series (1914)		£4.00	£40.00
A	C	25	Cries of London, 2nd series (1916):			
			A Blue back		£1.00	£25.00
			B Black back (unissued)		£7.00	—
A	C	50	Curious Beaks (1929)		80p	£40.00
A	C	50	Cycling (1939):			
			A Home issue — adhesive, with I.T.C. clause		90p	£45.00
			B Irish issue:			
			1 Adhesive, with large green numerals		£1.50	—
			2 Non-adhesive, with large green numerals		£1.50	—
			C Channel Islands issue — adhesive, without I.T.C. clause		£1.50	£75.00
	C		Dandies (1932):			
A		50	A Small size		40p	£20.00
B		25	B Large size		£1.80	£45.00
A	C	50	Decorations and Medals (unissued) (c1940)		£2.00	£100.00
A	C	50	Derby and Grand National Winners (1933):			
			A Cards		£1.70	£85.00
			B Transfers		50p	£25.00
	C		Dogs (1924) — Scenic backgrounds:			
A		50	A Small size		£1.00	£50.00
J		12	B Extra-large size		£3.25	£40.00
	C		Dogs — Full length:	H.668		
A		50	A Small size (1931):			
			1 Cards		90p	£45.00
			2 Transfers		50p	£25.00
B		25	B Large size (1933)		£2.60	£65.00
	C		Dogs — Heads:			
A		50	A Small size — Home issue (1929)		£1.00	£50.00
A		25	B Small size — Irish issue, 'A Series of 25', with I.T.C. clause (1927)		£2.00	£50.00
A		25	C Small size — Irish issue, '2nd Series of 25', with I.T.C. clause (1929)		£2.00	£50.00
			D Small size — Overseas issue, without I.T.C. clause (1927) — see Overseas section			
B		20	E Large size — Home issue, 'A Series of 20' (1926)		£2.75	£55.00
B		20	F Large size — Home issue, '2nd Series of 20' (1928)		£2.75	£55.00

Size	*Print-ing*	*Number in set*		*Handbook reference*	*Price per card*	*Complete set*
JOHN PLAYER & SONS, Nottingham *(continued)*						
A	C	50	Dogs' Heads (silver-grey backgrounds) (1940)		£3.00	—
A	C	50	Dogs' Heads by Biegel (unissued) (c1955)		90p	£45.00
B	C	25	Dogs — Pairs and Groups (unissued) (c1955)		£1.40	£35.00
A	C	50	Drum Banners and Cap Badges (1924):			
			A Base panel joining vertical framelines		90p	£45.00
			B Fractional space between the above		80p	£40.00
A	C	25	Egyptian Kings and Queens, and Classical Deities (1911)		£2.00	£50.00
J	C	10	Egyptian Sketches (1915)	H.351	£4.00	£40.00
	C	25	*England's Military Heroes (1898):	H.352		
A1			A Wide card		£40.00	—
A1			*A1 Wide card plain back*		£40.00	—
—			B Narrow card (68 × 28mm)		£32.00	—
—			*B2 Narrow card, plain back* (68 × 28mm)		£30.00	—
	C	25	England's Naval Heroes (1897):	H.353		
A1			A Wide card		£40.00	—
—			B Narrow card (68 × 28mm)		£26.00	£650.00
	C	25	England's Naval Heroes (1898), descriptions on back:	H.353		
A1			A Wide card		£40.00	—
A1			*A2 Wide card, plain back*		£40.00	—
—			B Narrow card (68 × 29mm)		£28.00	£700.00
—			*B2 Narrow card, plain back* (68 × 29mm)		£28.00	—
A	C	25	Everyday Phrases by Tom Browne (1901):	H.354		
			A Thickcard		£18.00	£450.00
			B Thin card		£18.00	£450.00
B	BW	25	Fables of Aesop (1927)		£2.40	£60.00
	C	20	Famous Authors and Poets (1902):			
A			A Wide card		£30.00	£600.00
—			B Narrow card (67 × 30mm)		£20.00	£400.00
B	C	25	Famous Beauties (1937):			
			A Home issue — with I.T.C. clause		£1.80	£45.00
			B Channel Islands issue — without I.T.C. clause		£2.40	£60.00
A	C	50	Famous Irish-Bred Horses (1936)		£3.50	£175.00
A	C	50	Famous Irish Greyhounds (1935)		£5.50	—
J	C	10	Famous Paintings (1913)	H.355	£3.50	£35.00
A	C	50	Film Stars — 'Series of 50' (1934)		£1.20	£60.00
A	C	50	Film Stars — 'Second Series ...':			
			A Home issue — Album 'price one penny' (1934)		90p	£45.00
			B Irish issue — Album offer without price (1935)		£1.60	£80.00
A	C	50	Film Stars — Third Series:			
			A Home issue — titled 'Film Stars — with I.T.C. clause (1938)		80p	£40.00
			B Irish issue — titled 'Screen Celebrities' (1939)		£2.00	—
			C Channel Islands issue — titled 'Film Stars', without I.T.C. clause (1938)		£1.50	£75.00
B	BW	25	Film Stars — Large size (1934):			
			A Home issue — with Album offer		£3.00	£75.00
			B Irish issue — without Album offer		£6.00	—
A	C	50	Fire-Fighting Appliances (1930)		£1.60	£80.00
A	C	50	Fishes of the World (1903)	H.66	£2.40	£120.00
A	C	50	Flags of the League of Nations (1928)		50p	£25.00
A	C	50	Football Caricatures by 'Mac' (1927)		£1.40	£70.00
A	C	50	Footballers Caricatures by 'Rip' (1926)		£1.40	£70.00
A	C	50	Footballers, 1928 (1928)		£1.80	£90.00
A	C	25	Footballers, 1928-9 — '2nd Series' (1929)		£1.80	£45.00
—	C	?	Football Fixture Folders (1946-61)		£13.00	—

Size	*Printing*	*Number in set*		*Handbook reference*	*Price per card*	*Complete set*
			JOHN PLAYER & SONS, Nottingham *(continued)*			
	C		Fresh-Water Fishes:			
A		50	A Small size, Home issue:			
			1 Pink card (1933)		£1.40	£70.00
			2 White card (1934)		£1.60	£80.00
B		25	B Large size, Home issue — adhesive (1935)		£2.60	£65.00
B		25	C Large size, Irish issue — non-adhesive (1935)		£5.00	£125.00
A	C	25	From Plantation to Smoker (1926)		32p	£8.00
	C	50	Gallery of Beauty (1896):	H.356		
			A Wide Card:			
A			I Set of 50		£22.00	—
A			II 5 Alternative Pictures		£60.00	—
			B Narrow Card official cut:			
—			I Set of 50		£20.00	—
—			II 5 Alternative Pictures		£60.00	—
	C		Game Birds and Wild Fowl:			
A		50	A Small size (1927)		£1.50	£75.00
B		25	B Large size (1928)		£5.00	£125.00
A	C	25	Gems of British Scenery (1914)		£1.20	£30.00
	C		Gilbert and Sullivan — 'A Series of ...':			
A		50	A Small size (1925)		£1.10	£55.00
J		25	B Extra-large size (1926)		£3.40	£85.00
	C		Gilbert and Sullivan — '2nd Series of ...':			
A		50	A Small size (1927)		£1.10	£55.00
B		25	B Large size (1928)		£4.00	£100.00
B	C	25	Golf (1939):			
			A Home issue — with I.T.C. clause		£7.50	£190.00
			B Channel Islands issue — without I.T.C. clause		£7.00	£175.00
A	C	25	Hidden Beauties (1929)		30p	£7.50
A	C	25	Highland Clans (1908)		£5.00	£125.00
A	C	50	Hints on Association Football (1934)	H.669	90p	£45.00
J	C	10	Historic Ships (1910):			
			A Thick card		£5.00	£50.00
			B Thin card		£5.00	£50.00
	C		History of Naval Dress:			
A		50	A Small size (1930)		£1.20	£60.00
B		25	B Large size (1929)		£2.00	£50.00
A	C	50	International Air Liners:			
			A Home issue — Album 'price one penny', with I.T.C. clause (1936)		50p	£25.00
			B Irish issue — Album offer without price, with I.T.C. clause (1937)		£1.00	£50.00
			C Channel Islands issue — without Album offer or I.T.C. clause (1936)		£1.00	£50.00
A	C	25	Irish Place Names — 'A Series of 25' (1927)		£3.20	£80.00
A	C	25	Irish Place Names — '2nd Series of 25' (1929)		£3.20	£80.00
	C	50	Kings and Queens of England (1935):	H.670		
A			A Small size		£1.60	£80.00
B			B Large size		£2.60	£130.00
A	C	50	Life on Board a Man of War in 1805 and 1905 (1905)	H.38	£2.40	£120.00
A	C	25	Live Stock (1925)		£4.00	£100.00
A	C	50	Military Head-Dress (1931)		£1.20	£60.00
A	C	50	Military Series (1900)		£22.00	—
A	C	50	Military Uniforms of the British Empire Overseas (1938):			
			A Home issue — adhesive, with I.T.C. clause		80p	£40.00
			B Channel Islands issue:			
			1 Adhesive, without I.T.C. clause		£1.50	£75.00
			2 Non-adhesive, without I.T.C. clause		£1.50	£75.00

JOHN PLAYER & SONS, Nottingham *(continued)*

Size	*Printing*	*Number in set*		*Handbook reference*	*Price per card*	*Complete set*
A	C	25	Miniatures (1916)		44p	£11.00
A	C	50	Modern Naval Craft (1939):			
			A Home issue — adhesive, with I.T.C. clause		50p	£25.00
			B Irish issue — non-adhesive		£1.00	—
			C Channel Islands issue — adhesive, without I.T.C. clause		90p	£45.00
A	C	50	Motor Cars — 'A Series of 50' (1936):			
			A Home issue — Album 'price one penny'		£1.40	£70.00
			B Irish issue — Album offer without price		£2.20	—
			C Channel Islands issue — without Album offer		£2.00	£100.00
A	C	50	Motor Cars — 'Second Series ...' (1937):			
			A Home issue — with I.T.C. clause		£1.00	£50.00
			B Channel Islands issue — without I.T.C. clause		£1.80	£90.00
B	U	20	Mount Everest (1925)		£4.50	£90.00
A	C	25	Napoleon (1915)	H.364	£2.00	£50.00
A	C	50	National Flags and Arms:			
			A Home issue — Album 'price one penny' (1936)		40p	£20.00
			B Irish issue — Album offer without price (1937)		£1.00	£50.00
			C Channel Islands issue — without Album offer (1936)		80p	£40.00
B	C	25	The Nation's Shrines (1929)		£2.00	£50.00
	C		Natural History:			
A		50	A Small size (1924)		35p	£17.50
J		12	B Extra-large size — 'A Series of 12' (1923)		£1.25	£15.00
J		12	C Extra-large size — '2nd Series of 12' (1924)		£1.25	£15.00
B	C	24	A Nature Calendar (1930)		£5.00	£125.00
	C		Nature Series:			
A		50	Small card (1908)		£1.40	£70.00
J		10	Extra-large card (Birds) (1908)		£12.00	—
J		10	Extra-large card (Animals) (1913)		£6.00	£60.00
A	C	50	Old England's Defenders (1898)		£22.00	—
B	C	25	'Old Hunting Prints' (1938):			
			A Home issue — with I.T.C. clause		£3.00	£75.00
			B Channel Islands issue — without I.T.C. clause		£4.00	—
B	C	25	Old Naval Prints (1936):			
			A Home issue — with I.T.C. clause		£2.60	£65.00
			B Channel Islands issue — without I.T.C. clause		£4.00	—
J	BW	25	Old Sporting Prints (1924)		£4.40	£110.00
B	C	25	Picturesque Bridges (1929)		£2.80	£70.00
B	C	25	Picturesque Cottages (1929)		£3.60	£90.00
B	C	25	Picturesque London (1931)		£4.40	£110.00
A	C	25	Players — Past and Present (1916)		90p	£22.50
A	C	25	Polar Exploration (1915)		£2.60	£65.00
A	C	25	Polar Exploration, 2nd series (1916)		£2.20	£55.00
B	C	25	Portals of the Past (1930)		£2.20	£55.00
A	C	50	Poultry (1931):	H.671		
			A Cards		£1.80	£90.00
			B Transfers		50p	£25.00
A	C	25	Products of the World:			
			A Thick card (1909)		80p	£20.00
			B Thin card (1908)		£1.20	£30.00
A	C	50	Products of the World — Scenes only (1928)		30p	£15.00
A	C	25	Racehorses (1926)		£5.40	£135.00
A	U	40	Racing Caricatures (1925)		90p	£36.00
B	C	25	Racing Yachts (1938):			
			A Home issue — with I.T.C. clause		£3.80	£95.00
			B Channel Islands issue — without I.T.C. clause		£5.00	—

Size	Printing	Number in set		Handbook reference	Price per card	Complete set

JOHN PLAYER & SONS, Nottingham *(continued)*

A	C	50	RAF Badges (1937):			
			A Home issue — with I.T.C. clause:			
			1 Without motto		60p	£30.00
			2 With motto		60p	£30.00
			B Channel Islands issue — without I.T.C. clause		£1.00	£50.00
A	C	50	*Regimental Colours and Cap Badges (1907)	H.73	£1.30	£65.00
A	C	50	*Regimental Colours and Cap Badges — Territorial Regiments (1910):			
			A Blue back		£1.30	£65.00
			B Brown back		£1.30	£65.00
A	C	50	Regimental Standards and Cap Badges (1930)		80p	£40.00
J	C	10	Regimental Uniforms — see 'Allied Cavalry'			
A	C	50	Regimental Uniforms (1-50):			
			A Blue back (Jul. 1912)		£2.20	£110.00
			B Brown back (Jul. 1914)		£2.40	£120.00
A	C	50	Regimental Uniforms (51-100) (1914)		£1.40	£70.00
A	C	50	Riders of the World:	H.358		
			A Thick grey card (1905)		£1.60	£80.00
			B Thinner white card (1914)		£1.60	£80.00
—	P	6	The Royal Family (101 × 154mm) (1902)	H.359	—	£270.00
—	C	1	The Royal Family (55 × 66mm) (1937)		—	£2.50
—	P	? 30	Rulers and Views (101 × 154mm) (1902)	H.363	£100.00	—
			Screen Celebrities — see Film Stars			
A	C	50	Sea Fishes:			
			A Home issue — Album 'price one penny', with I.T.C. clause (1935)		40p	£20.00
			B Irish issue — Album offer without price, with I.T.C. clause (1937)		£1.00	—
			C Channel Islands issue — without Album or I.T.C. clause (1935)		80p	£40.00
A	C	50	A Sectional Map of Ireland (1937)		£2.50	—
A	U	1	A Sectional Map of Ireland Joker (1937)		—	£15.00
A	C	25	Shakespearean Series (1914)		£1.60	£40.00
B	C	20	Ship-Models (1926)		£2.50	£50.00
A	C	50	Shipping (unissued) (c1955)		£1.50	£75.00
A	C	25	Ships' Figureheads (1912):			
			A Numerals 'sans serif'		£2.80	£70.00
			B Numerals with serif		£2.60	£65.00
B	C	25	Ships' Figure-Heads (1931)		£2.00	£50.00
—	C	8	Snap Cards (93 × 65mm) (c1930)	H.672	£7.00	—
A	C	50	Speedway Riders (1937)		£1.80	£90.00
A	BW	? 148	Stereoscopic Series (c1900)	H.357	£125.00	—
A	C	50	Straight Line Caricatures (1926)		60p	£30.00
A	C	25	Struggle for Existence (1923)		32p	£8.00
A	C	50	Tennis (1936)	H.524	90p	£45.00
A	C	25	Those Pearls of Heaven (1914)		£1.40	£35.00
A	BW	66	Transvaal Series (1902):	H.360		
			A Black front		£5.00	—
			B Violet-black front		£5.00	—
B	C	25	Treasures of Britain (1931)		£1.60	£40.00
A	C	25	Treasures of Ireland (1930)		£2.00	£50.00
B	C	25	Types of Horses (1939):			
			A Home issue — with I.T.C. clause		£4.00	£100.00
			B Channel Islands issue — without I.T.C. clause		£4.60	—
A	C	50	Uniforms of the Territorial Army (Oct. 1939)		90p	£45.00
A	C	50	Useful Plants and Fruits (1904)	H.361	£2.50	£125.00
A	C	25	Victoria Cross (1914)		£2.60	£65.00

Size	*Print-ing*	*Number in set*		*Handbook reference*	*Price per card*	*Complete set*

JOHN PLAYER & SONS, Nottingham *(continued)*

A	C	90	War Decorations and Medals (1927)		80p	£70.00
	C		Wild Animals:	H.673		
A		50	A Small size — 'Wild Animals' Heads' (1931)		70p	£35.00
A		25	B Small transfers, number in series not stated (1931)		£1.50	—
A		50	C Small transfers — 'A Series of 50' (1931)		50p	£25.00
B		25	D Large size — 'Wild Animals — A Series of ...' (1927)		£1.80	£45.00
B		25	E Large size — 'Wild Animals — 2nd Series ...' (1932)		£1.80	£45.00
A	C	50	Wild Animals of the World (1902):	H.77		
			A 'John Player & Sons Ltd.'		£3.00	£150.00
			B 'John Player & Sons, Branch, Nottingham'		£4.50	—
			C1 As B, 'Branch' omitted but showing traces of some or all of the letters		£4.50	—
			C2 As B. New printing with 'Branch' omitted		£3.00	£150.00
A2	C	45	Wild Animals of the World, narrow card (1902):	H.77		
			A 'John Player & Sons Ltd.'		£5.00	£225.00
			B 'John Player & Sons, Branch, Nottingham'		£7.00	—
			C1 As B, 'Branch' omitted but showing traces of some or all of the letters		£5.00	—
			C2 As B. New printing with 'Branch' omitted		£5.00	£225.00
	C		Wild Birds:			
A		50	A Small size (1932):			
			1 Cards		50p	£25.00
			2 Transfers		40p	£20.00
B		25	B Large size (1934)		£2.80	£70.00
B	C	25	Wild Fowl (1937)		£3.20	£80.00
A	C	50	Wonders of the Deep (1904)	H.365	£2.00	£100.00
A	C	25	Wonders of the World:	H.362		
			A Blue back (1913)		80p	£20.00
			B Grey back (1926)		£1.40	£35.00
J	C	10	Wooden Walls (1909):			
			A Thick card		£6.00	£60.00
			B Thin card		£6.00	£60.00
A	C	25	Wrestling and Ju-Jitsu:			
			A Blue back (1911)		£2.20	£55.00
			B Grey back (1925)		£1.60	£40.00
A	C	26	Your Initials (transfers) (1932)		70p	£18.00
B	C	25	Zoo Babies (1938):			
			A Home issue — with I.T.C. clause		80p	£20.00
			B Channel Islands issue — without I.T.C. clause		£2.00	—

POST-1960 ISSUES

G	C	30	African Wildlife (1990)		50p	£15.00
—	BW	9	Basket Ball Fixtures (114 × 71mm) (1972)		£6.00	—
	C	44	Black Jack (1984):	H.896		
—			A Size 75 × 35mm		£1.00	—
—			B Size 80 × 47mm		60p	—
G2			C Size 90 × 47mm		60p	—
G	C	32	Britain's Endangered Wildlife:			
			A Grandee Issue (1984)		25p	£8.00
			B Doncella Issue (1984)		30p	£9.00
H2	C	30	Britain's Maritime History (1989)		40p	£12.00
G	C	30	Britain's Nocturnal Wildlife:			
			A Grandee Issue (1987)		27p	£8.00
			B Doncella Issue (1987)		£1.00	£30.00

Size	Printing	Number in set		Handbook reference	Price per card	Complete set

JOHN PLAYER & SONS, Nottingham *(continued)*

G	C	30	Britain's Wayside Wildlife (1988)		30p	£9.00
G	C	30	Britain's Wild Flowers:			
			A Grandee Issue (1986)		25p	£7.50
			B Doncella Issue (1986)		60p	£18.00
G	C	32	British Birds (1980)		60p	£18.00
G	C	32	British Butterflies:			
			A Grandee Issue (1983)		40p	£13.00
			B Doncella Issue (1984)		60p	£19.00
G	C	30	British Mammals:			
			A Grandee Issue (1982):			
			1 Imperial Tobacco Ltd		27p	£8.00
			2 Imperial Group PLC		33p	£10.00
			B Doncella Issue (1983)		50p	£15.00
G	C	32	Country Houses and Castles (1981)		25p	£8.00
—	U	116	Corsair Game (63 × 38mm) (1965)	H.897	£1.00	—
H2	C	32	Exploration of Space (1983)		20p	£6.50
G	C	28	Famous MG Marques (1981)		90p	£25.00
G	C	24	The Golden Age of Flying (1977)	H.898	25p	£6.00
G	C	1	The Golden Age of Flying Completion Offer (1977)	H.898	—	£3.50
G	C	24	The Golden Age of Motoring (1975):	H.899		
			A With set completion offer		£3.50	—
			B Without set completion offer		27p	£6.50
G	C	24	The Golden Age of Sail (1978)		25p	£6.00
G	C	1	The Golden Age of Sail Completion Offer (1978)		—	£3.50
G	C	24	The Golden Age of Steam (1976)	H.900	27p	£6.50
G	C	1	The Golden Age of Steam Completion Offer (1976)	H.900	—	£3.50
G	U	7	Grandee Limericks (1977)		£10.00	—
H2	C	30	History of Britain's Railways (1987)		70p	£21.00
H2	C	30	History of British Aviation (1988)		80p	£24.00
H2	C	30	History of Motor Racing (1986):			
			A Imperial Tobacco Ltd		90p	£27.00
			B Imperial Group PLC		£1.20	£36.00
G	C	24	History of the VC (1980)		£1.00	£24.00
G	C	1	History of the VC completion offer (1980)		—	£5.00
—	BW	5	Jubilee Issue (70 × 55mm) (1960)	H.901	£1.50	£7.50
G	C	30	The Living Ocean:			
			A Grandee Issue (1985)		25p	£7.50
			B Doncella Issue (1985)		40p	£12.00
H2	C	32	Myths and Legends (1982)		£1.00	£32.00
G	C	24	Napoleonic Uniforms (1979)		25p	£6.00
G	C	1	Napoleonic Uniforms Completion Offer (1979)		—	£4.00
G	C	7	Panama Puzzles (1975)		£6.00	—
G	BW	6	Play Ladbroke Spot-Ball (1975)		£6.00	—
G	C	6	Play Panama Spot Six (1977)		£6.00	—
G1	C		Player Clues:	H.902		
		?	A Closing Date 30-1-87, red headings		50p	—
		?	B Closing Date 31-7-87, blue headings		50p	—
G1	C		Player Games:	H.903		
		?	A Closing Date 28-1-83		60p	—
		?	B Closing Date 29-7-83		60p	—
		?	C Closing Date 30-12-83		60p	—
		?	D Closing Date 30-4-84		60p	—
		?	E Closing Date 31-8-84		60p	—
		?	F Closing Date 31-1-85		60p	—
G1	C	?	Player Prize Closing Date 29-1-88	H.904	50p	—

Size	Print-ing	Number in set		Handbook reference	Price per card	Complete set

JOHN PLAYER & SONS, Nottingham *(continued)*

Size	Print-ing	Number in set		Handbook reference	Price per card	Complete set
G1	C		Player Quiz:	H.905		
		?	A Closing Date 31-7-85, green headings		50p	—
		?	B Closing Date 28-2-86, red headings		50p	—
		?	C Closing Date 31-7-86 blue headings		50p	—
	C	50	Supercars (1987):	H.906		
—			A Size 90 × 35mm		60p	—
G2			B Size 90 × 47mm		60p	—
	C	60	Superdeal (1985):	H.907		
—			A Size 75 × 35mm		60p	—
—			B Size 80 × 47mm		60p	—
—			C Size 90 × 35mm		60p	—
G2			D Size 90 × 47mm		60p	—
	C	108	Superyear 88 (1988):	H.908		
—			A Size 90 × 35mm		60p	—
G2			B Size 90 × 47mm		60p	—
—	U	4	Tom Thumb Record Breakers (82 × 65mm) (1976)	H.909	£6.00	—
G	C	25	Top Dogs (1979)		£1.20	£30.00
—	C	4	Vanguard Limericks (80 × 45mm) (1981)	H.910	£2.00	—
H2	C	32	Wonders of the Ancient World (1984)		40p	£12.50
H2	C	30	Wonders of the Modern World (1985)		30p	£9.00
G	C	6	World of Gardening (1976)		£10.00	—
	C	156	World Tour (1986):	H.911		
—			A Size 80 × 35mm		60p	—
—			B Size 80 × 47mm		60p	—
—			C Size 90 × 35mm		60p	—
G2			D Size 90 × 47mm		60p	—
OVERSEAS ISSUES						
A	C	50	Aeroplane Series (1926)		£2.40	—
A	C	50	Arms and Armour (1926)		£3.00	£150.00
		50	Beauties 1st series (1925):			
—	P		A Black and white fronts (63 × 41mm)		£1.60	£80.00
—	PC		B Coloured fronts (63 × 44mm)		£1.80	£90.00
—	PC	50	Beauties 2nd series (63 × 41mm) (1925)		£1.60	£80.00
D2	C	52	Birds of Brilliant Plumage (1927)		£3.50	—
A	C	25	Bonzo Dogs (1923)		£5.00	—
A	C	50	Boy Scouts (1924)		£3.50	—
—	C	25	British Live Stock (80 × 54mm) (1924)		£7.50	—
A	C	50	Butterflies (Girls) (1928)		£6.00	—
A	C	25	Dogs (Heads) (1927)		£1.60	£40.00
D	C	32	Drum Horses (1911)		£8.00	—
D2	C	25	Flag Girls of All Nations (1908)		£8.00	—
A	C	50	Household Hints (1928-29)		£1.00	£50.00
A	C	50	Lawn Tennis (1928)		£4.50	—
A	C	50	Leaders of Men (1925)		£2.50	£125.00
A	U	48	Pictures of the East (1931)		£2.40	£120.00
A	C	25	Picturesque People of the Empire (1928)		£2.20	£55.00
—	C	53	Playing Cards (68 × 45mm) (1929)		£1.40	—
A	U	50	Pugilists in Action (1928)		£4.50	—
A	C	50	Railway Working (1926)		£2.00	£100.00
A	P	50	The Royal Family at Home and Abroad (1927)		£2.50	—
A	C	50	Ships Flags and Cap Badges (1930)		£2.00	£100.00
A	C	50	Signalling series (1926)		£2.00	—
A	C	25	Whaling (1930)		£3.00	£75.00

JAS. PLAYFAIR & CO., London

Size	Print-ing	Number in set		Handbook reference	Price per card	Complete set
A	C	25	How to Keep Fit — Sandow Exercises (c1912)	H.136	£32.00	—

Size	Print-ing	Number in set		Handbook reference	Price per card	Complete set

THE PREMIER TOBACCO MANUFACTURERS LTD, London

D	U	48	Eminent Stage and Screen Personalities (1936)	H.569	£1.80	—
K2	C	52	*Miniature Playing Cards (c1935)		£7.50	—
—	BW		Stage and Screen Personalities (57 × 35mm) (1937):	H.674		
		100	A Back in grey		£1.50	—
		50	B Back in brown (Nos. 51-100)		£2.20	—

PRITCHARD & BURTON LTD, London

A2	C	51	*Actors and Actresses — 'FROGA B and C' (c1900):	H.20		
			A Blue back		£22.00	—
			B Grey-black back		£75.00	—
A	C	15	*Beauties 'PAC' (c1900)	H.2	£60.00	—
D	BW	20	*Boer War Cartoons (1900)	H.42	£120.00	—
A1	C		*Flags and Flags with Soldiers (c1902):	H.41		
			A Flagstaff Draped:			
		30	1st printing		£18.00	£540.00
		15	2nd printing		£20.00	—
		15	B Flagstaff not Draped (Flags only)		£20.00	—
D	U	25	*Holiday Resorts and Views (c1902)	H.366	£20.00	—
A	C	40	*Home Colonial Regiments (c1901)	H.69	£55.00	—
D	U	25	*Royalty Series (1902)	H.367	£22.00	—
D	U	25	*South African Series (1901)	H.368	£22.00	—
A2	C	25	*Star Girls (c1900)	H.30	£220.00	—

G. PRUDHOE, Darlington

C	C	30	*Army Pictures, Cartoons, etc (c1916)	H.12	£120.00	—

JAMES QUINTON LTD, London

A	C	26	*Actresses — 'FROGA A' (c1900)	H.20	£200.00	—

RAY & CO. LTD, London

—	C		*Flags of The Allies (Shaped) (c1915):	H.49		
		1	A Grouped Flag 'All Arms' Cigarettes		£80.00	—
		5	B Allies Flags 'Life Ray' Cigarettes		£80.00	—
A	BW	25	War Series — 1-25 — Battleships (c1915)	H.472	£15.00	—
A	C	75	War Series — 26-100 — British and Foreign Uniforms (c1915)	H.472	£12.00	—
A	C	24	War Series — 101-124 — British and Dominion Uniforms (c1915)	H.472	£25.00	—

RAYMOND REVUEBAR, London

—	P	25	Revuebar Striptease Artists (72 × 46mm) (1960)		£18.00	—

RECORD CIGARETTE & TOBACCO CO., London

—	U	? 2	Gramophone Records (100mm Diameter) (c1935)	H.675	£100.00	—
—	U	? 34	The 'Talkie' Cigarette Card — (gramophone record on reverse) (70mm square) (c1935):			
			A Back 'Record Tobacco Company'		£50.00	—
			B Back 'Record Cigarette Company'		£50.00	—

J. REDFORD & CO., London

A	BW	20	*Actresses — 'BLARM' (c1900)	H.23	£75.00	—
A2	C	25	*Armies of the World (c1901)	H.43	£60.00	—

Size	Printing	Number in set		Handbook reference	Price per card	Complete set

J. REDFORD & CO., London *(continued)*

A2	C	25	*Beauties — 'GRACC' (c1899)	H.59	£130.00	—
A2	C	30	*Colonial Troops (c1902)	H.40	£50.00	—
D	C	24	*Nautical Expressions (c1900)	H.174	£80.00	—
D2	C	40	*Naval and Military Phrases (c1904)	H.14	£60.00	—
A	C	25	Picture Series (c1905)	H.369	£65.00	—
A	C	25	Sports and Pastimes Series 1 (c1905)	H.225	£80.00	—
D1	BW	50	Stage Artistes of the Day (c1908)	H.370	£20.00	—

RELIANCE TOBACCO MFG. CO. LTD

A2	C	24	British Birds (c1935)	H.604	£5.00	—
A2	C	35	*Famous Stars* (c1935)	H.572	£5.00	—

RICHARDS & WARD

A1	P	? 13	*Beauties — 'Topsy Cigarettes' (c1900)	H.371	£750.00	—

A.S. RICHARDSON, Luton

—	U	12	*Manikin Cards (82 × 51mm) (c1920)	H.481	£120.00	—

THE RICHMOND CAVENDISH CO. LTD, London

A2	C	26	*Actresses — 'FROGA A' (c1900)	H.20	£32.00	—
D2	BW	28	*Actresses — 'PILPI I' (c1902)	H.195	£15.00	—
D	P	50	*Actresses 'PILPI II' (c1902)	H.196	£11.00	—
A	U		*Actresses Photogravure, 'Smoke Pioneer Cigarettes' back (c1905):	H.372		
		50	I Reading bottom to top		£8.00	£400.00
		? 179	IIA Reading top to bottom. Different subjects		£7.00	—
		? 13	B Plain back		£11.00	—
A	C	14	*Beauties 'AMBS' (1899):	H.373		
			A 'The Absent Minded Beggar' back:			
			i '1st Verse' back		£45.00	—
			ii '2nd Verse' back		£45.00	—
			iii '3rd Verse' back		£45.00	—
			iv '4th Verse' back		£45.00	—
			v 'Chorus (1st verse)' back		£45.00	—
			vi 'Chorus (2nd verse)' back		£45.00	—
			vii 'Chorus (3rd verse)' back		£45.00	—
			viii 'Chorus (4th verse)' back		£45.00	—
			B 'The Soldiers of The Queen' back:			
			i '1 Britons once did' back		£45.00	—
			ii '2 War clouds gather' back		£45.00	—
			iii '3 Now we're roused' back		£45.00	—
			iv 'Chorus' back		£45.00	—
A	C	52	*Beauties — 'ROBRI' playing card inset (c1898)	H.374	£45.00	—
—	C	40	*Medals (34 × 72mm) (c1900)	H.200	£20.00	£800.00
A2	C	20	Music Hall Artistes (c1902)	H.202	£50.00	—
A	C	12	*Pretty Girl Series — 'RASH' (c1900)	H.8	£50.00	—
A	C	20	*Yachts (c1900):	H.204		
			A Gold on black back		£65.00	—
			B Black on white back		£65.00	—

OVERSEAS ISSUES

D	C	28	Chinese Actors and Actresses (1922)	W.361	£4.00	—
A	P	50	Cinema Stars (1926)		£3.50	—

Size	Printing	Number in set		Handbook reference	Price per card	Complete set

RIDGWAYS, Manchester

—	C	? 2	*Play Up' Sporting Shields (c1895)	H.718	£150.00	—

R. ROBERTS & SONS, London

A2	C	26	*Actresses — 'FROGA A' (c1900)	H.20	£75.00	—
A	C	25	*Armies of the World (c1900):	H.43		
			A 'Fine Old Virginia' back		£50.00	—
			B Plain back		£50.00	—
A2	C	50	*Beauties — 'CHOAB' (c1900):	H.21		
			1-25 without borders to back		£70.00	—
			26-50 with borders to back		£85.00	—
—	C	50	*Beautiful Women (60 × 43mm) (c1900)	H.284	£250.00	—
A2	C	50	*Colonial Troops (c1902)	H.40	£40.00	—
A	BW	28	*Dominoes (c1905)		£80.00	—
K1	C	52	*Miniature Playing Cards (c1905):			
			A Blue background		£65.00	—
			B Pink background		£65.00	—
			C Yellow background		£65.00	—
D2	C	24	*Nautical Expressions (c1900):	H.174		
			A 'Navy Cut Cigarettes' on front		£60.00	—
			B Firm's name only on front		£60.00	—
A2	C	70	Stories without words (c1905)		£60.00	—
A2	C	25	*Types of British and Colonial Troops (c1900)	H.76	£50.00	—

ROBINSON & BARNSDALE LTD, London

—	C	1	*Advertisement Card — Soldier, 'Colin Campbell Cigars' (29 × 75mm) (c1897):	H.764		
			A With equal 'E' back		—	£200.00
			B With unequal 'E' back		—	£150.00
—	BW	? 24	*Actresses, 'Colin Campbell Cigars' (c1898):	H.375		
			A Size 43 × 70mm		£140.00	—
			B Officially cut narrow — 32 × 70mm		£140.00	—
A	P	? 33	*Actresses, 'Cupola' Cigarettes (c1898)	H.376	£250.00	—
A1	P		*Beauties — collotype (c1895):	H.377		
		? 9	A 'Our Golden Beauties' back in black		£250.00	—
		? 18	B 'Nana' back in red on white		£250.00	—
		? 1	C 'Nana' back in vermillion on cream		£250.00	—
A	C	? 1	*Beauties — 'Blush of Day' (c1898)		£300.00	—
—	C	? 16	*Beauties — 'Highest Honors' (44 × 73mm) (c1895)	H.379	£350.00	—
A2	U	? 3	Beauties 'KEWA II' (c1895)	H.139	£350.00	—

E. ROBINSON & SONS LTD, Stockport

A1	C	10	*Beauties 'ROBRI' (c1900):	H.374		
			A 'Forget-Me-Not Mixture' back		£60.00	—
			B 'Gold Flake Honeydew' back		£60.00	—
			C 'Gold Leaf Navy Cut' back		£60.00	—
			D 'Jack's Best Tobacco' back		£60.00	—
			E 'Jack Tar Navy Cut' back		£60.00	—
			F 'Man Friday Mixture' back		£60.00	—
			G 'Reliable Tobaccos' back		£60.00	—
			H 'Stockport Snuff' back		£60.00	—
			I 'Thin Twist & Thick Twist' back		£60.00	—
			J 'Three Decker Cigarettes' back		£60.00	—
A	BW	? 49	Derbyshire and the Peak (c1905)	H.380	£225.00	—
A2	C	25	Egyptian Studies (c1914)		£25.00	—
A	C	25	King Lud Problems (c1934)	H.638	£22.00	—

Size	Printing	Number in set		Handbook reference	Price per card	Complete set

E. ROBINSON & SONS LTD, Stockport *(continued)*

A	C	6	Medals and Decorations of Great Britain (c1905):	H.484		
			A Vertical back with firm's name		£250.00	—
			B Horizontal back with 'General Favourite Onyx'		£500.00	—
A2	C	40	Nature Studies (c1912)		£22.00	—
A2	C	25	Regimental Mascots (1916)		£70.00	—
A	C	25	Types of British Soldiers (1900)	H.144	£400.00	—
A2	C	25	Wild Flowers (c1915)		£20.00	£500.00

ROMAN STAR CIGARS

C	C	26	*Actresses 'FROGA A' (c1900)	H.20	£175.00	—
A	C	25	*Beauties 'BOCCA' (c1900)	H.39	£175.00	—

ROTHMAN'S LTD, London

	C		Beauties of the Cinema (1936):	H.605		
D1		40	A Small size		£1.60	£65.00
—		24	B Circular cards, 64mm diam:			
			1 Varnished		£4.00	£100.00
			2 Unvarnished		£4.00	£100.00
A2	P	24	Cinema Stars — Small size (c1925)		£1.60	£40.00
B	P	25	Cinema Stars — Large size (c1925)		£1.00	£25.00
—	C	30	Country Living (Consulate) (112 × 102mm) (1973)		—	£15.00
—	C	6	Diamond Jubilee Folders (127 × 95mm) (1950)		£12.00	—
C2	C	50	Football International Stars (unissued) (1984)	H.912	—	£25.00
C	U	36	Landmarks in Empire History (c1936)		£1.25	£45.00
		?	Metal Charms (c1930)		£4.00	—
D1	U	50	Modern Inventions (1935)		£1.10	£55.00
B2	P	54	New Zealand (c1930)		£1.00	£55.00
D1	U	24	Prominent Screen Favourites (1934)	H.568	£1.20	£30.00
A2	BW	50	'Punch Jokes' (c1935)		55p	£27.50
A1	C	5	Rare Banknotes (1970)		£4.00	—

WM. RUDDELL LTD, Dublin and Liverpool

K	U	? 3	*Couplet Cards (c1925)	H.676	£30.00	—
D	C	25	Grand Opera Series (1924)		£7.40	£185.00
A2	C	25	Rod and Gun (1924)		£7.00	£175.00
D	C	50	Songs that will Live for Ever (c1925)		£4.00	£200.00

RUTHERFORD

A	BW	? 6	Footballers (c1900)	H.765	£2000.00	—

I. RUTTER & CO., Mitcham

D	BW	15	*Actresses — 'RUTAN' (c1900):	H.381		
			A Rubber-stamped on plain back		£90.00	—
			B Red printed back		£60.00	—
			C *Plain back*		£35.00	—
A	BW	1	Advertisement Card 'Tobacco Bloom' (1899)	H.485	—	£1000.00
A	BW	7	*Boer War Celebrities (c1901)	H.382	£55.00	—
D1	C	54	*Comic Phrases (c1905)	H.223	£18.00	—
A	BW	20	Cricketers Series (1901)	H.29	£325.00	—
C	C		*Flags and Flags with Soldiers (c1902):	H.41		
		15	A Flagstaff Draped, 2nd printing		£26.00	—
		15	B Flagstaff not Draped (Flags only)			
			(a) white back		£26.00	—
			(b) cream back		£26.00	—

Size	*Print-ing*	*Number in set*		*Handbook reference*	*Price per card*	*Complete set*

I. RUTTER & CO., Mitcham *(continued)*

C	C	24	*Girls, Flags and Arms of Countries (c1900):	H.383		
			A Blue back		£35.00	—
			B *Plain back*		£25.00	—
A	C	25	Proverbs (c1905):	H.384		
			A Green Seal on front		£45.00	—
			B Red Seal on front		£45.00	—
A	C	25	*Shadowgraphs (c1905)	H.44	£40.00	—

S.D.V. TOBACCO CO. LTD, Liverpool

A	BW	16	British Royal Family (c1901)	H.28	£600.00	—

ST. PETERSBURG CIGARETTE CO. LTD, Portsmouth

A	BW	? 13	Footballers (c1900)	H.410	£1500.00	—

SALMON & GLUCKSTEIN LTD, London

—	C	1	*Advertisement Card ('Snake Charmer' Cigarettes) (73 × 107mm) (c1897)	H.767	—	£500.00
C	C	15	*Billiard Terms (c1905):			
			A Small numerals		£80.00	—
			B Larger numerals		£80.00	—
A	C	12	British Queens (c1897)	H.480	£45.00	—
—	C	30	*Castles, Abbeys and Houses (76 × 73mm) (c1906):			
			A Brown back		£18.00	—
			B Red back		£25.00	—
C	C	32	*Characters from Dickens (c1903)	H.385	£28.00	—
A	C	25	Coronation Series (1911)		£12.00	£300.00
—	U	25	*Famous Pictures — Brown photogravure (57 × 76mm) (c1910)	H.386	£10.00	£250.00
—	U	25	*Famous Pictures — Green photogravure (58 × 76mm) (c1910)	H.387	£9.00	£225.00
A2	C	6	Her Most Gracious Majesty Queen Victoria (1897):	H.388		
			A Thin card		£50.00	£300.00
			B Thick card		£50.00	£300.00
A	C	50	The Great White City (c1908)		£13.00	£650.00
C	C	40	Heroes of the Transvaal War (1901)	H.389	£15.00	£600.00
D2	C	25	Magical Series (1923)		£7.00	£175.00
C	C	30	*Music Hall Celebrities (c1902)		£55.00	—
—	C	25	*Occupations (64 × 18mm) (c1898)	H.390	£550.00	—
C	C	20	'Owners and Jockeys' Series (c1900)	H.392	£85.00	—
—	C	48	*The Post in Various Countries (41 × 66mm) (c1900)	H.391	£25.00	—
A2	C	6	*Pretty Girl Series — 'RASH' (c1900)	H.8	£65.00	—
—	C	22	Shakespearian Series (c1902):	H.393		
			A Large format, frame line back (38 × 69mm)		£35.00	—
			B Re-drawn, small format, no frame line back (37 × 66mm)		£35.00	—
A	C	25	*Star Girls (c1900):	H.30		
			A Red back		£120.00	—
			B Brown back, different setting		£120.00	—
A	C	25	Traditions of the Army and Navy (c1917):			
			A Large numerals		£16.00	£400.00
			B Smaller numerals, back redrawn		£16.00	£400.00
A2	C	25	Wireless Explained (1923)		£6.00	£150.00

Size	Printing	Number in set		Handbook reference	Price per card	Complete set

SALMON & GLUCKSTEIN LTD, London *(continued)*

SILKS

Size	Printing	Number in set		Handbook reference	Price per card	Complete set
—	C	50	*Pottery Types (paper-backed) (83 × 55mm) (c1915):	H.505-17		
			A Numbered on front and back		£4.00	—
			B Numbered on back only		£4.00	—

W. SANDORIDES & CO. LTD, London

Size	Printing	Number in set		Handbook reference	Price per card	Complete set
	U	25	Aquarium Studies from the London Zoo (1925):	H.607		
C2			A Small size:			
			1 Small lettering on back		£3.60	£90.00
			2 Larger lettering on back		£3.60	£90.00
B1			B Large size		£3.60	£90.00
	C	25	Cinema Celebrities (1924):	H.530		
C2			A Small size		£2.60	£65.00
—			B Extra-large size (109 × 67mm)		£4.00	£100.00
	C	25	Cinema Stars (export) (c1924):	H.530		
C2			A Small size, with firm's name at base of back		£6.00	—
C2			B Small size, 'Issued with Lucana Cigarettes		£6.00	—
C2			C Small size, 'Issued with Big Gun Cigarettes ...'		£8.00	—
—			D Extra-large size (109 × 67mm) 'Issued with Big Gun Cigarettes		£2.60	£65.00
—			E Extra-large size (109 × 67mm) issued with Lucana 66		£8.00	—
	U	50	Famous Racecourses (1926) — 'Lucana':	H.608		
C2			A Small size		£4.00	£200.00
B1			B Large size		£5.00	£250.00
C2	U	50	Famous Racehorses (1923):	H.609		
			1A Back in light brown		£3.20	£160.00
			1B Back in dark brown		£3.20	£160.00
			2 As 1A, with blue label added, inscribed 'Issued with Sandorides Big Gun Cigarettes ...'		£12.00	—
—	BW	12	London Views (57 × 31mm) (c1936) — see Teofani			
A	C	25	Sports & Pastimes — Series 1 — 'Big Gun Cigarettes (c1924)	H.225	£12.00	—

SANSOM'S CIGAR STORES, London

Size	Printing	Number in set		Handbook reference	Price per card	Complete set
—	P	? 2	*London Views (52 × 37mm) (c1915)	H.768	£600.00	—

NICHOLAS SARONY & CO., London

Size	Printing	Number in set		Handbook reference	Price per card	Complete set
	C	50	Around the Mediterranean (1926):	GP.404		
C2			A Small size		£1.20	£60.00
B1			B Large size		£1.20	£60.00
—	U	? 7	Boer War Scenes (67 × 45mm) (c1901)	GP.701	£800.00	—
	U	25	Celebrities and Their Autographs, Nd 1-25 (1923):			
C1			A Small size		£1.00	£25.00
B1			B Large size		£1.00	£25.00
	U	25	Celebrities and Their Autographs, Nd 26-50 (1924):			
C1			A Small size:			
			1 Small numerals		£1.00	£25.00
			2 Large numerals		£1.00	£25.00
B1			B Large size:			
			1 Small numerals		£1.00	£25.00
			2 Large numerals		£1.00	£25.00

ILLUSTRATIONS

CASTELLA CIGARS
HARDY
Supermarine Spitfire

1

2

Strathmore CIGARETTES
HAWKER HURRICANE SINGLE-SEAT FIGHTER

3

4

Railway Locomotives
Taddy & Co Cigarettes
"KING" CLASS EXPRESS LOCO. "KING GEORGE V" G.W.R. No 7

5

'Bullet' Train

6

LÆLIA ANCEPS

7

CASTELLA CIGARS
Chittaranjan 2-8-4T

8

9

10

11

12

13

14

15

16

17

18

19

20

21

22

23

24

25

26

27

28

29

30

31

32

33

34

35

36

37

38

39

40

41

42

43

44

45

46

47

48

49

50

51

52

53

54

55

56

57

58

59

60

61

62

63

64

65

66

67

68

69

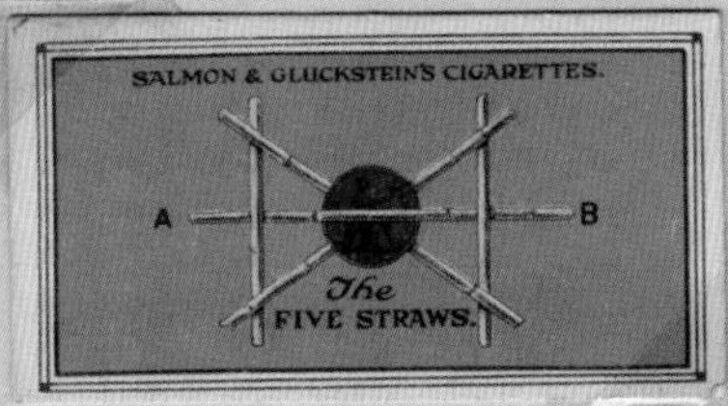

70

71

72

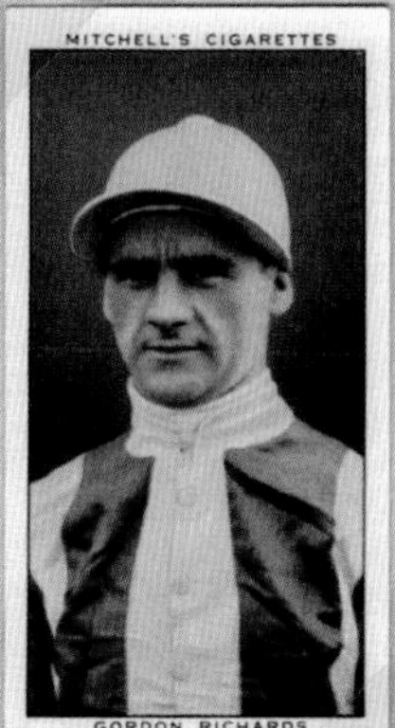

73

74

75

76

77

78

79

80

81

82

83

84

Size	*Print-ing*	*Number in set*		*Handbook reference*	*Price per card*	*Complete set*

NICHOLAS SARONY & CO., London *(continued)*

	U	25	Celebrities and Their Autographs. Nd 51-75 (1924):			
C1			A Small size		£1.00	£25.00
B1			B Large size		£1.00	£25.00
	U	25	Celebrities and Their Autographs, Nd 76-100 (1925):			
C1			A Small size		£1.00	£25.00
B1			B Large size		£1.00	£25.00
A2	U	50	Cinema Stars — Set 7 (1933)	GP.703	£1.50	£75.00
—	U		Cinema Stars — Postcard size (137 × 85mm):			
		38	'of a Series of 38 Cinema Stars' (1929)		£9.00	—
		42	'of a second Series of 42 Cinema Stars' (c1930)		£5.00	£210.00
		50	'of a third Series of 50 Cinema Stars' (c1930)		£5.00	£250.00
		42	'of a fourth Series of 42 Cinema Stars' (c1931)		£5.00	£210.00
		25	'of a fifth Series of 25 Cinema Stars' (c1931)		£5.00	£125.00
D	U	25	Cinema Studies (1929)		£1.10	£27.50
	C	25	A Day on the Airway (1928):			
C2			A Small size		£1.40	£35.00
B2			B Large size		£1.40	£35.00
A2	P	54	Life at Whipsnade Zoo (1934)	GP.415	60p	£32.50
	BW	25	Links with the Past — First 25 subjects, Nd 1-25 (1925):	GP.711		
C1			A Small size		50p	£12.50
B			B Large size		60p	—
	BW	25	Links with the Past — Second 25 subjects (1926):	GP.711		
C			A Home issue, Nd 26-50:			
			1 Small size		50p	£12.50
B			2 Large size, descriptive back		40p	£10.00
B			3 Large size, advertisement back		£1.80	—
			B Sydney issue, Nd 1-25:			
C			1 Small size		£1.00	£25.00
B			2 Large size		£1.00	£25.00
			C Christchurch issue, Nd 1-25:			
C			1 Small size		£1.00	£25.00
B			2 Large size		40p	£10.00
	BW	25	Museum Series (1927):	GP.712		
			A Home issue:			
C2			1 Small size		30p	£7.50
B			2 Large size, descriptive back		30p	£7.50
B			3 Large size, advertisement back		£1.00	£25.00
B			B Sydney issue, large size		70p	£17.50
			C Christchurch issue:			
C2			1 Small size		60p	£15.00
B			2 Large size		70p	£17.50
	P	36	National Types of Beauty (1928):	GP.417		
A2			A Small size		50p	£18.00
—			B Medium size (76 × 51mm)		40p	£14.00
	C	15	Origin of Games (1923):			
A			A Small size		£4.60	£70.00
B2			B Large size		£5.00	£75.00
	C	50	'Saronicks' (1929):	GP.414		
D2			A Small size		40p	£20.00
—			B Medium size (76 × 51 mm)		40p	£20.00
	C	50	Ships of All Ages (1929):			
D			A Small size		80p	£40.00
—			B Medium size (76 × 52mm)		£1.00	£50.00
D	C	25	Tennis Strokes (1923)		£3.40	£85.00

Size	Print-ing	Number in set		Handbook reference	Price per card	Complete set

T.S. SAUNT, Leicester

D	C	30	*Army Pictures, Cartoons etc (c1916)	H.12	£120.00	—

SCOTTISH CO-OPERATIVE WHOLESALE SOCIETY LTD, Glasgow ('S.C.W.S.')

A2	C	25	Burns (1924):	H.611		
			A Printed back:			
			1 White card		£2.60	—
			2 Cream card		£1.60	£40.00
			*B Plain back		£7.00	—
C	C	20	Dogs (1925)	H.211	£12.00	—
A2	C	25	Dwellings of All Nations (1924):	H.612		
			A Printed back:			
			1 White card		£3.50	—
			2 Cream card		£2.20	£55.00
			*B Plain back		£7.00	—
B	C	25	Famous Pictures (1924)		£8.00	—
H2	C	25	Famous Pictures — Glasgow Gallery (1927):			
			A Non-adhesive back		£2.20	£55.00
			B Adhesive back		£1.40	£35.00
H2	C	25	Famous Pictures — London Galleries (1927):			
			A Non-adhesive back		£2.20	£55.00
			B Adhesive back		£1.40	£35.00
A2	C	50	Feathered Favourites (1926):			
			A Grey borders		£2.50	£125.00
			B White borders:			
			1 Non-adhesive back		£2.50	£125.00
			2 Adhesive back		£1.80	£90.00
A	C	25	Racial Types (1925)		£8.00	£200.00
A2	C	50	Triumphs of Engineering (1926):			
			A Brown border		£2.50	£125.00
			B White border		£2.60	—
A2	C	50	Wireless (1924)		£4.50	£225.00

SELBY'S TOBACCO STORES, Cirencester

—	U	12	'Manikin' Cards (79 × 51mm) (c1920)	H.481	£120.00	—

SHARPE & SNOWDEN, London

A	U	? 1	*Views of England (c1905)	H.769	£750.00	—
A	U	? 23	*Views of London (c1905)	H.395	£350.00	—

W.J. SHEPHERD, London

A	U	25	*Beauties — 'FECKSA' (c1900)	H.58	£100.00	

SHORT'S, London

—	BW		*Short's House Views (c1925):	H.562		
		? 13	1 Numbered (75 × 60mm)		£60.00	—
		? 6	2 Unnumbered (77 × 69mm)		£40.00	—

JOHN SINCLAIR LTD, Newcastle-on-Tyne

D2	U	? 92	*Actresses (42 × 63 mm) (c1900)	H.396	£85.00	—

Size	Printing	Number in set		Handbook reference	Price per card	Complete set

JOHN SINCLAIR LTD, Newcastle-on-Tyne *(continued)*

Size	Printing	Number in set		Handbook reference	Price per card	Complete set
—	P		*Birds (1924):	H.613		
C		? 41	A Small size, back 'Specimen Cigarette Card' ...		£8.00	—
C		48	B Small size, descriptive back:			
			1 White front		£3.00	—
			2 Pinkish front		£3.00	—
—		50	C Large size (78 × 58mm)		£6.50	—
A	C	50	British Sea Dogs (1926)		£6.00	£300.00
	P		Champion Dogs — 'A Series of ...' (1938):			
A2		54	A Small size		75p	£40.00
B2		52	B Large size		75p	£40.00
	P		Champion Dogs — '2nd Series ...' (1939):			
A2		54	A Small size		£3.25	£175.00
B2		52	B Large size		£3.50	—
A2	P	50	English and Scottish Football Stars (1935)		£1.50	£75.00
A	P	54	Film Stars — 'A Series of 54 Real Photos' (1934)		£2.20	£120.00
A	P	54	Film Stars — 'A Series of Real Photos', Nd 1-54 (1937)		£1.70	£90.00
A	P	54	Film Stars — 'A Series of Real Photos', Nd 55-108 (1937)		£1.30	£70.00
	P		*Flowers and Plants (1924):	H.614		
C		? 37	A Small size, back 'Specimen Cigarette Card' ...		£7.50	—
C		96	B Small size, descriptive back:			
			1 White front		£2.50	—
			2 Pinkish front		£2.50	—
D	P	? 52	Football Favourites (c1910)		£170.00	—
A	BW	4	*North Country Celebrities (c1905)	H.397	£70.00	£280.00
D	P	? 55	Northern Gems (c1902)		£70.00	—
A	C	50	Picture Puzzles and Riddles (c1910)		£27.00	—
A	P	54	Radio Favourites (1935)		£1.50	£80.00
K2	C	53	Rubicon Cards (miniature playing cards) (1933):			
			A Without overprint		£6.00	—
			B With red overprint		£8.00	—
A	C	50	Trick Series (c1910)		£30.00	—
A	BW	50	Well-Known Footballers — North Eastern Counties (1938)		£1.20	£60.00
A	BW	50	Well-Known Footballers — Scottish (1938)		£1.20	£60.00
D2	C	50	World's Coinage (c1915)	H.398	£20.00	£1000.00

SILKS

Size	Printing	Number in set		Handbook reference	Price per card	Complete set
—	C	? 1	The Allies (140 × 100mm) (numbered 37) (c1915) ...	H.501-2	—	£35.00
—	C		**Flags — Set 2 (70 × 52mm) (unbacked and anonymous) (c1915):*	H.501-2		
		? 12	*A Numbered Nos 25-36*		£14.00	—
			B Unnumbered:			
		? 24	*1 Caption in red*		£8.00	—
		? 24	*2 Caption in myrtle-green*		£7.00	—
		? 24	*3 Caption in bright green*		£7.00	—
		? 24	*4 Caption in blue*		£8.00	—
		? 25	*5 Caption in black*		£12.00	—
—	C		**Flags — Set 11 (unbacked and anonymous) (c1915):*	H.501-11		
		50	*'Fourth Series' (49 × 70mm)*		£6.00	—
		50	*'Fifth Series' (49 × 70mm)*		£6.00	—
		50	*'Sixth Series':*			
			1 *Nos 1-25 (49 × 70mm)*		£7.00	—
			2 *Nos 26-50 (68 × 80mm)*		£7.00	—
		? 10	*'Seventh Series' (115 × 145mm)*		£60.00	—
—	C	50	*Regimental Badges I (paper backed) (70 × 52mm) (c1915)	H.502-1	£6.00	—

Size	Printing	Number in set		Handbook reference	Price per card	Complete set

JOHN SINCLAIR LTD, Newcastle-on-Tyne *(continued)*

—	C	? 24	**Regimental Colours II (unbacked and anonymous) (c1915):*	H.502-7		
			1 Nos 38-49 (No. 49 not seen) (76 × 70mm)		£13.00	—
			2 Nos 50-61 (65 × 51mm)		£13.00	—

ROBERT SINCLAIR TOBACCO CO. LTD, Newcastle-on-Tyne

C2	C		Billiards by Willie Smith (1928):			
		10	1 First set of 10		£9.00	£90.00
		15	2 Second Set of 15		£11.00	£165.00
		3	3 Third Set of 25 (Nos 26-28 only issued)		£16.00	£48.00
A2	U	28	Dominoes (c1900)		£60.00	—
			*Footballers (c1900):	H.399		
A2	U	? 4	A Mauve Collotype		£1500.00	—
D2	BW	? 16	B Black & White Collotype		£1000.00	—
D	C	12	*Policemen of the World (c1899)	H.164	£200.00	—
	C	12	The 'Smiler' Series (1924):			
A			A Small size (inscribed '... 24 cards'),		£7.00	—
H			B Large size		£12.00	—

SILKS. Unbacked silks, inscribed with initials 'R.S.' in circle.

—	C	4	*Battleships and Crests (73 × 102mm) (c1915)	H.499-1	£60.00	—
—	C	10	*Flags (70 × 51 mm) (c1915)	H.499-2	£26.00	—
—	C	6	*Great War Area — Cathedrals and Churches (140 × 102mm) (c1915)	H.499-3	£45.00	—
—	C	10	*Great War Heroes (70 × 51 mm) (c1915)	H.499-4	£38.00	—
—	C	1	*Red Cross Nurse (73 × 102mm) (c1915)	H.499-5	—	£50.00
—	C	5	*Regimental Badges (70 × 51 mm) (c1915)	H.499-6	£32.00	—

J. SINFIELD, Scarborough

A	U	24	*Beauties — 'HUMPS' (c1900)	H.222	£1000.00	—

SINGLETON & COLE LTD, Shrewsbury

A	C	50	*Atlantic Liners (1910)		£24.00	—
A	C	25	Bonzo Series (1928)	H.678	£8.00	£200.00
D1	BW	50	*Celebrities — Boer War Period (c1901):	H.400		
			25 Actresses		£20.00	£500.00
			25 Boer War Celebrities		£20.00	£500.00
A2	BW	35	Famous Boxers (1930):			
			A Numbered		£16.00	—
			B Unnumbered		£45.00	—
A2	BW	25	Famous Film Stars (1930)		£11.00	—
A	BW	35	Famous Officers — Hero Series (1915):			
			A1 'Famous Officers' on back toned card		£15.00	£525.00
			A2 'Famous Officers' thin white card		£35.00	—
			B 'Hero Series' on back		£400.00	—
D1	BW	50	*Footballers (c1905)		£150.00	—
C	C	40	*Kings and Queens (1902)	H.157	£22.00	—
—	U	12	'Manikin' Cards (77 × 49mm) (c1920)	H.481	£110.00	—
A	C	25	Maxims of Success (c1905):	H.401		
			A Orange border		£30.00	—
			B Lemon yellow border		£250.00	—

Size	Printing	Number in set		Handbook reference	Price per card	Complete set

SINGLETON & COLE LTD, Shrewsbury *(continued)*

A	BW		Orient Royal Mail Line (c1905):	H.402		
		8	A 'Orient-Pacific Line' Manager's back		£65.00	—
		8	B 'Orient Royal Mail Line' Singleton and Cole back		£45.00	—
		10	C 'Orient Line' Manager's back (5 ports)		£45.00	—
		10	D 'Orient Line' Managers back (11 ports)		£45.00	—
A	C	25	Wallace Jones — Keep Fit System (c1910)		£26.00	—
SILKS						
—	C	110	Crests and Badges of the British Army (paper-backed) (66 × 40mm) (c1915)	H.502-2	£4.00	—

F. & J. SMITH, Glasgow

36 page reference book — £4.50

A	C	25	*Advertisement Cards (1899)	H.403	£220.00	—
A	C	50	Battlefields of Great Britain (1913):			
			A 'Albion Gold Flake Cigarettes' back		£15.00	—
			B 'Auld Brig Flake' back		£15.00	—
			C 'Cut Golden Bar Twilight Brand' back		£15.00	—
			D 'Glasgow Mixture Cigarettes' back		£15.00	—
			E 'Glasgow Mixture Tobacco' back		£15.00	—
			F 'Goodwill Virginia' back		£15.00	—
			G 'Kashan Cigarettes' back		£15.00	—
			H 'No. 1 Mixture' back		£15.00	—
			I 'Orchestra Cigarettes' back		£15.00	—
			J 'Pinewood Cigarettes' back		£15.00	—
			K 'Pinewood Mixture' back		£15.00	—
			L 'Squaw Thick Black Tobacco' back		£15.00	—
			M 'Studio Cigarettes' back		£15.00	—
			N 'Sun Cured Mixture' back		£15.00	—
			O 'Wild Geranium Cigarettes' back		£15.00	—
A1	BW	25	*Boer War Series 'Studio' Cigarettes back (1900)		£70.00	—
A	C	50	*Boer War Series (1900)		£30.00	—
D	BW		*Champions of Sport (1902):	H.404		
		50	A Red back. Numbered, multi-backed		£90.00	—
		50	B Blue back. Unnumbered		£90.00	—
A	C	25	'Cinema Stars' (1920):	H.615		
			A 'Compeer Cigarettes' back		£12.00	—
			B 'Glasgow Mixture Mild, Medium & Full' back		£12.00	—
			C 'Kashan Cigarettes' back		£12.00	—
			D 'Luxury Mixture' back		£12.00	—
			E 'Orchestra Cigarettes, Mild & Medium' back		£12.00	—
			F 'Pinewood Cigarettes' back		£12.00	—
			G 'Studio Cigarettes' back		£12.00	—
			H 'Sun Cured Mixture' back		£12.00	—
A	U	50	Cricketers (1912)		£16.00	£800.00
A	U	20	Cricketers, 2nd Series, Nd 51-70 (1912)		£30.00	£600.00
A	U	50	Derby Winners (1913)		£15.00	£750.00
A	C	50	Famous Explorers (1911)		£16.00	£800.00
A	C	50	Football Club Records, 1913 to 1917 (1918)		£18.00	£900.00
A	C	50	Football Club Records, 1921-22 (1922)		£18.00	£900.00
D	U	120	*Footballers, brown back (1902)		£45.00	—
A	U	50	*Footballers, blue back Nd 1-52 (Nos 1 and 13 not issued) (1910):			
			A Black portrait		£14.00	—
			B Brown portrait		£14.00	—

Size	*Printing*	*Number in set*		*Handbook reference*	*Price per card*	*Complete set*

F. & J. SMITH, Glasgow *(continued)*

A	U	50	*Footballers, blue back. Nd 55-104 (Nos 53 and 54 not issued) (1910):			
			A Black portrait		£14.00	—
			B Brown portrait		£14.00	—
A	U	150	*Footballers, yellow frame line (1914):			
			A Pale blue back		£14.00	—
			B Deep blue back		£14.00	—
A	C	50	Fowls, Pigeons and Dogs (1908)	H.64	£10.00	£500.00
A	C	25	Holiday Resorts (1925)		£8.00	£200.00
A	C		*Medals:	H.71		
		20	A Unnumbered — thick card (1902)		£15.00	£300.00
		50	B Numbered. 'F. & J. Smith' thick card, multi-backed (1902)		£11.00	£550.00
		50	C Numbered. 'The Imperial Tobacco Co.' very thin card (1903)		£35.00	—
		50	D Numbered. 'The Imperial Tobacco Company' thin card, multi-backed (1906)		£11.00	£550.00
A	C	50	Nations of the World (1923)	H.454	£6.50	£325.00
A	C	50	Naval Dress and Badges:	H.172		
			A Descriptive back, multi-backed (1911)		£10.00	£500.00
			B Non-descriptive back, multi-backed (1914)		£10.00	£500.00
A	C	50	Phil May Sketches:	H.72		
			A Blue-grey back, multi-backed (1908)		£10.00	—
			B Brown back (1924):			
			1 'Albion (Empire Grown) Smoking Mixture' back		£6.50	—
			2 'Glasgow Smoking Mixture' back		£6.50	—
			3 'High Class Virginia Cigarettes' back		£6.50	—
			4 'Seal Virginia Cigarettes' back		£6.50	—
A	C	25	Prominent Rugby Players (1924)		£12.00	£300.00
A	C	40	Races of Mankind (1900):	H.483		
			A Series title on front, multi-backed		£45.00	—
			*B Without series title, multi-backed		£65.00	—
A	C	25	Shadowgraphs (1915):			
			A Glasgow Mixture, Mild, Medium & Full		£8.00	—
			B Orchestra Cigarettes		£8.00	—
			C Pinewood Cigarettes		£8.00	—
			D Pinewood Mixture		£8.00	—
			E Squaw Thick Black Tobacco		£8.00	—
			F Studio Cigarettes		£8.00	—
			G Sun Cured Mixture		£8.00	—
A	C	50	*A Tour Round the World:			
			A Script Advertisement back (1904)		£22.00	—
			B Post-card format back (1905)		£40.00	—
A	C	50	A Tour Round the World (titled series, multi-backed) (1906)	H.75	£11.00	£550.00
A	BW	25	War Incidents (1914):			
			A White back		£8.00	£200.00
			B Toned back		£8.00	£200.00
A	BW	25	War Incidents, 2nd series (1915):			
			A White back		£8.00	£200.00
			B Toned back		£8.00	£200.00

SNELL & CO., Plymouth and Devonport

A	BW	25	*Boer War Celebrities — 'STEW' (c1901)	H.105	£225.00	—

Size	*Print-ing*	*Number in set*		*Handbook reference*	*Price per card*	*Complete set*

SOCIETE JOB, London (and Paris)

A	C	25	British Lighthouses (c1925)		£8.00	£200.00
—	U		*Cinema Stars (c1926):	H.616		
		48	A Unnumbered size (58 × 45mm):			
			1 Complete Set		—	£75.00
			2 46 different (minus Love, Milovanoff)		£1.00	£46.00
		43	B Unnumbered size (58 × 36mm)		£3.00	—
		?	C Numbered 100-192 (56 × 45mm) (sepia)		£4.00	—
		? 1	D Numbered 39 (57 × 45mm) (reddish brown)		£10.00	—
D	BW	25	*Dogs (1911)	H.406	£26.00	£650.00
D	BW	25	*Liners (1912)	H.407	£32.00	—
D1	C	52	*Miniature Playing Cards (c1925)		£7.00	—
A2	C	25	Orders of Chivalry (1924)		£3.60	£90.00
A2	C	25	Orders of Chivalry (Second series) (1927)		£3.60	£90.00
A2	C	3	Orders of Chivalry (unnumbered) (1927)		£8.00	£24.00
D	BW	25	*Racehorses — 1908-09 Winners (1909)	H.408	£26.00	£650.00

LEON SOROKO, London

—	U	6	Jubilee series (1935):			
			A Small size (75 × 41mm)		£175.00	—
			B Large size (83 × 73mm)		£175.00	—

SOUTH WALES TOB. MFG CO. LTD, Newport and London

A	BW	? 91	Game of Numbers (c1910)		£80.00	—
A	U	25	*Views of London (c1910)	H.409	£26.00	£650.00

SOUTH WALES TOBACCO CO. (1913) LTD, Newport

D	C	30	*Army Pictures, Cartoons, etc. (c1916)	H.12	£120.00	—

S.E. SOUTHGATE & SON, London

A1	C	25	*Types of British and Colonial Troops (c1900)	H.76	£130.00	—

T. SPALTON, Macclesfield

D	C	30	*Army Pictures, cartoons etc (c1916)	H.12	£120.00	—

SPIRO VALLERI & CO.

A	BW	? 10	Noted Footballers (c1905)	H.772	£2000.00	—

G. STANDLEY, Newbury

—	U	12	'Manikin' Cards (77 × 49mm) (c1920)	H.481	£120.00	—

A. & A.E. STAPLETON, Hastings

—	U	12	*'Manikin' Cards (79 × 51mm) (c1920)	H.481	£120.00	—

H. STEVENS & CO., Salisbury

A1	C	20	*Dogs (1923)	H.211	£11.00	—
A1	U	25	*Zoo series (1926)	H.588	£7.00	—

A. STEVENSON, Middleton

A	U	50	War Portraits (1916)	H.86	£100.00	—

Size	*Printing*	*Number in set*		*Handbook reference*	*Price per card*	*Complete set*

ALBERT STOCKWELL, Porthcawl

D	C	30	*Army Pictures, Cartoons, etc (c1916)	H.12	£120.00	—

STRATHMORE TOBACCO CO. LTD, London

—	U	25	British Aircraft (76 × 50mm) (1938)		£3.00	£75.00

TADDY & CO., London

32 page reference book — £4.50

—	U	? 72	*Actresses — collotype (40 × 70mm) (c1897)	H.411	£120.00	—
A	C	25	*Actresses — with Flowers (c1900)		£90.00	—
A	BW	37	Admirals and Generals — The War (c1915):			
			A 25 Commoner Cards	H.412	£18.00	—
			B 12 Scarce Cards (Nos 8, 9, 10, 13, 14, 17, 18, 21, 22, 23, 24, 25)		£40.00	—
A	BW	25	Admirals and Generals — The War (South African printing) (c1915)	H.412	£35.00	—
A	C	25	Autographs (c1910)	H.413	£22.00	£550.00
A	C	20	Boer Leaders: (c1901)			
			A White back		£25.00	£500.00
			B Cream back		£25.00	—
A	C	50	British Medals and Decorations — Series 2 (c1905)		£13.00	£650.00
A	C	50	British Medals and Ribbons (c1903)		£13.00	£650.00
A	C	20	*Clowns and Circus Artistes (c1915)	H.414	£900.00	—
C2	C	30	Coronation series (1902):			
			A Grained card		£24.00	—
			B Smooth card		£24.00	—
A	BW	238	County Cricketers (c1907)	H.415	£40.00	—
A	C	50	Dogs (c1900)	H.487	£32.00	—
C	U	5	*English Royalty — collotype (c1898)	H.416	£850.00	—
A	C	25	Famous Actors — Famous Actresses (c1903)		£22.00	£550.00
A	BW	50	Famous Horses and Cattle (c1912)		£110.00	—
A2	C	25	Famous Jockeys (c1905):	H.417		
			A Without frame line — blue title		£36.00	—
			B With frame line — brown title		£32.00	—
A	BW	50	Footballers (export issue) (c1906)	H.418	£100.00	—
A	C	25	'Heraldry' series (c1910)		£22.00	£550.00
A	C	25	Honours and Ribbons (c1910)		£26.00	£650.00
C	C	10	Klondyke series (c1900)		£70.00	£700.00
C	BW	60	Leading Members of the Legislative Assembly (export issue) (c1900)		£850.00	—
A	C	25	*Natives of the World (c1900)	H.419	£70.00	—
A	C	25	Orders of Chivalry (c1911)	H.301	£22.00	£550.00
A	C	25	Orders of Chivalry, second series (c1912)	H.301	£26.00	£650.00
A	BW		Prominent Footballers — Grapnel and/or Imperial back:	H.420		
		? 596	A Without 'Myrtle Grove' footnote (1907)		£25.00	—
		? 403	B With 'Myrtle Grove' footnote (1908-9)		£25.00	—
A	BW	? 409	Prominent Footballers — London Mixture back (1913-14)	H.420	£45.00	—
—	C	20	*Royalty, Actresses, Soldiers (39 × 72mm) (c1898)	H.421	£225.00	—
A	C	25	'Royalty' series (c1908)		£20.00	£500.00
A	C	25	*Russo-Japanese War (1-25) (1904)		£22.00	£550.00
A	C	25	*Russo-Japanese War (26-50) (1904)		£26.00	£650.00
A	BW	16	South African Cricket Team 1907	H.422	£60.00	—
A	BW	26	South African Football Team 1906-07	H.423	£25.00	—
A	C	25	Sports and Pastimes — Series 1 (c1912)	H.225	£24.00	£600.00
A	C	25	Territorial Regiments — Series 1 (1908)		£24.00	£600.00

Size	Print-ing	Number in set		Handbook reference	Price per card	Complete set

TADDY & CO., London *(continued)*

A	C	25	Thames series (c1903)		£36.00	£900.00
C	C	20	Victoria Cross Heroes (1-20) (c1900)		£75.00	—
C	C	20	Victoria Cross Heroes (21-40) (c1900)		£75.00	—
A	C	20	VC Heroes — Boer War (41-60) (1901):			
			A White back		£22.00	—
			B Toned back		£22.00	£440.00
A	C	20	VC Heroes — Boer War (61-80) (1901):			
			A White back		£22.00	—
			B Toned back		£22.00	£440.00
A	C	20	VC Heroes — Boer War (81-100) (1902):			
			A White back		£24.00	—
			B Toned back		£24.00	£480.00
A	C	25	Victoria Cross Heroes (101-125) (1905)		£60.00	—
A2	BW	2	*Wrestlers (c1910)	H.424	£300.00	—

TADDY & CO., London and Grimsby

—	C	8	Advertisement Cards, three sizes (1980)		60p	£5.00
A	C	26	Motor Cars, including checklist (1980):			
			A 'Clown Cigarettes' back		40p	£10.00
			B 'Myrtle Grove Cigarettes' back		40p	£10.00
A	C	26	Railway Locomotives including checklist (1980):			
			A 'Clown Cigarettes' back		50p	£12.00
			B 'Myrtle Grove Cigarettes' back		40p	£10.00

W. & M. TAYLOR, Dublin

A	C	8	European War series (c1915):	H.129		
			A 'Bendigo Cigarettes' back		£45.00	—
			B 'Tipperary Cigarettes' back		£45.00	—
A	U	25	*War series — 'Muratti II' (c1915):	H.290		
			A 'Bendigo Cigarettes' back		£60.00	—
			B 'Tipperary Cigarettes' back		£18.00	£450.00

TAYLOR WOOD, Newcastle

C	C	18	Motor Cycle series (c1914)	H.469	£120.00	—

TEOFANI & CO. LTD, London

(Cards mostly without Teofani's name.)

C2	U	25	Aquarium Studies from the London Zoo ('Lucana' cards with green label added, inscribed 'Issued with Teofani Windsor Cigarettes') (c1925)	H.607	£12.00	—
D1	U	50	Cinema Celebrities (c1928):			
			A 'Presented with Broadway Novelties'		£5.00	—
			B 'Presented with these well-known ...'		£3.50	—
	C	25	Cinema Stars (c1928):	H.530		
			1 *Anonymous printings:*			
C2			A *Small size*		£7.00	—
			B *Extra-large size (109 × 67mm)*		£7.00	—
			2 Teofani printings:			
C2			A Small size — 'Issued with Blue Band Cigarettes		£7.00	—
C2			B Small size — 'Three Star Cigarettes'		£7.00	—
C2			C Small size — 'Three Star Magnums'		£7.00	—
C2			D Small Size — 'The Favourite Cigarettes'		£7.00	—
—			E Extra-large size (109 × 67mm) — 'Three Star Magnums'		£7.00	—

Size	Printing	Number in set		Handbook reference	Price per card	Complete set

TEOFANI & CO. LTD, London *(continued)*

Size	Printing	Number in set		Handbook reference	Price per card	Complete set
D	U	25	*Famous Boxers — 'Issued with The 'Favourite Magnums ...' (c1925)	H.721	£11.00	—
C2	P	32	Famous British Ships and Officers — 'Issued with these High Grade Cigarettes' (1934)		£4.00	£130.00
B1	U	50	Famous Racecourses ('Lucana' cards with mauve label added, inscribed 'Issued with The Favourite Cigarettes' (c1926)	H.608	£20.00	—
A	U	? 24	Famous Racehorses (c1925)	H.609	£12.00	—
—	BW	12	**Film Actors and Actresses (56 × 31mm) (plain back)* (1936)	H.618	£1.50	£18.00
C2	C	20	*Great Inventors (c1924)*	H.213	£5.00	—
A	C	20	**Head Dresses of Various Nations (plain back)* (c1925)		£16.00	—
—	BW	12	**London Views (57 × 31mm)* (c1936):	H.620		
			A *Plain back*		50p	£6.00
			B Back 'Our Agent Raoul Savon' with brand name:			
			i 'Big Gun' back		£5.00	—
			ii 'Fine' back		£5.00	—
			iii 'Hudavend' back		£5.00	—
			iv 'K.O.G.' back		£5.00	—
			v 'Lucana 66' back		£5.00	—
			vi 'Lucana C.T.' back		£5.00	—
			vii 'Palace' back		£5.00	—
			viii 'Pharoah's' back		£5.00	—
			ix 'Teofani No. 1' back		£5.00	—
			x 'Three Dogs' back		£5.00	—
			xi 'Three Star' back		£5.00	—
			xii 'West End' back		£5.00	—
D2	U	48	*Modern Movie Stars and Cinema Celebrities* (1934)	H.569	£1.00	£50.00
A	C	50	**Natives in Costume (plain back)* (c1925)		£16.00	—
A2	C	24	Past and Present — Series A — The Army (1938):			
			A With framelines		£2.00	£50.00
			B Without framelines		£1.70	£40.00
A2	C	24	Past and Present — Series B — Weapons of War (1938)		£1.00	£25.00
A2	C	4	Past and Present — Series C — Transport (1940)	H.679	£5.00	—
C	U	50	Public Schools and Colleges — 'Issued with these Fine Cigarettes' (c1924)	H.575	£3.60	—
D	C	50	Ships and Their Flags — 'Issued with these well-known cigarettes' (c1925)	GP.124	£4.00	£200.00
A	C	25	Sports and Pastimes Series I — 'Smoke these cigarettes always' (c1925)	H.225	£14.00	—
—	P	22	**Teofani Gems I — Series of 22 (53 × 35mm) (plain back)* (c1925)		£3.00	—
—	P	28	**Teofani Gems II — Series of 28 (53 × 35mm) (plain back)* (c1925)		£1.00	—
—	P	36	**Teofani Gems III — Series of 36 (53 × 35mm) (plain back)* (c1925)		£3.00	—
—	P	2	Teofani Gems — unnumbered (53 × 35mm) (plain back) (c1925)		£3.00	£6.00
A2	P	36	Views of the British Empire — 'Issued with these Famous Cigarettes' (c1928):			
			A Front in black and white		£1.25	£45.00
			B Front in light brown		£1.25	£45.00
C	U	50	Views of London — 'Issued with these World Famous Cigarettes' (c1925)	H.577	£3.00	—
C2	U	24	*Well-Known Racehorses* (c1924)	H.609	£10.00	—
A	C	50	**World's Smokers (plain back)* (c1925)		£16.00	—

Size	Printing	Number in set		Handbook reference	Price per card	Complete set

TEOFANI & CO. LTD, London *(continued)*

Size	Printing	Number in set		Handbook reference	Price per card	Complete set
	U	50	Zoological Studies (c1924):	H.578		
C			A Standard Size		£3.50	—
B1			B Large Size		£7.00	—
OVERSEAS ISSUE						
H1	BW	50	Teofani's Icelandic Employees (1930)		£7.00	—
H	P	50	Theatre Artistes and Scenes (c1930)		£25.00	—

TETLEY & SONS LTD, Leeds

Size	Printing	Number in set		Handbook reference	Price per card	Complete set
A2	C	1	*'The Allies' (grouped flags) (c1915)	H.425	—	£1000.00
A	U	50	War Portraits (c1916)	H.86	£100.00	—
D	C	25	World's Coinage (1914)	H.398	£70.00	—

THEMANS & CO., Manchester

Size	Printing	Number in set		Handbook reference	Price per card	Complete set
A	—	55	Dominoes (Sunspot brand issue) (c1914)		£80.00	—
C	C	18	Motor Cycle series (c1914)	H.469	£85.00	—
A	C	? 2	Riddles and Anecdotes (c1913)	H.426	£1000.00	—
A	U	50	*War Portraits (1916)	H.86	£60.00	—
—	C	14	War Posters (63 × 41 mm) (c1916)	H.486	£350.00	—
SILKS						
			Anonymous silks with blue border, plain board backing. Reported also to have been issued with firm's name rubber stamped on backing.			
—	C		**Miscellaneous Subjects* (c1915):	H.500		
		? 8	*Series B1 – Flags (50 × 66mm)*		£10.00	—
		? 3	*Series B2 – Flags (50 × 66mm)*		£10.00	—
		? 12	*Series B3 – Regimental Badges (50 × 66mm)*		£7.00	—
		? 12	*Series B4 – Ship's Badges (50 × 66mm)*		£20.00	—
		? 7	*Series B5 – British Views and Scenes (50 × 66mm)*		£20.00	—
		? 48	*Series B6 – Film Stars (50 × 66mm)*		£10.00	—
		? 2	*Series C1 – Flags (65 × 55mm)*		£10.00	—
		? 3	*Series C2 – Flags (70 × 65mm)*		£10.00	—
		? 4	*Series C3 – Regimental Badges (64 × 77mm)*		£10.00	—
		? 2	*Series C4 – Crests of Warships (64 × 77mm)*		£10.00	—
		? 1	*Series D1 – Royal Standard (138 × 89mm)*		£15.00	—
		? 1	*Series D2 – Shield of Flags (138 × 89mm)*		£15.00	—
		? 1	*Series D3 – Regimental Badge (138 × 89mm)*		£15.00	—
		? 1	*Series D5 – British Views and Scenes (138 × 89mm)*		£20.00	—
		? 14	*Series D6 – Film Stars (138 × 89mm)*		£10.00	—

THOMSON & PORTEOUS, Edinburgh

Size	Printing	Number in set		Handbook reference	Price per card	Complete set
D2	C	50	Arms of British Towns (c1905)		£17.00	£850.00
A	BW	25	*Boer War Celebrities — 'STEW' (c1901)	H.105	£60.00	—
A	C	20	European War series (c1915)	H.129	£15.00	£300.00
A	C	25	*Shadowgraphs (c1905)	H.44	£45.00	—
A	C	41	VC Heroes (c1915):	H.427		
			A Front with firm's name at base:			
			i 40 Different (minus No. 6)		£13.50	£540.00
			ii Number 6		—	£60.00
			B Front with firm's name at top		£60.00	—
			C Without firm's name, with 'Pure Virginia Cigarettes'		£13.50	£555.00

TOBACCO SUPPLY SYNDICATE, London (T.S.S.)

Size	Printing	Number in set		Handbook reference	Price per card	Complete set
D	C	24	*Nautical Expressions (c1900)	H.174	£120.00	—

Size	Printing	Number in set		Handbook reference	Price per card	Complete set

TOM NODDY

Size	Printing	Number in set		Handbook reference	Price per card	Complete set
—	C	12	Children of the Year Series (140 × 90mm) (1904)		£100.00	—

TURKISH MONOPOLY CIGARETTE CO. LTD

Size	Printing	Number in set		Handbook reference	Price per card	Complete set
—	C	? 16	*Scenes from the Boer War (113 × 68mm, folded in three) (c1901)	H.478	£500.00	—

UNITED KINGDOM TOBACCO CO., London

Size	Printing	Number in set		Handbook reference	Price per card	Complete set
A	C	50	Aircraft — 'The Greys Cigarettes' (1938)	GP.5	£1.80	£90.00
—	U	48	Beautiful Britain — 'The Greys Cigarettes' (140 × 90mm) (1929)	GP.406	£1.70	£85.00
—	U	48	Beautiful Britain — Second series 'The Greys Cigarettes' (140 × 90mm) (1929)	GP.407	£1.50	£75.00
A2	C	25	British Orders of Chivalry and Valour — 'The Greys Cigarettes' (1936)	GP.43	£1.40	£35.00
A	U	24	Chinese Scenes (1933)		75p	£18.00
A2	U	32	Cinema Stars — Set 4 (1933)	GP.53	£1.70	£55.00
A2	U	50	Cinema Stars — Set 7 (1934):	GP.703		
			A *Anonymous back*		£2.50	£125.00
			B Back with firm's name		£1.70	£85.00
A2	C	36	Officers Full Dress (1936)		£2.00	£70.00
A2	C	36	Soldiers of the King — 'The Greys Cigarettes' (1937)	GP.127	£2.00	£70.00

UNITED SERVICES MANUFACTURING CO. LTD, London

Size	Printing	Number in set		Handbook reference	Price per card	Complete set
A1	C	50	Ancient Warriors (1938)		£2.00	£100.00
A	C	25	Ancient Warriors (1954)		£4.00	—
A1	BW	50	Bathing Belles (1939)	H.592	90p	£45.00
D	U	100	Interesting Personalities (1935)		£3.25	—
D	U	50	Popular Footballers (1936)		£5.00	—
D	U	50	Popular Screen Stars (1937)		£4.00	—

UNITED TOBACCONISTS' ASSOCIATION LTD

Size	Printing	Number in set		Handbook reference	Price per card	Complete set
A	C	10	*Actresses — 'MUTA' (c1900)	H.265	£200.00	—
A2	C	12	*Pretty Girl Series 'RASH' (c1900)	H.8	£500.00	—

WALKER'S TOBACCO CO. LTD, Liverpool

Size	Printing	Number in set		Handbook reference	Price per card	Complete set
C	P	60	*British Beauty Spots (c1925)	H.553	£20.00	—
A	BW	28	*Dominoes 'Old Monk' issue (1908)		£65.00	—
D2	U	28	*Dominoes 'W.T.C.' Monogram back (c1925)	H.535-2	£6.00	—
A2	P	32	Film Stars — 'Tatley's Cigarettes' (1936)	H.623	—	£70.00
			31 Different (minus Lombard)		£1.50	£46.00
A2	P	48	*Film Stars — Walker's name at base (1937)	H.623	£4.50	—

WALTERS TOBACCO CO. LTD, London

Size	Printing	Number in set		Handbook reference	Price per card	Complete set
B	U	6	Angling Information (wording only) (1939)	H.624	£1.50	£9.00

E.T. WATERMAN, Coventry

Size	Printing	Number in set		Handbook reference	Price per card	Complete set
D	C	30	*Army Pictures, Cartoons, etc. (1916)	H.12	£120.00	—

WEBB & RASSELL, Reigate

Size	Printing	Number in set		Handbook reference	Price per card	Complete set
A	U	50	War Portraits (1916)	H.86	£100.00	—

Size	Printing	Number in set		Handbook reference	Price per card	Complete set

H.C. WEBSTER (Q.V. Cigars)

—	BW	? 7	*Barnum and Bailey's Circus (60 × 42mm) (c1900)	H.428	£350.00	—

HENRY WELFARE & CO., London

D	P	? 22	Prominent Politicians (c1911)	H.429	£70.00	—

WESTMINSTER TOBACCO CO. LTD, London

Inscribed 'Issued by the Successors in the United Kingdom to the Westminster Tobacco Co., Ltd.' For other issues without the above see Overseas Issues.

A2	P	36	Australia — 'First Series' (1932)		25p	£9.00
A2	P	36	*Australia, Second Series, plain back, unissued.* (1933)	H.680	25p	£9.00
A2	P	48	British Royal and Ancient Buildings (1925):			
			A Unnumbered, without descriptive text		80p	£40.00
			B Numbered, with descriptive text		£1.00	£50.00
A2	P	48	British Royal and Ancient Buildings — 'A Second Series ...' (1926)		40p	£20.00
A2	P	36	Canada — 'First Series' (1927)		70p	£25.00
A2	P	36	Canada — 'Second Series' (1928)		70p	£25.00
A2	P	48	Indian Empire — 'First Series' (1926)		40p	£20.00
A2	P	48	Indian Empire — 'Second Series' (1927)		40p	£20.00
A2	P	36	New Zealand — 'First Series' (1929)		50p	£18.00
A2	P	36	New Zealand — 'Second Series' (1930)		25p	£9.00
A2	P	36	South Africa — 'First Series' (1930)		70p	£25.00
A2	P	36	South Africa — 'Second Series' (1931)		70p	£25.00

OVERSEAS ISSUES

—	BW	332	Adamsons Oplevelser (68 × 50mm) (1930)		£20.00	—
—	P	50	Beauties (63 × 48mm) (1924)		£3.00	—
—	P	100	Beautiful Women (65 × 49mm) (1915)		£3.00	—
—	C	50	Birds, Beasts and Fishes (63 × 48mm) (1923)		£2.80	—
			British Beauties (1915):			
—	CP	102	A Coloured (60 × 41mm)		£4.00	—
—	P	86	B Uncoloured (57 × 41mm)		£4.00	—
A2	P	48	British Royal and Ancient Buildings (1925)		£1.00	£50.00
—	C	50	Butterflies and Moths (70 × 42mm) (1920)		£2.80	—
A2	P	36	Canada 1st series (1926)		£1.00	£36.00
A2	P	36	Canada 2nd series (1928)		£1.00	£36.00
D2	U	30	Celebrated Actresses (1921)		£5.50	—
—	C	25	Champion Dogs (anonymous back) (95 × 67mm) (1934)		£5.00	—
A	BW	100	Cinema Artistes green back (1929-33)		£3.25	—
A	BW	50	Cinema Artistes grey back (1929-33)		£3.25	—
A	C	48	Cinema Celebrities (1935)		£3.00	—
A	P	50	Cinema Stars (1926)		£3.00	—
—	P	50	Cinema Stars (63 × 48mm) (1930)		£3.20	—
—	CP	50	Cinema Stars (63 × 48mm) (1930)		£3.20	—
—	C	27	Dancing Girls (63 × 44mm) (1917)		£6.00	—
A	C	50	Do You Know (1922)		£2.50	—
D2	C	24	Fairy Tale (booklets) (1926)		£6.50	—
—	C	100	Famous Beauties (64 × 48mm) (1916):			
			A Captions in brown		£2.30	—
			B Captions in blue		£2.50	—
—	U	35	Famous Fighting Ships of Various Nations (138 × 92mm) (c1910)		£50.00	—

Size	Printing	Number in set		Handbook reference	Price per card	Complete set

WESTMINSTER TOBACCO CO. LTD, London *(continued)*

		52	Film Favourites (64 × 48mm) (1927):			
—	P		A Uncoloured		£4.00	—
—	CP		B Coloured		£4.00	—
—	U	50	Film Personalities (64 × 48mm) (1931)		£4.50	—
—	C	50	Garden Flowers of the World (70 × 50mm) (1917)		£3.00	—
A1	U	40	The Great War Celebrities (1914)		£8.50	—
A2	P	48	Indian Empire 1st series (1925)		£1.00	£50.00
A2	P	48	Indian Empire 2nd series (1926)		£1.00	£50.00
—	P	50	Islenzkar Eimskipamyndir (Trawlers) (77 × 52mm) (1931)		£3.00	£150.00
—	P	50	Islenzkar Landslagmyndir (Views) (77 × 52mm) (1928)		£2.20	£110.00
—	P	50	Islenzkar Landslagmyndir 2nd series (Views) (77 × 52mm) (1929)		£2.20	£110.00
A1	C	40	Merrie England Studies (1914)		£8.00	—
A	BW	36	Modern Beauties (1938)		£3.50	—
—	CP	52	Movie Stars (63 × 48mm) (1925)		£3.50	—
A2	P	36	New Zealand 1st series (1928)		£1.25	£42.00
A2	P	36	New Zealand 2nd series (1929)		£1.25	£42.00
—	C	53	Playing Cards (63 × 41mm) (1934):			
			A With Exchange Scheme		£3.00	—
			B Without Exchange Scheme		£3.00	—
—	C	55	Playing Cards (72 × 49mm) (1934):			
			A Blue back		£2.00	—
			B Red back		£2.00	—
A	P	50	Popular Film Stars (1926)		£3.50	—
A2	P	36	South Africa 1st series (1928)		£1.00	£36.00
A2	P	36	South Africa 2nd series (1928)		£1.00	£36.00
—	C	49	South African Succulents (72 × 50mm) (1936)		30p	£15.00
—	C	100	Stage and Cinema Stars, captions in grey (63 × 47mm) (1921)		£2.25	—
—	C	100	Stage and Cinema Stars, captions in black (63 × 47mm) (1921)		£3.00	—
—	CP	50	Stars of Filmland (63 × 48mm) (1927):			
			A 'Westminster' lettering brown on white		£3.50	—
			B 'Westminster' lettering white on brown		£3.50	—
C2	C	50	Steamships of the World (1920)		£10.00	—
—	C	50	Uniforms of All Ages (69 × 47mm) (1917)		£11.00	—
A	P	50	Views of Malaya (1930)		£7.00	—
D	C	25	Wireless (1923)		£5.00	—
—	C	50	Women of Nations (70 × 49mm) (1922)		£4.50	—
A	BW	50	The World of Tomorrow (1938)		£1.50	£75.00
SILK ISSUES						
—	C	50	Garden Flowers of the World (82 × 51mm) (c1914)		£6.00	—
—	C	24	Miniature Rugs (93 × 52mm) (1924)		£18.00	—

WHALE & CO.

A	C	? 11	Conundrums (c1900)	H.232	£400.00	—

M. WHITE & CO., London

—	BW	20	*Actresses — 'BLARM' (c1900)	H.23	£200.00	—

WHITFIELD'S, Walsall

D	C	30	*Army Pictures, Cartoons etc. (c1916)	H.12	£120.00	—

Size	Printing	Number in set		Handbook reference	Price per card	Complete set

WHITFORD & SONS, Evesham

C2	C	20	*Inventors series (c1924)	H.213	£45.00	—

WHOLESALE TOBACCO SUPPLY CO., London ('Hawser' Cigarettes)

A	C	25	Armies of the World (c1902)	H.43	£70.00	—
A	C	40	Army Pictures (c1902)	H.69	£100.00	—

P. WHYTE, England

D	C	30	*Army Pictures, Cartoons, etc. (1916)	H.12	£120.00	—

W. WILLIAMS & CO., Chester

A	U	30	Aristocrats of the Turf (c1925)	H.554	£8.00	£240.00
A	U	36	Aristocrats of the Turf 2nd series (c1925)	H.554	£14.00	—
A	BW	25	*Boer War Celebrities 'STEW' (c1901)	H.105	£75.00	—
A	C	25	Boxing (c1924)	H.311	£10.00	£250.00
A	C	50	Interesting Buildings (c1910)	H.70	£13.00	£650.00
A	BW	12	Views of Chester (c1910)	H.430	£33.00	£400.00
A	BW	12	Views of Chester — As It Was (c1910):	H.430		
			A Toned card		£33.00	£400.00
			B Bleuté card		£33.00	—

W.D. & H.O. WILLS, Bristol

212 page reference book The Card Issues of W.D. & H.O. Wills (2011 Edition)— £25.00

NOTE: The Imperial Tobacco Co. clause (I.T.C. clause) appears on Home issues dated between 1902 and 1940, excluding those issued in the Channel Islands. For series without I.T.C. clause, see the Overseas section.

A	U		*Actresses — collotype (c1894):			
		25	A 'Wills' Cigarettes'	W.2-1	£100.00	—
		43	B 'Wills's Cigarettes'	W.2-2	£100.00	—
A	C	20	*Actresses, brown type-set back (c1895)	W.3-A	£1000.00	—
A	C	52	*Actresses, brown scroll back, with PC inset (c1898)	W.3-C	£17.00	£900.00
A	C	52	*Actresses, grey scroll back (c1897):	W.3-D		
			A Without PC inset		£17.00	£900.00
			B With PC inset		£17.00	£900.00
A	U		*Actresses and Beauties — collotype, 'Three Castles' and 'Firefly' front (c1895):	W.2-4		
		? 125	Actresses		£100.00	—
		? 33	Beauties		£100.00	—
A	C		*Advertisement Cards:	W.1		
		? 4	1888 issue (cigarette packets)		£2000.00	—
		? 1	1889-90 issue (serving maid)		£800.00	—
		? 11	1890-93 issues (tobacco packings)		£1000.00	—
		? 3	1893 issue (showcards):			
			A 'Autumn Gold Cigarettes' back		£350.00	—
			B 'Best Bird's Eye Cigarettes' back		£350.00	—
			C 'Eothen Cigarettes' back		£350.00	—
			D 'Passing Clouds' back		£350.00	—
			E 'Pole Star Cigarettes' back		£350.00	—
			F 'Sahara Cigarettes' back		£350.00	—
			G 'The Three Castles Cigarettes' back		£350.00	—
		? 6	1893-94 issue (posters)		£350.00	—
B	BW	1	Advertisement Card — Wants List (1935)		—	75p
—	C	4	*Advertisement Postcards of Wills Packings (139 × 88mm) (1902)	W.398	£150.00	—

W.D. & H.O. WILLS, Bristol *(continued)*

Size	*Print-ing*	*Number in set*		*Handbook reference*	*Price per card*	*Complete set*
A	C		Air Raid Precautions (1938):	W.123		
		50	A Home issue — adhesive back, with I.T.C. clause		90p	£45.00
		40	B Irish issue — non-adhesive back		£1.50	—
		50	C Channel Islands issue – adhesive back, without I.T.C. clause		£1.20	£60.00
A	C	50	Allied Army Leaders (1917)	W.35	£1.70	£85.00
A	C	50	Alpine Flowers (1913)		90p	£45.00
A	C	48	Animalloys (sectional) (1934)	W.124	40p	£20.00
A	C	50	*Animals and Birds in Fancy Costumes (c1896)	W.4	£45.00	—
B	C	25	Animals and Their Furs (1929)		£1.80	£45.00
A	C	50	Arms of the Bishopric (1907)		£1.00	£50.00
A	C	50	Arms of the British Empire (1910)	W.40	80p	£40.00
B	C	25	Arms of the British Empire — 'First Series' (1931)		£1.80	£45.00
B	C	25	Arms of the British Empire — 'Second Series' (1932)		£1.80	£45.00
A	C	50	Arms of Companies (1913)		80p	£40.00
A	C	50	Arms of Foreign Cities (1912):	W.42		
			A White card		80p	£40.00
			B Cream card		90p	—
			C As A, with 'Mark'		£1.00	—
B	C	42	Arms of Oxford and Cambridge Colleges (1922)		£1.40	£60.00
B	C	25	Arms of Public Schools — '1st Series' (1933)		£2.00	£50.00
B	C	25	Arms of Public Schools — '2nd Series' (1934)		£2.00	£50.00
B	C	25	Arms of Universities (1923)		£1.60	£40.00
A	C	50	Association Footballers 'Frameline' back (1935)	W.134	£1.30	£65.00
			A Home issue – with I.T.C. clause		£1.30	£65.00
			B Channel Islands issue – without I.T.C. clause		£2.50	£125.00
A	C	50	Association Footballers — 'No frameline' back (1939):	W.135		
			A Home issue — adhesive back		£1.30	£65.00
			B Irish issue — non-adhesive back		£2.40	£120.00
B	C	25	Auction Bridge (1926)		£2.20	£55.00
A	C	50	Aviation (1910)	W.46	£2.50	£125.00
A	U	? 20	*Beauties — collotype (c1894):	W.2-3		
			A 'W.D. & H.O. Wills' Cigarettes'		£175.00	—
			B 'Firefly' Cigarettes		£175.00	—
A1	C	? 10	*Beauties ('Girl Studies'), type-set back (c1895)	W.3-B	£1200.00	—
A	C		*Beauties, brown backs (c1897):	W.3-E		
		52	A With PC inset — scroll back		£20.00	£1000.00
		10	B As A, 10 additional pictures		£70.00	—
		? 53	C 'Wills' Cigarettes' front, scroll back		£175.00	—
		? 29	D 'Wills' Cigarettes' front, type-set back		£250.00	—
K	C	52	*Beauties, miniature cards, PC inset, grey scroll back (c1896)	W.3-F	£26.00	—
B	C	25	Beautiful Homes (1930)		£2.60	£65.00
A	C	50	Billiards (1909)		£2.20	£110.00
—	—	10	Boer War Medallions (c1901)	W.18	£90.00	—
A	C	50	*Borough Arms (1-50):			
			A Scroll back, unnumbered (1904)	W.19	£1.00	£50.00
			B Scroll back, numbered on front (1904)		£10.00	—
			C Descriptive back, numbered on back (1905)		£1.00	£50.00
			D 2nd Edition — 1-50 (1906)		80p	£40.00
A	C	50	*Borough Arms (51-100):	W.19		
			A 2nd Series (1905)		70p	£35.00
			B 2nd Edition, 51-100 (1906)		70p	£35.00
A	C	50	*Borough Arms (101-150):	W.19		
			A 3rd Series, Album clause in grey (1905)		90p	£45.00
			B 3rd Series, Album clause in red (1905)		70p	£35.00
			C 2nd Edition, 101-150 (1906)		70p	£35.00

Size	Printing	Number in set		Handbook reference	Price per card	Complete set

W.D. & H.O. WILLS, Bristol *(continued)*

Size	Printing	Number in set		Handbook reference	Price per card	Complete set
A	C	50	*Borough Arms (151-200), 4th series (1905)	W.19	70p	£35.00
A	C	24	*Britain's Part in the War (1917)		£1.00	£25.00
A	C	50	British Birds (1917)		£1.40	£70.00
A	C	50	British Butterflies (1927)	W.156	£1.10	£55.00
B	C	25	British Castles (1925)		£2.80	£70.00
—	BW	1	British Commanders in the Transvaal War 1899-1900 (booklet) (206 × 114mm) (1900):	W.511		
			A With 'Bristol & London' on front		—	£100.00
			B Without 'Bristol & London' on front		—	£100.00
—	C	12	The British Empire (133 × 101mm) (c1930)		£9.00	—
B	C	25	British School of Painting (1927)		£1.40	£35.00
—	BW	48	British Sporting Personalities (66 × 52mm) (1937)		£1.00	£50.00
A	C	50	Builders of the Empire (1898):	W.20		
			A White card		£8.00	£400.00
			B Cream card		£8.00	£400.00
B	C	40	Butterflies and Moths (1938)		90p	£36.00
A	C	1	*Calendar for 1911 (1910)		—	£15.00
A	C	1	*Calendar for 1912 (1911)		—	£10.00
B	C	25	Cathedrals (1933)		£4.80	£120.00
B	U	25	Celebrated Pictures (1916):	W.165		
			A Deep brown back		£2.00	£50.00
			B Yellow-brown back		£1.80	£45.00
B	U	25	Celebrated Pictures, 2nd Series (1916)	W.166	£2.20	£55.00
A	C	50	Celebrated Ships (1911)		£1.20	£60.00
A	C	25	Cinema Stars — 'First Series' (1928)		£1.60	£40.00
A	C	25	Cinema Stars — 'Second Series' (1928)		£1.60	£40.00
A	U	50	Cinema Stars — 'Third Series' (1931)		£2.00	£100.00
—	C	12	Cities of Britain (133 × 101mm) (c1930)		£9.00	—
A	C	60	Coronation Series (1902):	W.6		
			A 'Wide arrow' type back		£6.00	£360.00
			B 'Narrow arrow' type back		£6.00	£360.00
A	C	50	The Coronation Series (1911)		£1.00	£50.00
A	C	50	*Cricketers (1896)	W.7	£85.00	—
A	C		Cricketers Series, 1901:	W.8		
		50	A With Vignette		£24.00	—
		25	B Without Vignette		£24.00	—
A	C		Cricketers (1908):	W.58		
		25	A 1-25 'Wills' S' at top front		£9.00	£225.00
		50	B 1-50 'Wills's' at top front		£7.50	£375.00
A	C	50	Cricketers, 1928 (1928)	W.178	£1.80	£90.00
A	C	50	Cricketers — '2nd Series' (1929)		£1.80	£90.00
B	C	25	Dogs (1914)		£3.60	£90.00
B	C	25	Dogs, 2nd Series (1915)		£3.60	£90.00
A	C	50	Dogs — Light backgrounds (1937):	W.187		
			A Home issue — adhesive back, with I.T.C. clause		60p	£30.00
			B Irish issue — non-adhesive back		£1.50	£75.00
			C Channel Islands issue – adhesive back, without I.T.C. clause		£1.20	£60.00
A	C		*Double Meaning (1898):	W.5		
		50	A Without PC inset		£10.00	£500.00
		52	B With PC inset		£10.00	£520.00
A	C		Do You Know:			
		50	'A Series of 50' (1922)	W.188	50p	£25.00
		50	'2nd Series of 50' (1924)	W.189	50p	£25.00
		50	'3rd Series of 50' (1926)	W.190	50p	£25.00
		50	'4th Series of 50' (1933)	W.191	60p	£30.00

Size	*Print-ing*	*Number in set*		*Handbook reference*	*Price per card*	*Complete set*

W.D. & H.O. WILLS, Bristol *(continued)*

A	C	50	Engineering Wonders (1927)	W.193	£1.00	£50.00
A	C	50	English Period Costumes (1929)		£1.00	£50.00
B	C	25	English Period Costumes (1927)	W.195	£2.60	£65.00
B	C	40	Famous British Authors (1937)		£1.75	£70.00
B	C	30	Famous British Liners — 'First Series' (1934)		£5.50	—
B	C	30	Famous British Liners — 'Second Series' (1935)		£3.60	£110.00
B	C	25	Famous Golfers (1930)		£16.00	—
A	C	50	Famous Inventions (1915)	W.60	£1.00	£50.00
A	C		A Famous Picture — (sectional):			
		48	Series No. 1 — 'Between Two Fires' (1930)	W.207	30p	£15.00
		48	Series No. 2 — 'The Boyhood of Raleigh' (1930)	W.208	30p	£15.00
		48	Series No. 3 — 'Mother and Son' (1931)	W.209	30p	£15.00
		48	'The Toast' (1931):	W.210		
			A Home issue — Series No. 4		50p	£24.00
			B Irish issue — Series No. 1		£2.00	—
		48	'The Laughing Cavalier' (1931):	W.211		
			A Home issue — Series No. 5:			
			1 No stop after numeral		40p	£20.00
			2 Full stop after numeral		40p	£20.00
			B Irish issue — Series No. 2		£2.00	—
		49	Series No. 6 — 'And When did you Last See Your Father?' (1932)	W.212	£1.00	£50.00
A	C	50	First Aid:			
			A Without Album Clause (1913)		£1.50	£75.00
			B With Album Clause (1915)		£1.50	£75.00
A	C	50	Fish & Bait (1910)	W.62	£2.80	£140.00
	C	6	Flags of the Allies (shaped) (1915)	W.67	£12.00	—
A	C	25	Flags of the Empire (1926)	W.215	£1.40	£35.00
A	C	25	Flags of the Empire — '2nd Series' (1929)		£1.00	£25.00
A	C	50	Flower Culture in Pots (1925)	W.217	45p	£22.50
B	C	30	Flowering Shrubs (1935)		£1.00	£30.00
A	C	50	Flowering Trees and Shrubs (1924)		70p	£35.00
A	U	66	*Football Series (1902)	W.22	£9.00	—
A	C	50	Garden Flowers (1933)	W.225	70p	£35.00
A	C	50	Garden Flowers by Richard Sudell (1939):	W.222		
			A Home issue – Album offer with price		25p	£12.50
			B Irish issue – Album offer without price		50p	£25.00
			C Channel Islands issue – no Album offer		50p	£25.00
B	C	40	Garden Flowers — New Varieties — 'A Series' (1938)		60p	£24.00
B	C	40	Garden Flowers — New Varieties — '2nd Series' (1939)		50p	£20.00
A	C	50	Garden Hints (1938):	W.226		
			A Home issue — Album offer with price		25p	£12.50
			B Irish issue — Album offer without price		40p	£20.00
			C Channel Islands issue – no Album offer		50p	£25.00
A	C	50	Gardening Hints (1923)	W.227	35p	£17.50
A	C	50	Garden Life (1914)	W.69	70p	£35.00
A	C	50	Gems of Belgian Architecture (1915)		60p	£30.00
A	C	50	Gems of French Architecture (1917):			
			A White card		£1.40	£70.00
			B Bleuté card		£1.60	—
			C Rough brown card		£1.60	—
A	P	50	Gems of Italian Architecture (1960) (reprint)	W.388	70p	£35.00
A	C	50	Gems of Russian Architecture (1916)		70p	£35.00
B	C	25	Golfing (1924)		£9.00	—
—	C	32	Happy Families (non-insert) (91 × 63mm) (c1935)		£5.00	—
B	C	25	Heraldic Signs and Their Origin (1925)	W.230	£1.80	£45.00

Size	*Print-ing*	*Number in set*		*Handbook reference*	*Price per card*	*Complete set*

W.D. & H.O. WILLS, Bristol *(continued)*

A	C	50	Historic Events (1912)	W.74	£1.20	£60.00
A2	P	54	Homeland Events (1932)	W.232	60p	£32.00
A	C	50	Household Hints (1927)	W.234	50p	£25.00
A	C	50	Household Hints — '2nd Series' (1930)		50p	£25.00
A	C	50	Household Hints (1936):	W.236		
			A Home issue — Album offer with price		25p	£12.50
			B Irish issue — Album offer without price		50p	£25.00
			C Channel Islands issue – no Album offer		50p	£25.00
A	BW	50	Hurlers (1927)		£1.80	£90.00
—	C	12	Industries of Britain (133 × 101mm) (c1930)		£9.00	—
A	C	25	Irish Beauty Spots (1929)		£4.40	—
A	C	25	Irish Holiday Resorts (1930)		£4.40	—
A	C	50	Irish Industries (1937):			
			A Back 'This surface is adhesive ...'		£3.00	—
			B Back 'Ask your retailer ...'		£1.20	£60.00
A	U	25	Irish Rugby Internationals (1928)		£12.00	—
A	C	50	Irish Sportsmen (1935)		£4.00	—
A	C	50	Japanese Series (c1900)	W.23	£37.00	—
B	C	40	The King's Art Treasures (1938)		30p	£12.00
	C		*Kings and Queens:	W.9		
A1		50	A Short card (1897):			
			a Grey back, thin card		£6.00	£300.00
			b Grey back, thick card		£6.00	£300.00
			c Brown back		£10.00	—
A			B Standard size card (1902):			
		51	a Blue-grey back with 5 substitute titles:			
			i 50 different		£6.00	£300.00
			ii Edward The Martyr		—	£50.00
		50	b Grey back, different design, thinner card		£13.00	—
B	C	25	Lawn Tennis, 1931 (1931)		£9.00	—
A	C	50	Life in the Hedgerow (c1950) (unissued)		50p	£25.00
A	C	50	Life in the Royal Navy (1939):	W.253		
			A Home issue – with Album offer		40p	£20.00
			B Channel Islands issue – without Album offer		50p	£25.00
A	C	50	Life in the Tree Tops (1925)	W.254	40p	£20.00
A	C	50	Life of King Edward VIII (1936) (unissued)		—	£1000.00
A	C		*Locomotive Engines and Rolling Stock:	W.24		
		50	A Without I.T.C. clause (1901)		£8.00	£400.00
		7	B As A, 7 additional cards (1901)		£30.00	—
		50	C With I.T.C. clause (1902)		£8.00	£400.00
A	C	50	Lucky Charms (1923)	W.256	60p	£30.00
A	C	50	*Medals (1902):	W.25		
			A White card		£2.80	£140.00
			B Toned card		£2.80	£140.00
A	C	50	Merchant Ships of the World (1924)	W.257	£1.40	£70.00
A	C	50	Military Motors (1916):			
			A Without 'Passed by Censor'		£1.80	£90.00
			B With 'Passed by Censor'		£1.80	£90.00
K2	C	53	*Miniature Playing Cards (1932-34):	W.260		
			A Home issue, blue back — 'narrow 52' (2 printings)		50p	£25.00
			B Home issue, blue back — 'wide 52' (4 printings)		50p	£25.00
			C Home issue, pink back (3 printings)		60p	—
			D Irish issue, blue back (7 printings)		£1.00	—
A	C	50	Mining (1916)	W.81	£1.50	£75.00
B	C	25	Modern Architecture (1931)		£1.60	£40.00

Size	Printing	Number in set		Handbook reference	Price per card	Complete set

W.D. & H.O. WILLS, Bristol *(continued)*

B	U	30	Modern British Sculpture (1928)		£1.30	£40.00
A	C	50	Musical Celebrities (1911)	W.83	£2.50	£125.00
A	C	50	Musical Celebrities — Second Series (1916):	W.83		
			Set of 50 with 8 substituted cards		£3.50	£175.00
			8 original cards (later substituted)		£275.00	—
A	C	25	*National Costumes (c1895)	W.26	£200.00	—
A	C	? 8	*National Types (c1893)	W.396	£1300.00	—
A	C	50	Naval Dress & Badges (1909)	W.84	£3.50	£175.00
A	C	50	Nelson Series (1905)	W.85	£5.50	£275.00
A	C	50	Old English Garden Flowers (1911)		£1.50	£75.00
A	C	50	Old English Garden Flowers, 2nd Series (1913)		£1.00	£50.00
B	C	25	Old Furniture — '1st Series' (1923)		£2.80	£70.00
B	C	25	Old Furniture — '2nd Series' (1924)		£2.80	£70.00
B	C	40	Old Inns — 'A Series of 40' (1936)		£3.00	£120.00
B	C	40	Old Inns — 'Second Series of 40' (1939)		£1.75	£70.00
B	C	25	Old London (1929)		£3.60	£90.00
B	C	30	Old Pottery and Porcelain (1934)		£1.20	£36.00
B	C	25	Old Silver (1924)		£2.40	£60.00
B	C	25	Old Sundials (1928)		£2.80	£70.00
A	C	20	Our Gallant Grenadiers (c1901):	W.27		
			A Deep grey on toned card		£32.00	—
			B Blue-grey on bluish card		£32.00	—
A	BW	50	Our King and Queen (1937):	W.286		
			A Home issue – with Album offer		30p	£15.00
			B Channel Islands issue – without Album offer		50p	£25.00
A	C	50	Overseas Dominions (Australia) (1915)	W.87	80p	£40.00
A	C	50	Overseas Dominions (Canada) (1914)		60p	£30.00
A	C	50	Physical Culture (1914)		£1.00	£50.00
—	—	1	Pinchbeck Medallion (1897)		£100.00	—
A	C	25	Pond and Aquarium 1st Series (c1950) (unissued)		32p	£8.00
A	C	25	Pond and Aquarium 2nd Series (c1950) (unissued)		32p	£8.00
A	U	100	*Portraits of European Royalty (1908):			
			Nos. 1-50		£1.50	£75.00
			Nos. 51-100		£1.50	£75.00
B	C	25	Public Schools (1927)		£2.40	£60.00
B	U	25	Punch Cartoons (1916):			
			A Toned card		£3.60	£90.00
			B Glossy white card		£6.00	—
B	U	25	Punch Cartoons — Second Series (1917)		£18.00	—
B	C	40	Puppies (c1950) (unissued)		—	—
B	C	40	Racehorses and Jockeys, 1938 (1939)		£2.25	£90.00
A	C	50	Radio Celebrities — 'A Series ...' (1934):	W.301		
			A Home issue — back 'This surface ...'		80p	£40.00
			B Irish issue — back 'Note. This surface ...'		£1.50	—
A	C	50	Radio Celebrities — 'Second Series — (1935):	W.302		
			A Home issue — back 'This surface ...'		50p	£25.00
			B Irish issue — back 'Note. This surface ...'		£1.30	—
A	C	50	Railway Engines (1924)	W.303	£1.20	£60.00
A	C	50	Railway Engines (1936):	W.304		
			A Home issue — back 'This surface ...'		£1.00	£50.00
			B Irish issue — back 'Note. This surface ...'		£1.50	£75.00
A	C	50	Railway Equipment (1939):	W.305		
			A Home issue – with Album offer		40p	£20.00
			B Channel Islands issue – without Album offer		60p	£30.00
A	C	50	Railway Locomotives (1930)		£1.70	£85.00
A	C	12	Recruiting Posters (1915)	W.92	£7.50	£90.00

Size	*Print-ing*	*Number in set*		*Handbook reference*	*Price per card*	*Complete set*

W.D. & H.O. WILLS, Bristol *(continued)*

A	C	50	The Reign of H. M. King George V (1935)		80p	£40.00
B	C	25	Rigs of Ships (1929)		£3.60	£90.00
A	C	50	Romance of the Heavens (1928):	W.313		
			A Thin card		£1.10	£55.00
			B Thick card		£1.10	£55.00
A	C	50	Roses (1912)	W.94	£1.60	£80.00
A	C	50	Roses, 2nd Series (1914)	W.94	£1.60	£80.00
A	C	50	Roses (1926)	W.94	£1.00	£50.00
B	C	40	Roses (1936)		£1.60	£65.00
—	BW	48	Round Europe (66 × 52mm) (1937)		40p	£20.00
A	C	50	Rugby Internationals (1929)		£2.00	£100.00
A	C	50	Safety First (1934):	W.321		
			A Home issue — 'This surface ...'		£1.20	£60.00
			B Irish issue — 'Note. This surface ...'		£2.00	—
A	C	50	School Arms (1906)	W.96	80p	£40.00
A	C	50	The Sea-Shore (1938):	W.322		
			A Home issue — adhesive with Album offer		30p	£15.00
			B Irish issue — non-adhesive		70p	£35.00
			C Channel Islands issue – adhesive without Album offer		50p	£25.00
A	C	50	Seaside Resorts (1899):	W.10		
			A 'Best Bird's Eye' back		£12.00	—
			B 'Capstan Navy Cut' back		£12.00	—
			C 'Gold Flake' back		£12.00	—
			D 'The Three Castles' back		£12.00	—
			E 'Traveller' back		£12.00	—
			F 'Westward Ho!' back		£12.00	—
A	U	40	Shannon Electric Power Scheme (1931)		£1.75	£70.00
A	C		*Ships:	W.11		
		25	A Without 'Wills' on front (1895):			
			a 'Three Castles' back		£30.00	£750.00
			b Grey scroll back		£30.00	£750.00
		50	B With 'Wills' on front, dark grey back (1896)		£20.00	—
		100	C Green scroll back on brown card (1898-1902):			
			i 1898-25, Group 1		£20.00	—
			ii 1898-50, Group 2		£20.00	—
			iii 1902-25 additional subjects, Group 3		£20.00	—
A	U	50	Ships' Badges (1925)	W.328	80p	£40.00
A	C	50	Signalling Series (1911)	W.97	£1.80	£90.00
A	C	50	*Soldiers and Sailors (c1894):	W.13		
			A Grey back		£45.00	—
			B Blue back		£45.00	—
A	C		*Soldiers of the World (1895-7):	W.12		
			A Without PC inset:			
		100	a With 'Ld.' back, thick card		£8.00	£800.00
		100	b With 'Ld.' back, thin card		£8.00	—
		100	c Without 'Ld.' back, thin card		£8.00	£800.00
		1	Additional card (as c) 'England, Drummer'		—	£140.00
		52	B With PC inset		£23.00	£1200.00
A	C	50	Speed (1930)		£1.50	£75.00
A	C	50	Speed (1938):	W.330		
			A Home issue — Album offer with price		40p	£20.00
			B Irish issue — Album offer without price		80p	£40.00
			C Channel Islands issue – no Album offer		50p	£25.00
A	C	50	Sports of All Nations, multi-backed (1900)	W.14	£11.00	£550.00

Size	Printing	Number in set		Handbook reference	Price per card	Complete set

W.D. & H.O. WILLS, Bristol *(continued)*

Size	Printing	Number in set		Handbook reference	Price per card	Complete set
A	C	50	Strange Craft (1931)		£1.00	£50.00
A	C	50	Time and Money in Different Countries (1906)	W.104	£1.80	£90.00
A	BW		Transvaal Series:	W.30		
		50	A With black border (1899)		£9.00	—
		66	Bi Without black border (1900-01)		£1.75	£115.00
		258	Bii Intermediate cards — additions and alternatives (1900-01)		£1.75	—
		66	C Final 66 subjects, as issued with 'Capstan' back (1902)		£6.00	—
B	C	40	Trees (1937)		£1.60	£65.00
B	C	25	University Hoods and Gowns (1926)		£3.00	£75.00
A	C		'Vanity Fair' Series (1902):	W.31		
		50	1st series		£7.00	£350.00
		50	2nd series		£7.00	£350.00
		50	Unnumbered — 43 subjects as in 1st and 2nd, 7 new subjects		£7.00	£350.00
A	C	50	Waterloo (c1916) (unissued)		£120.00	—
A	C		Wild Animals of the World (c1900):	W.15		
		50	A Green scroll back		£6.50	£325.00
		52	B Grey back, PC inset		£12.00	£600.00
		? 16	C Text back		£35.00	—
A	C	50	Wild Flowers (1923):	W.345		
			A With dots in side panels		70p	£35.00
			B Without dots in side panels		70p	£35.00
A	C	50	Wild Flowers — 'Series of 50' (1936):	W.346		
			A Home issue — back 'This surface ...'		50p	£25.00
			B Irish issue — back 'Note. This surface ...'		70p	—
			C Channel Islands issue – without Album offer or I.T.C. clause		60p	£30.00
A	C	50	Wild Flowers — '2nd Series.' (1937):	W.347		
			A Home issue — adhesive back, with Album offer		20p	£10.00
			B Irish issue — non-adhesive back		60p	£30.00
			C Channel Islands issue – adhesive back without Album offer		60p	£30.00
A	C	50	Wonders of the Past (1926)	W.348	60p	£30.00
A	C	50	Wonders of the Sea (1928)	W.349	50p	£25.00
A	C	25	The World's Dreadnoughts (1910)	W.115	£3.00	£75.00

POST-1965 ISSUES

Size	Printing	Number in set		Handbook reference	Price per card	Complete set
H2	C	30	Britain's Motoring History (1991)	W.416	£1.40	£42.00
—	C	6	Britain's Motoring History (149 × 104mm) (1991)	W.416	£1.25	—
H2	C	30	Britain's Steam Railways (1998)		£1.20	£36.00
G2	C	30	British Aviation (1994)	W.418	£1.20	£36.00
—	C	6	British Aviation (1994) Beer Mats	W418	50p	£3.00
	C	56	Caribbean Treasure Cruise (1985):	W.419		
—			A Size 75 × 35mm		60p	—
—			B Size 80 × 47mm		60p	—
G2	C	30	Classic Sports Cars (1996)		£1.20	£36.00
G2	C	30	Donington Collection (1993)	W.422	£1.20	£36.00
—	C	6	Donington Collection (1993) Beer Mats	W.422	£1.25	—
—	C	12	Embassy World Snooker Championship 17 April-3 May (80 × 47mm) (2004)	W.443	£3.00	—
	C	12	Embassy World Snooker Championship 16 April-2 May (2005):	W.444		
—			A Size 75 × 32mm		£3.00	—
—			B Size 80 × 47mm		£3.00	—
G2	BW	48	Familiar Phrases (1986)		£1.20	£60.00

Size	Printing	Number in set		Handbook reference	Price per card	Complete set

W.D. & H.O. WILLS, Bristol *(continued)*

Size	Printing	Number in set		Handbook reference	Price per card	Complete set
	C	26	Focus on What's What (1989):	W.425		
—			A Size 75 × 32mm		60p	—
—			B Size 80 × 47mm		60p	—
G2	C	10	Golden Era (1999)	W.426	£2.00	£20.00
H2	C	30	History of Britain's Railways (1987)	W.428	£1.20	£36.00
H2	C	30	History of Motor Racing (1987)	W.429	£1.50	—
G2	C	30	In Search of Steam (1992)	W.430	£1.20	£36.00
—	C	6	In Search of Steam (1992) Beer Mats	W.430	£1.25	—
G2	BW	5	Pica Punchline (1984)		£1.20	£6.00
H2	U	144	Punch Lines (1983)	W.433	80p	—
G2	U	288	Punch Lines (1983)	W.433	80p	—
G2	U	48	Ring the Changes (1985):	W.434		
			A With 'Wills' name		£1.20	—
			B Without 'Wills' Name		£1.20	—
—	C	12	Russ Abbot Advertising Cards (80 × 47mm) (1993)		£1.50	£18.00
	C	72	Showhouse (1988):	W.435		
—			A Size 60 × 43mm		60p	—
—			B Size 80 × 35mm		60p	—
—			C Size 68 × 47mm		60p	—
—			D Size 80 × 47mm		60p	—
G2			E Size 90 × 47mm		60p	—
G2	C	30	Soldiers of Waterloo (1995)		£1.20	£36.00
G2	BW	10	Spot the Shot (1986)		£2.50	—
G2	C	30	The Tank Story (1997)		£1.20	£36.00
			Three Castles Sailing Ship Model advertisement cards (1965):			
A	C	1	A View from Stern: Three Castles Filter:			
			I. Three Castles Cigarettes		—	£4.00
			II. In the eighteenth century		—	£1.50
A	C	1	B Views from Bows:			
			I. Three Castles Filter		—	£1.50
			II. Three Castles Filter magnum		—	£1.50
A	BW	1	C Sailing Ship Black Line Drawing		—	£5.00
A	BW	1	D Three Castles Shield Black Line Drawing		—	£5.00
—	C		200th Anniversary Presentation Packs (2 sets of Playing Cards) (1986)	W.661	—	£90.00
	C	?	Wheel of Fortune (1985):	W.439		
—			A Size 75 × 35mm		60p	—
—			B Size 80 × 47mm		60p	—
—	C	56	Wonders of the World (1986):	W.440		
			A Size 90 × 47mm		50p	£28.00
			B Size 80 × 47mm		70p	£40.00
			C Size 80 × 35mm		90p	—
C1	C	36	World of Firearms (1982)		25p	£9.00
C1	C	36	World of Speed (1981)		25p	£9.00

OVERSEAS ISSUES

Size	Printing	Number in set		Handbook reference	Price per card	Complete set
D2	U	50	Actors and Actresses, scroll backs in green (1905):	W.32		
			A Portraits in black and white		£3.50	—
			B Portraits flesh tinted		£2.75	—
D	U	30	Actresses — brown and green (1905) Scissors issue	W.116	£3.30	£100.00
D2	U	50	Actresses — four colours surround (c1904):	W.117		
			A Scissors issue		£7.00	—
			B Green scroll back issue		£2.80	—

Size	*Print-ing*	*Number in set*		*Handbook reference*	*Price per card*	*Complete set*

W.D. & H.O. WILLS, Bristol *(continued)*

D	U	30	Actresses — orange/mauve surround (c1916) Scissors issue:	W.118		
			A Surround in Orange		£2.50	£75.00
			B Surround in mauve		£1.50	£45.00
D2	U	100	Actresses (c1903):	W.34		
			A Capstan issue		£3.25	—
			B Vice Regal issue		£3.25	—
D	U		Actresses (c1903):	W.33		
		250	A Front portrait in black, border in red		£3.00	—
		50	B Front portrait in red, border in red		£3.00	—
D	BW	25	Actresses — Tabs type numbered (1902)	W.16	£20.00	—
D2	BW	50	Actresses — Tabs type unnumbered, Scissors issue (c1905)	W.119	£12.00	—
D	U	30	Actresses unicoloured I (1908):	W.120		
			A Scissors issue, back in red		£1.80	£55.00
			B Scissors issue, back in purple brown		£2.50	£75.00
A	U	30	Actresses — unicoloured II (c1908) Scissors issue	W.121	£2.00	£60.00
A	C	1	*Advertisement Card 'Capstan' (1902)	W.402	£300.00	—
A	C	50	Aeroplanes (1926)		£3.20	—
A	C	60	Animals (cut-outs) (1913):	W.37		
			A Havelock issue		£1.80	—
			B Wills' Specialities issue		£1.00	£60.00
	C	50	Animals and Birds:	W.17		
A			A With text, without title (c1902)		£15.00	—
D2			B Without text, with title (1912)		£5.00	—
D2			C Without text or title (1909)		£6.00	—
A	C	50	Arms and Armour (1910):	W.38		
			A Capstan issue		£2.00	—
			B Havelock issue		£3.00	—
			C Vice Regal issue		£2.00	—
			D United Service issue		£3.20	£160.00
A	C	50	Arms of the British Empire (1910):	W.40		
			A Backs in black		£1.10	£55.00
			B Wills' Specialities issue		£1.10	—
			C Havelock issue		£7.00	—
A	C	25	Army Life (1914) Scissors issue	W.133	£2.60	£65.00
—	U	50	Art Photogravures 1st series (1912):	W.43		
			A Size 67 × 33mm		80p	—
			B Size 67 × 44mm		80p	—
A	U	50	Art Photogravures 2nd series (1914)	W.44	80p	—
A	C	40	Australian Club Cricketers (1905):	W.59-1		
			A Dark blue backs		£18.00	—
			B Green backs		£18.00	—
			C Pale blue backs		£18.00	—
A	C	25	Australian and English Cricketers (1903)	W.59-2	£16.00	—
D2	U	25	Australian and English Cricketers (1909):	W.59-3		
			A Capstan issue:			
			i Framework in scarlet		£16.00	—
			ii Framework in blue		£16.00	—
			B Vice Regal issue:			
			i Framework in scarlet		£16.00	—
			ii Framework in blue		£16.00	—
D2	U	60	Australian and South African Cricketers (1910):	W.59-4		
			A Capstan issue:			
			i Framework in scarlet		£16.00	—
			ii Framework in blue		£16.00	—

Size	Printing	Number in set		Handbook reference	Price per card	Complete set
			W.D. & H.O. WILLS, Bristol *(continued)*			
D2	U	60	Australian & South African Cricketers (1910) *continued*:	W.59-4		
			B Havelock issue:			
			i Framework in scarlet		£38.00	—
			ii Framework in blue		£38.00	—
			C Vice Regal issue:			
			i Framework in scarlet		£16.00	—
			ii Framework in blue		£16.00	—
—	P	100	Australian Scenic Series (69 × 52mm) (1928)	W.138	90p	—
A	C	50	Australian Wild Flowers (1913):			
			A Wills' Specialities issue, grey-brown back		£1.00	£50.00
			B Wills' Specialities issue, green back		£2.00	—
			C Havelock issue		£3.50	—
A	C		Aviation (1910):	W.46		
		85	A Black backs 'Series of 85':			
			i Capstan issue		£3.00	—
			ii Vice Regal issue		£3.00	—
		75	B Black backs 'Series of 75':			
			i Capstan issue		£2.20	—
			ii Havelock issue		£3.00	—
			iii Vice Regal issue		£2.20	—
		75	C Green back 'Series of 75':			
			i Capstan issue		£2.40	—
			ii Havelock issue		£3.50	—
			iii Vice Regal issue		£2.40	—
D2	C	50	Aviation Series (1911):	W.47		
			A W.D. and H.O. Wills back		£3.50	—
			B Anonymous backs with album clause		£3.50	—
			C Anonymous backs without album clause		£3.50	—
A	C	? 95	Baseball Series (1912) Pirate issue	W.353	£500.00	—
A	U	40	Beauties — brown tinted (1913):	W.139		
			A Scissors issue		£1.70	£70.00
			B Star circle and leaves issue		£3.00	—
D2	U	30	Beauties — 'Celebrated Actresses' Scissors issue (c1912)	W.140	£4.50	—
A2	C	52	Beauties — Heads and shoulders set in background (1911):	W.141		
			A Scissors issue:			
			i Background to packets plain		£6.50	—
			ii Background to packets latticework design		£3.20	£170.00
			iii No packet back		£40.00	—
			B Star circle and leaves issue		£5.00	—
—	CP	50	Beauties 1st series (63 × 45mm) (1925)	W.142	£4.00	—
—	P	25	Beauties 1st Series (64 × 40mm) (1925)	W.142	£3.00	—
—	P	50	Beauties 2nd series (64 × 40mm) (1925)	W.143	£3.50	—
A2	C	32	Beauties — Picture Hats (1914):	W.144		
			A Scissors issue		£3.75	—
			B Star circle and leaves issue		£5.50	—
—	CP	72	Beauties — red star and circle back (70 × 47mm) (1923)	W.145	£12.00	—
D2	U	50	Beauties — red tinted (1905)	W.146	£2.40	£120.00
D	C	30	Beauties and Children (c1910) Scissors issue	W.147	£2.50	£75.00
A	P	50	Beautiful New Zealand (1928)		40p	£20.00
D2	C	50	Best Dogs of Their Breed (1914):	W.48		
			A Havelock issue		£7.50	—
			B Wills' Specialities issue		£5.00	—
			C Anonymous back, Wills' on front		£8.50	—

Size	*Print-ing*	*Number in set*		*Handbook reference*	*Price per card*	*Complete set*

W.D. & H.O. WILLS, Bristol *(continued)*

D2	C	30	Birds and Animals (1911) Ruby Queen issue	W.354	£3.00	—
D1	C	50	Birds, Beasts and Fishes (1924)	W.151	50p	£25.00
A	C	100	Birds of Australasia:			
			A Green backs (1912):			
			i Capstan issue		£1.50	£150.00
			ii Havelock issue		£2.50	—
			iii Vice Regal issue		£1.50	£150.00
			B Yellow backs (1915):			
			i Havelock issue		£2.50	—
			ii Wills' Specialities issue		£1.50	—
D	C	52	Birds of Brilliant Plumage:	W.152		
			A Four Aces issue (1924)		£3.25	—
			B Pirate Issue:			
			i With border on front (1916)		£4.00	—
			ii Without border on front (1916)		£4.00	—
			C Red star, circle and leaves issue (1914)		£4.50	—
D2	C	25	Birds of the East 1st series Ruby Queen issue (1912)	W.355	£1.60	£40.00
D2	C	25	Birds of the East 2nd series Ruby Queen issue (1927)	W.356	£1.60	£40.00
D2	C	36	Boxers (1911):	W.153		
			A Scissors issue		£10.00	—
			B Green star and circle issue		£10.00	—
D2	U		Britain's Defenders (1915):	W.51		
			A Wills' Specialities issue:			
		50	i Inscribed 'A Series of 50'		£1.50	£75.00
		8	ii Without inscription 'A Series of 50'		£10.00	—
		50	B Havelock issue		£2.50	—
		50	C Scissors issue:			
			i Red upright 'Scissors' packet		£1.60	£80.00
			ii Green upright 'Scissors' packet		£1.70	£85.00
			iii Red slanting 'Scissors' packet		£1.60	£80.00
		50	D Green star and circle issue		£2.00	—
D2	C	43	British Army Boxers (1913) Scissors issue		£6.00	—
D2	C	50	British Army Uniforms (c1910):	W.106		
			A Wild Woodbine issue		£6.00	£300.00
			B Flag issue		£5.00	—
			C Scissors issue		£5.00	£250.00
—	C	101	British Beauties (59 × 41mm) (c1915)	W.155	£2.25	—
A	C	50	British Empire Series (1912):			
			A Capstan issue		£1.00	£50.00
			B Havelock issue		£1.80	—
			C Vice Regal issue		£1.00	£50.00
A	P	48	British Royal and Ancient Buildings (1925)		50p	£25.00
A	BW	45	British Rugby Players (1930)		£2.50	—
A	U	50	Chateaux (1925)	W.167	£5.50	—
A	C	50	Children of All Nations (1925)		80p	£40.00
D2	C	100	China's Famous Warriors (1911) Pirate issue:			
			A First 25 subjects	W.357	£3.00	£75.00
			B Second 25 subjects	W.358	£3.00	£75.00
			C Third 25 subjects	W.359	£3.00	£75.00
			D Fourth 25 subjects	W.360	£3.00	£75.00
D2	C	28	Chinese Actors and Actresses (1907) Pirate issue	W.361	£3.00	—
D2	C	25	Chinese Beauties 1st Series (1907) Pirate issue:	W.362		
			A Vertical back		£2.00	£50.00
			B Horizontal back		£2.20	£55.00
D2	C	25	Chinese Beauties 2nd series (1909) Pirate issue:	W.363		
			A With framelines on front		£2.00	£50.00
			B Without framelines on front		£2.00	£50.00

Size	Print-ing	Number in set		Handbook reference	Price per card	Complete set
W.D. & H.O. WILLS, Bristol *(continued)*						
D2	C	30	Chinese Children's Games (1911) Ruby Queen issue	W.364	£2.50	—
D2	C	50	Chinese Costumes Pirate issue (1928)	W.365	£5.00	—
—	C	25	Chinese Pagodas (1911) Pirate issue (138 × 88mm)	W.366	£50.00	—
D2	U	50	Chinese Proverbs brown (138 × 88mm) (1928):	W.367		
			A Pirate issue		£1.60	—
			B Ruby Queen issue		£5.00	—
D2	C	50	Chinese Proverbs coloured (1914-16) Pirate issue:	W.368		
			A Back in blue:			
			i Without overprint		£1.60	—
			ii With overprint		£1.60	—
			B Back in olive green		£1.60	—
D2	C	40	Chinese Trades (c1905) Autocar issue	W.369	£7.00	—
D2	C	50	Chinese Transport (1914) Ruby Queen issue	W.370	£3.50	—
D2	U	50	Cinema Stars Four Aces issue (1926):	W.172		
			A Numbered		£1.80	£90.00
			B Unnumbered		£2.00	£100.00
D2	U	25	Cinema Stars (1916) Scissors issue	W.173	£2.40	£60.00
A1	P	50	Cinema Stars (1926)	W.382	£5.00	—
A	C	50	Coaches and Coaching Days (1925)		£2.00	£100.00
A	C		Conundrums (c1900):	W.21		
		25	A With album clause		£12.00	—
		25	B Without album clause		£12.00	—
		25	C Without album clause redrawn		£12.00	—
		50	D Without album clause inscribed '50 Different'		£12.00	—
—	C	68	Crests and Colours of Australian Universities, Colleges and Schools (70 × 48mm) (1929)	W.176	80p	£55.00
A	P	63	Cricketers (c1925)	W.59-5	£8.00	—
A	U	25	Cricketer Series (1902)	W.59-6	£130.00	—
A	U	50	Cricketer Series (1901)	W.59-7	£130.00	—
A	P	48	Cricket Season 1928-29	W.177	£3.50	—
D2	C	27	Dancing Girls (1915) Scissors issue:	W.180		
			A Inscribed '28 Subjects' (No. 3 not issued)		£3.00	—
			B Inscribed '27 Subjects'		£3.00	—
D2	C	25	Derby Day Series (1914):	W.181		
			A Scissors issue:			
			i With title		£8.00	—
			ii Without title		£10.00	—
			B Star and circle issue		£9.00	—
A	C	50	Dogs — Scenic backgrounds (1925)		£1.00	£50.00
—	C	20	Dogs — Heads 1st series (70 × 63mm) (1927):			
			A Wills' World Renown Cigarettes issue:			
			i With album clause		£3.50	—
			ii Without album clause		£3.50	—
			B Three Castles and Vice Regal Cigarettes issue		£3.50	—
—	C	20	Dogs — Heads 2nd series (70 × 63mm) (1927)		£3.50	—
D2	C	32	Drum Horses (1909):	W.192		
			A Scissors issue:			
			i Vertical format, open Scissors packet		£9.00	—
			ii Horizontal format, closed Scissors packet		£7.00	—
			B United Service issue		£6.50	—
			C Green star, circle and leaves issue		£7.50	—
A	P	25	English Cricketers (1926)		£3.00	£75.00
—	C	25	English Period Costumes (70 × 55mm) (1928):	W.195		
			A White card		£1.80	—
			B Cream card		£1.80	£45.00
—	P	10	English Views & Buildings (145 × 108mm) (c1928)	W.407	£12.00	—

Size	*Print-ing*	*Number in set*		*Handbook reference*	*Price per card*	*Complete set*

W.D. & H.O. WILLS, Bristol *(continued)*

	BW		Etchings (of Dogs) (1925):			
A		26	A Small size English language issues:			
			i With 'Gold Flake Cigarettes'		£7.00	—
			ii Without 'Gold Flake Cigarettes'		£2.50	—
A		26	B Small size Dutch language issues:			
			i With framelines to back		£8.00	—
			ii Without framelines to back		£8.00	—
—		26	C Medium size (78 × 54mm)		£5.00	—
D	C	25	The Evolution of the British Navy (1915)		£3.00	£75.00
		10	Famous Castles (c1928):	W.408		
—	P		A Size 145 × 108mm		£10.00	—
—	U		B Size 140 × 75mm		£10.00	—
	U		Famous Film Stars (1934):			
A		100	A Small size		£1.50	—
—		100	B Medium size (67 × 53mm):			
			i White card		£2.50	—
			ii Cream card		£2.50	—
—	P	100	Famous Film Stars (68 × 51mm) (c1936)		£3.40	—
A2	U	50	Famous Footballers (1914):			
			A Scissors issue		£10.00	—
			B Star and circle issue		£10.00	—
A	C	50	Famous Inventions (without ITC clause) (1926)	W.60	£1.00	£50.00
D2	U	75	Film Favourites Four Aces issue (1928)		£1.70	—
A	C	50	Fish of Australasia (1912):			
			A Capstan issue		£1.20	£60.00
			B Havelock issue		£2.50	—
			C Vice Regal issue		£1.20	£60.00
D2	C		Flag Girls of All Nations (1908):	W.64		
		50	A Capstan issue		£2.00	—
		50	B Vice Regal issue		£2.00	—
		25	C United Service issue		£2.80	£70.00
		25	D Scissors issue:			
			i Numbered		£10.00	—
			ii Unnumbered		£10.00	—
		25	E Green star, circle and leaves issue		£2.80	£70.00
—	C	8	Flags, shaped metal (1915)	W.65	£9.00	—
D2	C	126	Flags and Ensigns (1903)	W.66	£1.50	—
A	C	25	Flags of the Empire (no ITC clause) (1926)	W.215	£7.00	—
D2	C		Flowers Purple Mountain issue (1914):			
		20	A Numbered	W.371	£12.00	—
		100	B Unnumbered	W.372	£12.00	—
D2	C	50	Football Club Colours Scissors/Special Army Quality issue (1907)	W.220	£9.00	—
A	C	28	Football Club Colours and Flags (1913):	W.68		
			A Capstan issue		£5.00	—
			B Havelock issue		£7.00	—
	U	200	Footballers (1933):			
A			A Small size		£1.70	—
—			B Medium size (67 × 52mm)		£3.50	—
—	C	? 5	Footballers Shaped Die Cut (59 × 30mm) (1910)	W.404	£150.00	—
D2	C	50	Girls of All Nations (1908):	W.73		
			A Capstan issue		£2.50	—
			B Vice Regal issue		£2.50	—
			C Green star, circle and leaves issue		£2.60	—
D2	C	25	Governor-General of India Scissors issue (1912)	W.229	£7.40	—
—	C	25	Heraldic Signs and Their Origins (77 × 59mm) (1925)	W.230	£1.60	£40.00

Size	Printing	Number in set		Handbook reference	Price per card	Complete set

W.D. & H.O. WILLS, Bristol *(continued)*

Size	Printing	Number in set		Handbook reference	Price per card	Complete set
D2	C	30	Heroic Deeds (1913) Scissors issue		£4.00	—
A	C	50	Historic Events (1913):	W.74		
			A Wills' Specialities issue		£1.20	£60.00
			B Havelock issue		£2.20	—
—	C	25	History of Naval Dress (75 × 55mm) (1930)		£35.00	—
A2	P	50	Homeland Events (1927)	W.233	70p	£35.00
A2	C	50	Horses of Today (1906):	W.75		
			A Capstan issue		£3.00	—
			B Havelock issue		£5.00	—
			C Vice Regal issue		£3.00	—
A	C	50	Household Hints (1927):	W.236		
			A With 'Wills' Cigarettes' at top back		60p	—
			B Without 'Wills' Cigarettes' at top back		£1.50	—
D2	C		Houses of Parliament (c1912):	W.237		
		33	A Pirate issue		£1.40	£45.00
		32	B Star and circle issue		£2.25	£72.00
D2	C	50	Indian Regiments (1912):	W.239		
			A Scissors issue		£9.00	—
			B Star and circle issue		£9.00	—
A	C	2	Indian Series – see Bukhsh Ellallie & Co.			
A	C	50	Interesting Buildings (1905)	W.76	£2.50	£125.00
D2	BW	67	International Footballers Season 1909-1910:	W.242		
			A Scissors issue (1910)		£11.00	—
			B United Services issue (1910)		£11.00	—
			C Flag issue (1911)		£11.00	—
A	U	5	Islands of the Pacific (c1916)	W.375	£225.00	—
D2	C	50	Jiu-Jitsu (c1910):			
			A Scissors issue		£6.50	—
			B Flag issue		£6.00	—
D1	C	53	Jockeys and Owners Colours with PC inset Scissors issue (1914)		£8.00	—
A	C	50	Lighthouses (1926)		£1.80	£90.00
A	U		Maori Series (c1900):	W.77		
		100	A White border		£90.00	—
		? 44	B Green border. Numbered bottom left		£90.00	—
		? 3	C Green border. Numbered top left		£200.00	—
		? 4	D Green border. Unnumbered		£200.00	—
		? 100	E White border. Plain back (anonymous)		£75.00	—
A	C	45	Melbourne Cup Winners (1906)	W.78	£8.00	—
A	C	50	Merchant Ships of the World (1925) (without I.T.C. clause)	W.257	£1.20	£60.00
A1	C	40	Merrie England Studies (Male) (1916)	W.79	£7.00	—
A	U	24	Merveilles du Monde (1927)	W.258	£7.00	—
A	BW	25	Military Portraits (1917) Scissors issue		£4.00	—
—	C	25	Miniatures — oval medallions (62 × 45mm) (1914)	W.261	£55.00	—
K2	C	52	Miniature Playing Cards Scissors issue (1906)		£11.00	—
A	U	50	Modern War Weapons (1915):	W.82		
			A Wills' Specialities issue		£2.00	—
			B Havelock issue		£3.00	—
A	C	25	Modes of Conveyance (1928) Four Aces issue		£2.00	£50.00
A	C	48	Motor Cars (1923)		£2.00	£100.00
A	P	50	Motor Cars (1927)		£1.80	£90.00
A	C	50	Motor Cycles (1926)		£3.20	£160.00
A1	P	48	Movie Stars (1927)		£3.50	—
D2	BW	50	Music Hall Celebrities (1911) Scissors issue	W.269	£6.50	—
A	C	50	National Flags and Arms (1938)		£1.50	—

Size	*Printing*	*Number in set*		*Handbook reference*	*Price per card*	*Complete set*

W.D. & H.O. WILLS, Bristol *(continued)*

—	C	25	The Nation's Shrines (71 × 55mm) (1928)		£1.40	£35.00
A	P	50	Nature Studies (1928)		£1.50	—
A	C	50	New Zealand Birds (1925)		£1.20	£60.00
A	P	50	New Zealand — Early Scenes and Maori Life (1926)		50p	£25.00
A	P	50	New Zealand Footballers (1927)		£1.50	£75.00
A	U	50	New Zealand Race Horses (1928):			
			A Cream card		£1.00	£50.00
			B White card		£1.00	—
A	C	50	N.Z. Butterflies, Moths and Beetles (1925)		£1.00	£50.00
A	C	25	Past and Present (1929)		£1.40	£35.00
A1	C	50	Past and Present Champions (1908):	W.89		
			A Capstan Cigarette issue		£10.00	—
			B Capstan Tobacco issue		£10.00	—
A	C	25	Picturesque People of the Empire (1928)		£1.40	£35.00
A	C	25	Pirates and Highwaymen (1925)		£1.60	£40.00
A	C	25	Police of the World (1910)	W.290	£10.00	—
—	C	70	Practical Wireless (69 × 62mm) (1923)		£8.00	—
D2	C		Products of the World — Maps and Scenes (1913):	W.293		
		50	A Pirate issue		£1.30	—
		25	B Green star, circle and leaves issue		£1.80	—
A	C	50	Products of the World — Scenes only (1929)		50p	£25.00
A	C	50	Prominent Australian and English Cricketers (1907)	W.59-8	£14.00	—
D2	C	23	Prominent Australian and English Cricketers (1907)	W.59-9	£18.00	—
D2	BW	59	Prominent Australian and English Cricketers (1911):	W.59-10		
			A Capstan issue:			
			i 'A Series of 50'		£13.00	—
			ii 'A Series of .../A Series of 59'		£16.00	—
			B Vice Regal issue:			
			i 'A Series of 50'		£13.00	—
			ii 'A Series of .../A Series of 59'		£16.00	—
			C Havelock issue		£40.00	—
D2	C	25	Puzzle Series (1910) Scissors/United Service issue:	W.298		
			A Background blue-green		£7.00	—
			B Background light yellow		£7.00	—
D	C	50	Races of Mankind (1911)		£12.00	—
A	C	50	Railway Engines (1924)	W.303	£1.30	£65.00
A	C	50	Railway Working (1927)		£2.20	—
A	C	50	Regimental Colours and Cap Badges (1907):			
			A Scissors issue		£1.50	£75.00
			B United Service issue:			
			i Red back		£1.50	£75.00
			ii Blue back		£1.50	£75.00
D2	C	33	Regimental Pets (1911) Scissors issue	W.309	£6.00	—
A	C	50	Regimental Standards and Cap Badges (1928)		80p	£40.00
A	C	50	Riders of the World:	W.93		
			A Capstan/Vice Regal/Pennant/Wills' Specialities issue (1913)		£1.60	—
			B Havelock issue (1913)		£3.20	—
			C Back in red-brown (1931)		£1.20	£60.00
A	C	50	Romance of the Heavens (1928) (No ITC clause)		£1.50	—
D2	C	25	Roses (1912):	W.373		
			A Purple Mountain issues:			
			i With Wills' Cigarettes on front		£6.00	—
			ii Without Wills' Cigarettes on front		£6.00	—
			B Plain backs with Wills' Cigarettes on front		£6.00	—
A	P	50	The Royal Family at Home and Abroad (1927)		£1.50	—

Size	Print-ing	Number in set		Handbook reference	Price per card	Complete set
			W.D. & H.O. WILLS, Bristol *(continued)*			
A	C	50	Royal Mail (with Wills' Cigarettes on fronts) (1913):	W.95		
			A Capstan issue		£4.00	£200.00
			B Havelock issue (without Wills' Cigarettes on fronts)		£5.00	—
			C Vice Regal issue		£4.00	£200.00
			D With anonymous backs		£6.00	—
			E With plain back		£6.00	—
A	P	50	The Royal Navy (1929)		£1.80	£90.00
A	BW	100	Royalty, Notabilities and Events 1900-1902 (1902)	W.28	£3.00	—
D1	U	27	Rulers of the World (1911)	W.320	£7.50	—
D2			Russo-Japanese Series (1905):	W.29		
	BW	100	A Fronts in black		£2.00	£200.00
	U	50	B Fronts in red		£8.00	—
A	C	50	Safety First (1937)	W.321	80p	£40.00
B	CP	48	Scenes from the Empire (1939)		£1.80	£90.00
D2	C	30	Semaphore Signalling (1910)		£3.50	£105.00
A	P	50	Ships and Shipping (1928)		90p	£45.00
D2	C	36	Ships and Their Pennants (1913)		£5.50	—
A	C	50	Ships' Badges (1925)	W.328	90p	£45.00
A	C	50	Signalling Series (1912):	W.97		
			A Capstan issue		£1.30	£65.00
			B Havelock issue		£2.50	—
			C Vice Regal issue		£1.30	£65.00
D2	BW	40	Sketches in black and white (1905)	W.98	£2.50	—
	C		Soldiers of the World (1903):	W.12		
A		50	A Numbered		£9.00	—
D2		75	B Unnumbered		£10.00	—
A	BW	100	South African Personalities (1894)	W.99	£125.00	—
—	P	10	Splendours of New Zealand (140 × 75mm) (c1928)		£10.00	—
D2	C	30	Sporting Girls (1913) Scissors issue	W.331	£8.00	—
	P	50	A Sporting Holiday in New Zealand (1928):	W.332		
A			A Small size		70p	£35.00
—			B Medium size (70 × 57mm)		90p	£45.00
D2	C	25	Sporting Terms (1905):	W.100		
			A Capstan issue		£15.00	—
			B Vice Regal issue		£15.00	—
D	C	50	Sports of the World (1917)		£5.00	—
D2		50	Stage and Music Hall Celebrities (1904) (Portrait in oval frame):	W.102		
	BW		A Capstan issue		£3.50	—
	BW		B Vice Regal issue		£3.50	—
	U		C Havelock issue		£4.50	—
D2	BW	50	Stage and Music Hall Celebrities (1908) (Portrait in oblong frame)	W.103	£3.50	—
D1	P	52	Stars of the Cinema (1926):			
			A Text back		£5.00	—
			B Four Aces issue		£5.00	—
A	C	50	Time and Money in Different Countries (1908):	W.104		
			A Capstan issue		£1.60	—
			B Havelock issue		£2.80	—
			C Vice Regal issue:			
			i With album clause		£1.60	£80.00
			ii Without album clause		£1.60	£80.00
A	C	50	A Tour Round the World (1907)	W.105	£3.00	—
D2	C	50	Types of the British Army (1912):	W.106		
			A Capstan issue		£2.40	—
			B Vice Regal issue		£2.40	—

Size	Print-ing	Number in set		Handbook reference	Price per card	Complete set

W.D. & H.O. WILLS, Bristol *(continued)*

Size	Print-ing	Number in set		Handbook reference	Price per card	Complete set
A	C	50	Types of the Commonwealth Forces (1910):	W.107		
			A Capstan issue		£2.60	—
			B Vice Regal issue		£2.60	—
			C Havelock issue		£5.00	—
A	C	25	United States Warships (1911):	W.108		
			A Capstan issue		£3.00	—
			B Havelock issue		£5.00	—
			C Vice Regal issue		£3.00	—
A	P	50	Units of the British Army and RAF (1928)		60p	£30.00
A	C	50	USS Co's Steamers (1930)		£2.60	—
A	C	50	VCs (1926)		£2.00	£100.00
D2	C	25	Victoria Cross Heroes (1915):			
			A Havelock issue		£4.00	—
			B Wills' Specialities issue		£2.60	£65.00
			C Scissors issue		£3.20	£80.00
A	C	10	Victorian Football Association (1908):	W.110		
			A Capstan on front		£4.50	—
			B Havelock on front		£6.50	—
A	C	19	Victorian Football League (1908):	W.111		
			A Capstan on front		£4.50	—
			B Havelock on front		£6.50	—
—	P	215	Views of the World (66 × 28mm) (1908):	W.112		
			A Numbers 1-50 plain backs (anonymous)		£1.00	—
			B Numbers 51-215 blue back Capstan issue		£1.00	—
			C Numbers 51-215 green back Vice Regal issue		£1.00	—
A	C	25	Village Models Series (1925):			
			A Small size		£1.40	£35.00
			B Medium size		£6.00	—
D2	C	50	War Incidents 1st series (1915):	W.113		
			A Wills' Specialities issue		£2.40	—
			B Havelock issue		£3.50	—
			C Scissors issue		£2.50	£125.00
D2	C	50	War Incidents 2nd series (1915):	W.113		
			A Wills' Specialities issue		£3.00	£150.00
			B Havelock issue		£5.00	—
A	BW	50	War Pictures (1915):	W.114		
			A Wills' Specialities issue		£1.40	£70.00
			B Havelock issue		£2.50	—
A	C	50	Warships (1926)		£1.80	£90.00
D2	C	30	What It Means (1916) Scissors issue		£1.50	£45.00
	C		Wild Animals (1934):			
A		50	A Small size titled 'Wild Animals' Heads		70p	£35.00
—		25	B Medium size titled 'Wild Animals' (69 × 55mm)		£1.40	£35.00
A	C	50	Wild Animals of the World (1906):	W.15		
			A Bristol and London issue		£12.00	—
			B Celebrated Cigarettes issue		£6.00	£300.00
			C Star, circle and leaves issue		£8.50	—
A	C	25	Wonders of the World (1926)		£1.20	£30.00
A	C	25	The World's Dreadnoughts (1910):	W.115		
			A Capstan issue		£2.40	—
			B Vice Regal issue		£2.40	—
			C No ITC clause		£2.60	£65.00
A	P	50	Zoo (1927):			
			A Scissors issue without descriptive back		£5.00	—
			B Wills' issue with descriptive back		30p	£15.00
—	P	50	Zoological Series (70 × 60mm) (1922)		£1.80	—

Size	Print-ing	Number in set		Handbook reference	Price per card	Complete set

W.D. & H.O. WILLS, Bristol *(continued)*

SILK ISSUES 1911-17

Size	Print-ing	Number in set		Handbook reference	Price per card	Complete set
—	C	50	Arms of the British Empire (70 × 48mm)	W.126	£3.00	—
—	C	50	Australian Butterflies (70 × 51mm)		£3.00	—
—	C	50	Birds and Animals of Australia (70 × 48mm)		£3.20	—
			Crests and Colours of Australian Universities, Colleges and Schools (70 × 48mm):			
—	C	50	A Numbered		£3.00	—
—	C	1	B Unnumbered		£25.00	—
—	C	1	Flag (Union Jack) (162 × 112mm)		£30.00	—
—	C	28	Flags of 1914-18 Allies (64 × 42mm):	W.214		
			A Backs with letterpress in capitals		£2.25	—
			B Backs with letterpress in small lettering		£2.25	—
—	C	13	*Flags on Lace* (71 × 50mm)	W.405	£6.00	—
A	C	38	Kings and Queens of England	W.251	£4.50	—
—	C	50	Popular Flowers (72 × 51mm):			
			A Backs inscribed 'Now being inserted in the large packets'		£4.50	—
			B Backs inscribed 'Now being inserted in the 1/- packets'		£4.50	—
—	C	67	War Medals (82 × 53mm)	W.341	£3.50	—

WILSON & CO., Ely

A	U	50	War Portraits (1916)	H.86	£100.00	—

W. WILSON, Birmingham

D	C	30	*Army Pictures. Cartoons, etc (1916)	H.12	£120.00	—
A	U	50	War Portraits (1916)	H.86	£100.00	—

HENRI WINTERMANS (UK) LTD

G	C	30	Disappearing Rain Forest (1991)		40p	£12.00
G	C	30	Wonders of Nature (1992)		40p	£12.00

A. & M. WIX, London and Johannesburg

—	—		Cinema Cavalcade (50 coloured, 200 black and white; sizes — 70 small, 110 large, 70 extra-large):			
		250	'A Series of 250 ...' ('Max Cigarettes') (1939)		£1.20	—
		250	'2nd Series of 250 ...' ('Max Cigarettes') (1940)		£1.40	—
A2	C	100	Film Favourites — 'Series of 100 ...' (c1937)	H.581-1	£2.50	—
A2	C	100	Film Favourites — '2nd Series of 100 ...' (1939)	H.581-2	£2.50	—
A2	C	100	Film Favourites — '3rd Series of 100 ...' (c1939)	H.581-3	£1.40	£140.00
J1	C	100	*Men of Destiny (folders) (P.O. Box 5764, Johannesburg) (c1935)		£2.00	—
—	C	250	Speed Through the Ages (171 small, 79 large) (1938):	H.583		
			A Back in English and Afrikaans		32p	£80.00
			B Back in English		40p	£100.00
—	C	250	This Age of Power and Wonder (170 small, 80 large) ('Max Cigarettes') (c1935)		30p	£75.00

J. WIX & SONS LTD, London

—	C	80	Bridge Favours and Place Cards (diecut) (1937)	H.681	£18.00	—
—	C	50	Bridge Hands (140 × 105mm) (1930)	H.682	£30.00	—
C	C	50	Builders of Empire — 'Kensitas' (1937)		60p	£30.00

J. WIX & SONS LTD, London *(continued)*

Size	*Print-ing*	*Number in set*		*Handbook reference*	*Price per card*	*Complete set*
—	U	42	Card Tricks by Jasper Maskelyne (c1935):	H.535-3		
			A Size 70 × 34mm		£6.00	—
			B Size 70 × 47mm		£6.00	—
A2	C	50	Coronation (1937):			
			A J. Wix back:			
			1 Linen finish		25p	£12.50
			2 Varnished		60p	£30.00
			B 'Kensitas' back		25p	£12.50
	C		Henry:	H.625		
			'A Series of ...' (1935):			
B1		50	A Large size		80p	£40.00
—		25	B Extra-large size		£3.00	£75.00
			'2nd Series ...' (1935):			
B1		50	A Large size:			
			i With album price		£1.00	£50.00
			ii Without album price		£3.00	—
—		25	B Extra-large size:			
			i Last line of text 'Throat'		£3.00	£75.00
			ii Last line of text 'Your Throat'		£6.00	—
B1		50	3rd Series, nothing after 'copyright reserved' (1936)		80p	£40.00
B1		50	4th Series, with full stop after 'copyright reserved' (1936)		70p	£35.00
B1		50	5th Series, with dash after 'copyright reserved' (1936)		60p	£30.00
	U		Jenkynisms:			
			A 'The K4's' Series (c1932):			
B2		102	I Known as 1st Series	H.636-1	80p	—
B2		50	II Known as 2nd Series	H.636-2	80p	£40.00
B2		30	III Known as 3rd Series	H.636-3	80p	—
B2		1	IV Known as 4th Series	H.636-4	—	£2.50
			B The Red Bordered series (c1932):			
	U	50	I Series of Quotations:	H.637-1		
A2			A Size 65 × 38mm		£4.00	—
—			B Size 69 × 54mm		£4.00	—
	U		II 'Today's Jenkynisms':	H.637-2		
A2			A Size 65 × 38mm:			
		? 44	i Without letter		£4.00	—
		? 30	ii Series B		£4.00	—
		? 19	iii Series C		£4.00	—
		? 34	iv Series D		£4.00	—
—			B Size 69 × 54mm:			
		? 44	i Without letter		£4.00	—
		? 30	ii Series B		£4.00	—
		? 19	iii Series C		£4.00	—
		? 34	iv Series D		£4.00	—
—	C		Ken-cards (102 × 118mm):			
		12	Series 1 Starters/Snacks (1969)		—	£5.00
		12	Series 2 Main Courses (1969)		—	£5.00
		12	Series 3 Desserts (1969)		—	£5.00
		12	Series 4 Motoring (1969)		—	£5.00
		12	Series 5 Gardening (1969)		—	£5.00
		12	Series 6 Do It Yourself (1969)		—	£5.00
		12	Series 7 Home Hints (1969)		—	£5.00
		12	Series 8 Fishing (1969)		—	£5.00
	U	25	Love Scenes from Famous Films — 'First Series' (1932):			
C2			A Small size		£3.00	£75.00
B1			B Large size		£3.00	£75.00
—			C Extra-large size (127 × 88mm)		£6.00	—

Size	Print-ing	Number in set		Handbook reference	Price per card	Complete set

J. WIX & SONS LTD, London *(continued)*

Size	Print-ing	Number in set		Handbook reference	Price per card	Complete set
	U	19	Love Scenes from Famous Films — 'Second Series' (1932) (Nos. 5, 9, 13, 20, 23, 24 withdrawn):			
C2			A Small size		£2.50	£50.00
B1			B Large size		£3.00	£60.00
			C Extra-large size (127 × 88mm)		£7.50	—
K2	C	53	**Miniature Playing Cards (anonymous)* (c1935):	H.535-3		
			A Scroll design:			
			1 Red back		20p	£9.00
			2 Blue back		25p	£12.50
			B Ship design:			
			1 Red border — Nelson's 'Victory'		35p	£17.50
			2 Black border — Drake's 'Revenge'		35p	£17.50
U		25	Scenes from Famous Films — 'Third Series' (1933):			
C2			A Small size		£3.00	£75.00
—			B Extra-large size (127 × 88mm)		£7.50	—
SILKS						
—	C	48	British Empire Flags — 'Kensitas' (78 × 54mm) (1933)	H.496-4		
			A Inscribed 'Printed in U.S.A.'		90p	£45.00
			B Without the above		90p	£45.00
—	C	60	Kensitas Flowers — 'First Series', small (68 × 40mm) (1934):	H.496-1		
			A Back of folder plain		£3.00	—
			B Back of folder printed in green:			
			i Centre oval 19mm deep		£3.00	—
			ii Centre oval 22mm deep		£3.00	—
			iii As ii, inscribed 'washable ...'		£3.00	—
—	C	60	Kensitas Flowers — 'First Series', medium (76 × 55mm) (1934):	H.496-1		
			A Back of folder plain		£4.50	—
			B Back of folder printed in green:			
			i Line commencing 'Kensitas' 46mm long		£4.50	—
			ii Line commencing 'Kensitas' 50mm long		£4.50	—
			iii As ii, inscribed 'Washable'		£4.50	—
	C	30	Kensitas Flowers — 'First Series' Extra-large (138 × 96mm) (1934):	H.496-1		
			A Back of folder plain		£40.00	—
			B Back of folder printed in green:			
			i Word 'More' half in oval		£40.00	—
			ii Word 'More' outside oval		£40.00	—
			iii As ii, inscribed 'Washable'		£40.00	—
—	C	40	Kensitas Flowers — 'Second Series' (1935):	H.496-2		
			A Small size, 68 × 40mm			
			1 Nos 1-30		£6.00	—
			2 Nos. 31 to 40		£25.00	—
			B Medium size, 76 × 55mm			
			1 Nos 1-30		£6.00	—
			2 Nos. 31 to 40		£26.00	—
	C	60	National Flags — 'Kensitas' (78 × 54mm) (1934)	H.496-3	£1.15	£70.00
OVERSEAS ISSUE						
A2	P	24	Royal Tour in New Zealand (1928)		£13.00	—

WOOD BROS., England

—	BW	28	Dominoes (63 × 29mm) (c1910)		£70.00	—

Size	*Print-ing*	*Number in set*		*Handbook reference*	*Price per card*	*Complete set*

T. WOOD, Cleckheaton

D	C	30	*Army Pictures, Cartoons, etc (1916)	H.12	£120.00	–

JOHN J. WOODS, London

A	BW	? 23	*Views of London (c1905)	H.395	£250.00	–

W.H. & J. WOODS LTD, Preston

–	C	1	Advertisement Card 'Perfection Flake' (86 × 35mm) (c1900)	H.773	–	£1000.00
A2	U	25	Aesop's Fables (c1932)	H.518	£1.60	£40.00
A2	P	50	Modern Motor Cars (c1936)		£5.50	£275.00
D	C	25	Romance of the Royal Mail (c1933)		£1.20	£30.00
A	C	25	*Types of Volunteers and Yeomanry (c1902)	H.455	£34.00	£850.00

J. & E. WOOLF

A	U	? 5	*Beauties 'KEWA' (c1900)	H.139	£1000.00	–

M.H. WOOLLER, London

A	–	25	Beauties 'BOCCA' (c1900)		£1200.00	–

T.E. YEOMANS & SONS LTD, Derby

–	C	72	Beautiful Women (75 × 55mm) (c1900)	H.284	£250.00	–
A	U	50	War Portraits (1916)	H.86	£100.00	–

JOHN YOUNG & SONS LTD, Bolton

A2	C	12	Naval Skits (c1904)	H.457	£150.00	–
A2	C	12	*Russo-Japanese Series (1904)	H.456	£90.00	–

A. ZICALIOTTI

A	C	1	Advertisement Card 'Milly Totty' (c1900)	H.774	–	£1500.00

Size	Printing	Number in set		Handbook reference	Price per card	Complete set

ANONYMOUS SERIES

A WITH LETTERPRESS ON BACK OF CARD

Size	Printing	Number in set		Handbook reference	Price per card	Complete set
A2	C	20	*Animal Series — see Hill*			
			A 'The cigarettes with which ...' back			
			B Space at back			
A	U	? 35	**Beauties — 'KEW A' 'England Expects ...' back*	H.139	£125.00	—
D	BW	25	**Boxers, green back — see Cohen Weenen*			
A1	C	? 2	**Celebrities — Coloured. 1902 Calendar back — see Cohen Weenen*			
D	C	? 2	**Celebrities — 'GAINSBOROUGH I', 1902 Calendar back, gilt border to front — see Cohen Weenen*	H.90		
	C	25	*Cinema Stars — see Teofani:*	H.530		
C2			*A Small size*			
—			*B Extra-large size (109 × 67mm)*			
A2	U	50	*Cinema Stars — Set 7 — see United Kingdom Tobacco Co*	GP.703		
D2	C	25	*Cinema Stars — Set 8 — see Moustafa*	GP.542		
A2	C	50	*Evolution of the British Navy — see Godfrey Phillips*			
A2	BW	40	*Famous Film Stars, text in Arabic (two series) — see Hill*			
A2	C	50	*Famous Footballers — see Godfrey Phillips*			
A2	C	35	*Famous Stars — see Reliance Tobacco Mfg. Co.*	H.572		
C2	C	20	*Great Inventors — see Teofani*	H.213		
A2	C	20	**Interesting Buildings and Views, 1902 Calendar back — see Cohen Weenen*	H.96		
D2	U	48	*Modern Movie Stars and Cinema Celebrities — see Teofani*	H.569		
D2	C	? 1	**Nations, 1902 Calendar back — see Cohen Weenen*	H.97		
D2	C	25	*Pictures of World Interest — see Moustafa*			
A	C	25	**Types of British Soldiers, 'General Favourite Onyx' back — see E. Robinson*	H.144		
D	C	25	*V.C. Heroes (Nos. 51-75 — see Cohen Weenen)*			
A	C	41	*V.C. Heroes — 'Pure Virginia Cigarettes' — Dobson Molle & Co. Ltd — Printers — see Thomson and Porteous*	H.427		
D	U	50	**War Series (Cohen Weenen — Nos. 1-50)*	H.103		
C2	U	24	*Well-Known Racehorses — see Teofani*	H.609		

B WITH PLAIN BACK

Size	Printing	Number in set		Handbook reference	Price per card	Complete set
A	U	25	**Actors and Actresses — 'FROGA C'*	H.20	£12.00	—
D2	U	? 9	**Actresses — 'ANGLO'*	H.185	£90.00	—
	U		**Actresses — 'ANGOOD':*	H.187		
			A Brown tinted —			
		? 22	*i Thick board*		£40.00	—
		? 14	*ii Thin board*		£40.00	—
		? 10	*B Green tinted*		£60.00	—
		? 30	*C Black tinted*		£40.00	—
A1	BW	20	**Actresses — 'BLARM'*	H.23	£13.00	—
D	U	20	**Actresses — Chocolate tinted — see Hill*	H.207		
A	C	? 50	**Actresses — 'DAVAN':*	H.124		
			A Portrait in red only		£50.00	—
			B Portrait in colour		£50.00	—
D	BW	12	**Actresses — 'FRAN' — see Drapkin*	H.175		
A		26	**Actresses — 'FROGA A':*	H.20		
	C		i. Coloured		£12.00	—
	U		ii. Unicoloured		£12.00	—
A1	BW	10	**Actresses — 'HAGG A'*	H.24	£11.00	—

Size	Printing	Number in set		Handbook reference	Price per card	Complete set

ANONYMOUS SERIES *(continued)*

Size	Printing	Number in set		Handbook reference	Price per card	Complete set
A1	BW	? 13	*Actresses — 'HAGG B'*	H.24	£11.00	—
A	BW	15	*Actresses — 'RUTAN' — see Rutter*	H.381		
—	C	50	*Actresses Oval Card (as Phillips)*	H.324		
A1	U		*Actresses and Beauties — Collotype — see Ogden*	H.306		
C	C	20	*Animal Series — see Hill*			
—	C	? 12	*Arms of Cambridge Colleges (17 × 25mm) — see Kuit*	H.458		
—	C	? 12	*Arms of Companies (30 × 33mm) — see Kuit*	H.459		
A2	P	36	*Australia. Second Series — see Westminster*			
A2	BW	? 13	*Battleships — see Hill*	H.208		
A	C	25	*Beauties — 'BOCCA'*	H.39	£16.00	—
A		50	*Beauties — 'CHOAB':*	H.21		
	U		*A Unicoloured*		£12.00	—
	C		*B Coloured*		£12.00	—
A			*Beauties — 'FECKSA':*	H.58		
	U	50	*A Plum-coloured front*		£10.00	—
	C	? 6	*B Coloured front*		£50.00	—
D2	U	? 23	*Beauties — 'FENA'*	H.148	£50.00	—
A2	C	25	*Beauties — 'GRACC'*	H.59	£20.00	—
A	C	26	*Beauties — 'HOL'*	H.192	£12.00	—
A	U	? 14	*Beauties 'KEWA'*	H.139	£50.00	—
A	U	? 7	Beauties — 'NANA'	H.377	£150.00	—
D	BW	50	*Beauties — 'PLUMS'* (c1900)	H.186	£45.00	—
—	C	30	*Beauties — Oval card (36 × 60mm) — see Phillips*	H.244		
A2	P	18	*Beauties — see Marcovitch*	GP.490		
D1	U		*Bewlay's War Series:*	H.477		
		12	*1 Front without captions*		£20.00	—
		? 1	*2 Front with captions*		£30.00	—
A2	BW	20	*Boer War Cartoons*	H.42	£20.00	—
A	C		*Boer War and General Interest:*	H.13		
		? 20	*A Plain cream back*		£40.00	—
		? 22	*B Brown Leaf Design back*		£40.00	—
		? 12	*C Green Leaf Design back*		£40.00	—
		? 6	*D Green Daisy Design back*		£60.00	—
A2	BW	? 16	*Boer War Celebrities — 'CAG'*	H.79	£25.00	—
A		? 7	*Boer War Celebrities 'RUTTER':*	H.382		
	BW		*A Front in Black and White*		£35.00	—
	U		*B Front in light orange brown*		£35.00	—
D2	BW	20	*Boer War Generals — 'CLAM'*	H.61	£16.00	—
A1	BW	? 10	*Boer War Generals — 'FLAC'*	H.47	£16.00	—
D	C	25	*Boxer Rebellion — Sketches (1904)*	H.46	£12.00	—
A	C	54	*British Beauties (Phillips) (1-54)*	H.328		
A	C	54	*British Beauties (Phillips) (55-108) Matt*	H.328		
A1	P	60	*British Beauty Spots — see Coudens*	H.553		
B1	P	50	*British Castles, Nd. S.J.51-S.J.100 — see Pattreiouex*			
—	C	108	*British Naval Crests (74 × 52mm)*	H.504-4/GP.207	£3.50	—
A	C	12	*British Queens*	H.480	£30.00	—
A	BW	16	*British Royal Family*	H.28	£12.00	—
D2	CP	50	*Camera Studies — see Moustafa*			
B1	P	50	*Cathedrals and Abbeys. Nd. S.J.1-S.J.50 — see Pattreiouex*			
A	C	45	*Celebrities — Coloured (Cohen Weenen)*	GP.357		
D	C	39	*Celebrities — 'GAINSBOROUGH I' — see Cohen Weenen*	GP.358		
D	BW	? 147	*Celebrities — 'GAINSBOROUGH II' — see Cohen Weenen*	GP.359		

Size	Printing	Number in set		Handbook reference	Price per card	Complete set

ANONYMOUS SERIES *(continued)*

Size	Printing	Number in set		Handbook reference	Price per card	Complete set
A1	P	36	**Celebrities of the Great War (1916) — see Major Drapkin & Co*			
A	BW	? 12	*Celebrities of the Great War*	H.236	£90.00	—
A	C	25	**Charming Portraits — see Continental Cigarette Factory*	H.549		
A2	U	30	**Cinema Stars — Set 3*	GP.52	£2.00	—
A2	U	30	**Cinema Stars — Set 6 (1935)*	GP.55	£1.00	£30.00
A	C		**Colonial Troops:*	H.40		
		30	*A Cream card*		£15.00	—
		50	*B White card*		£15.00	—
—	C	110	**Crests and Badges of the British Army (74 × 52mm):*	GP.245		
			(a) Numbered		£4.00	—
			(b) Unnumbered		£3.00	—
A	BW	20	*Cricketers Series*	H.29	£225.00	—
A	C	50	*Dogs (as Taddy) (c1900):*	H.487		
			A Borders in green		£30.00	—
			B Borders in white		£30.00	—
A	C	25	**England's Military Heroes — see Player:*	H.352		
			A Wide card			
			B Narrow card			
A	C	25	**England's Naval Heroes — see Player:*	H.353		
			A Wide card			
			B Narrow card			
A	C	20	**The European War Series*	H.129	£10.00	—
—	BW	12	**Film Actors and Actresses (56 × 31mm) — see Teofani*	H.618		
A	C		**Flags, Arms and Types of Nations:*	H.115		
		24	*A Numbered*		£10.00	—
		? 2	*B Unnumbered*		£50.00	—
A	C		**Flags and Flags with Soldiers:*	H.41		
		30	*A Flagstaff Draped*		£10.00	—
		15	*B Flagstaff not Draped (Flags only)*		£10.00	—
A1	C	30	**Flags of Nations — see Cope*	H.114		
A1	C	24	**Girls, Flags and Arms of Countries — see Rutter*	H.383		
A	C	20	**Head Dresses of Various Nations — see Teofani*			
A	C	40	**Home and Colonial Regiments*	H.69	£10.00	—
A	—	20	**Inventors and Their Inventions — see Hill*	H.213		
—	C	? 9	**Irish Views (68 × 67mm) — see Lambkin*	H.585		
A	C	52	**Japanese Series, P.C. Inset — see Muratti*			
A1	P	? 2	**King Edward and Queen Alexandra*	H.460	£20.00	—
—	BW	12	**London Views (57 × 31mm) — see Teofani*	H.620		
C	C	20	**National Flag Series — see Hill*			
D	C	20	**Nations, gilt border — see Cohen Weenen*	GP.369		
A	C	50	**Natives in Costume — see Teofani*			
D	C	40	**Naval and Military Phrases:*	H.14		
			A Plain front (no border)		£10.00	—
			B Front with gilt border		£60.00	—
—	P	30	**Photographs (Animal Studies) (64 × 41mm)*	GP.337	£2.00	—
—	U	? 2	**Portraits — see Drapkin & Millhoff (48 × 36mm)*	H.461		
A	U	? 42	**Pretty Girl Series — 'BAGG'*	H.45	£20.00	—
A2	C	12	**Pretty Girl Series 'RASH' (c1897)*	H.8	£18.00	—
A1	C	20	**Prince of Wales Series*	H.22	£12.00	—
D	C	30	**Proverbs*	H.15	£12.00	—
—	C	? 48	**Regimental Colours II (76 × 70mm)*	H.502-7	£12.00	—
A	BW	19	*Russo-Japanese Series*	H.184	£20.00	—
A	C	20	*Russo-Japanese War Series*	H.100	£20.00	—
A	C	10	*Scenes from San Toy — see Richard Lloyd*	H.462		

Size	Printing	Number in set		Handbook reference	Price per card	Complete set

ANONYMOUS SERIES *(continued)*

Size	Printing	Number in set		Handbook reference	Price per card	Complete set
A	C	25	*Sports and Pastimes Series No. 1*	H.225	£12.00	—
A	C	25	**Star Girls*	H.30	£15.00	—
A1	BW	? 28	**Statuary (Hill A-D)*	H.218		
—	P	22	**Teofani Gems I — Series of 22 (53 × 35mm) — see Teofani*			
—	P	28	**Teofani Gems II — Series of 28 (53 × 35mm) see Teofani*			
—	P	36	**Teofani Gems III — Series of 36 (53 × 35mm) — see Teofani*			
A	C	25	**Types of British and Colonial Troops*	H.76	£20.00	—
A2	C	25	**Types of British Soldiers*	H.144	£12.00	—
—	U	? 24	*Views and Yachts (narrow, abt. 63 × 30mm)*	H.262-2	£50.00	—
D	BW	12	**Views of the World — see Drapkin*	H.176		
D	BW	8	**Warships — see Drapkin*	GP.426		
D			**War Series:*	H.103		
	U	? 2	*A Front in brown*		£30.00	—
	BW	? 4	*B Front in black and white*		£30.00	—
A	C	50	**World's Smokers — see Teofani*			

C WITH DESIGNS ON BACK

Size	Printing	Number in set		Handbook reference	Price per card	Complete set
A	BW	25	*Careless Moments (1922)*		80p	£20.00
D2	U	28	**Dominoes ("W.T.C." monogram back) — see Walker's Tobacco Co.*	H.535-2		
—	C	53	**Miniature Playing Cards (68 × 42mm) (red back, black cat trade mark in centre) — see Carreras*	H.535-1		
K2	C	53	**Miniature Playing Cards (blue scroll back) — see Godfrey Phillips*			
K2	C	53	**Miniature Playing Cards — see J. Wix:*	H.535-3		
			A Scroll design:			
			1 Red back			
			2 Blue back			
			B Ship design:			
			2 Black border — Drake's "Revenge"			
C			**Playing Cards and Dominoes — see Carreras:*	H.535-1		
C		52	*A Small size:*			
			1 Numbered			
			2 Unnumbered			
—		26	*B Large size (77 × 69mm):*			
			1 Numbered			
			2 Unnumbered			

D ANONYMOUS SERIES SILKS AND OTHER NOVELTY ISSUES

For Anonymous Metal Plaques — see International Tobacco Co.
For Anonymous Metal Charms — see Rothman's.
For Anonymous Miniature Rugs — see Godfrey Phillips.
For Anonymous Lace Motifs — see Carreras.
For Anonymous Woven Silks — see Anstie and J. Wix.
For Anonymous Printed Silks with Blue Borders — see Themans.

SECTION 2

FOREIGN TOBACCO ISSUERS

Size	*Number in set*		*Price per card*	*Complete set*

AFRICAN CIGARETTE CO. LTD, Egypt

	50	Actresses ALWICS (c1905)	£9.00	—
L	25	Auction Bridge (c1925)	£7.00	—

AFRICAN TOBACCO MANUFACTURERS, South Africa

A CARD ISSUES

L	29	All Blacks South African Tour (1928)	£18.00	—
	60	Animals (c1920):		
		A Cut Outs	£3.50	—
		B Not Cut Out	£3.50	—
	25	The Arcadia Fair (1924)	£10.00	—
MP	48	British Aircraft (1932)	£5.00	—
	50	Chinese Transport (1930)	£4.50	—
MP	48	Cinema Artistes (1930)	£4.00	—
	50	Cinema Stars "OMBI" Officers Mess Issue 1st Series (1921)	£1.80	£90.00
	50	Cinema Stars "OMBI" Officers Mess Issue 2nd Series (1921)	£2.00	£100.00
M	50	Famous and Beautiful Women (1938)	£2.50	—
L	50	Famous and Beautiful Women (1938)	£3.00	—
	33	Houses of Parliament (c1920)	£6.00	—
	58	Miniatures (c1925)	£6.00	—
MP	48	National Costume (1930)	£3.25	—
K	53	Playing Cards MP-SA Virginia Cigarettes (c1930)	£3.00	—
K	53	Playing Cards, OK Cigarettes (c1930)	£1.80	—
K	53	Playing Cards, Scotts Cigarettes (c1930)	£1.80	—
MP	48	Popular Dogs (1930)	£5.00	—
M	100	Postage Stamps, Rarest Varieties (1929)	£1.50	£150.00
M	80	Prominent NZ and Australian Rugby Players and Springbok 1937 Touring Team (1937)	£5.00	—
L	80	Prominent NZ and Australian Rugby Players and Springbok 1937 Touring Team (1937)	£3.00	—
	25	The Racecourse (1924)	£10.00	—
M	132	S. African Members of the Legislative Assembly (1921)	£40.00	—
M	100	The World of Sport (1938)	£4.00	—
L	100	The World of Sport (1938)	£3.50	—

B SILK ISSUES

M	30	Some Beautiful Roses (c1925)	£9.00	—
M	25	Types of British Birds (c1925)	£9.00	—
M	20	Types of British Butterflies (c1925)	£11.00	—
M	25	Types of Railway Engines (c1925)	£26.00	—
M	25	Types of Sea Shells (c1925)	£13.00	—

ALLEN & GINTER, USA

ALL SERIES ISSUED 1885-95

	?	Actors and Actresses (sepia photographic)	£6.00	—

Size	Number in set		Price per card	Complete set

ALLEN & GINTER, USA *(continued)*

Size	Number in set		Price per card	Complete set
	?	Actresses and Beauties (coloured)	£10.00	—
	50	American Editors	£32.00	—
L	50	American Editors	£40.00	—
L	50	The American Indian	£60.00	—
	50	Arms of All Nations	£25.00	—
	50	Birds of America	£14.00	£700.00
L	50	Birds of America	£27.00	—
	50	Birds of the Tropics	£16.00	£800.00
L	50	Birds of the Tropics	£28.00	—
	50	Celebrated American Indian Chiefs	£38.00	—
	50	City Flags	£14.00	—
	50	Fans of the Period	£28.00	—
	50	Fish from American Waters	£15.00	—
L	50	Fish from American Waters	£30.00	—
	50	Flags of All Nations (series title curved)	£10.00	£500.00
	48	Flags of All Nations (series title in straight line)	£10.00	£500.00
	50	Flags of All Nations, 2nd series	£12.00	£600.00
	47	Flags of the States and Territories	£13.00	—
	50	Fruits	£24.00	—
	50	Game Birds	£14.00	£700.00
L	50	Game Birds	£27.00	—
	50	General Government and State Capitol Buildings	£14.00	—
	50	Great Generals	£40.00	—
	50	Natives in Costume	£35.00	—
	50	Naval Flags	£15.00	£750.00
	50	Parasol Drill	£25.00	—
	50	Pirates of the Spanish Main	£40.00	—
	50	Prize and Game Chickens	£25.00	—
	50	Quadrupeds	£16.00	—
L	50	Quadrupeds	£30.00	—
	50	Racing Colors of the World:		
		A Front with white frame	£25.00	—
		B Front without white frame	£25.00	—
	50	Song Birds of the World	£14.00	£700.00
L	50	Song Birds of the World	£30.00	—
	50	Types of All Nations	£25.00	—
	50	Wild Animals of the World	£17.00	—
	50	The World's Beauties, 1st series	£24.00	—
	50	The World's Beauties, 2nd series	£24.00	—
	50	The World's Champions, 1st series	£50.00	—
	50	The World's Champions, 2nd series	£60.00	—
L	50	The World's Champions, 2nd series	£100.00	—
	50	The World's Decorations	£15.00	£750.00
L	50	The World's Decorations	£26.00	—
	50	World's Dudes	£24.00	—
	50	The World's Racers	£28.00	—
	50	World's Smokers	£22.00	—
	50	World's Sovereigns	£30.00	—

ALLEN TOBACCO CO., USA

Size	Number in set		Price per card	Complete set
L	?	Views and Art Studies (c1910)	£5.00	—

THE AMERICAN CIGARETTE CO. LTD, China

Size	Number in set		Price per card	Complete set
	10	Admirals and Generals Ref RB.118/155 (c1900)	£60.00	—
	25	Beauties Group 1 Ref RB.118/8 (c1900)	£18.00	—
	? 15	Beauties Group 2 Ref RB.118/21-2 (c1900)	£30.00	—

Size	Number in set		Price per card	Complete set

THE AMERICAN CIGARETTE CO. LTD, China *(continued)*

	53	Beauties with Playing Card inset Ref RB.118/23 (c1900)	£50.00	—
	50	Flowers Ref RB.118/161 (c1900)	£15.00	—

AMERICAN EAGLE TOBACCO CO., USA

	20	Actresses blue border (c1890):		
		A With firm's name	£80.00	—
		B 'Double 5' back	£70.00	—
	15	Actresses sepia (c1890)	£75.00	—
	15	Beauties 'PAC' (c1895)	£100.00	—
	36	Flags of Nations (c1890):		
		A Size 70 × 39mm	£35.00	—
		B Size 64 × 39mm	£35.00	—
	36	Flags of States (c1890):		
		A Size 70 × 39mm	£35.00	—
		B Size 64 × 39mm	£35.00	—
	50	Occupations for Women (c1895)	£70.00	—
		Photographic Cards Actresses (c1890):		
	? 33	A Size 69 × 37mm	£20.00	—
L	6	B Size 102 × 52mm	£30.00	—
	23	Presidents of the U.S. (c1890)	£60.00	—

THE AMERICAN TOBACCO COMPANY, USA

ALL SERIES ISSUED 1890-1902

A TYPESET BACK IN BLACK

	28	Beauties Domino Girls RB.118/66	£20.00	—
	25	Beauties Group 1 RB.118/4	£4.00	—
	? 1	Beauties Group 2 RB.118/20	—	—
	25	Beauties Group 3 RB.118/25	£4.00	—
	27	Beauties Group 3 RB.118/26	£4.00	£110.00
	25	Beauties Group 3 RB.118/27	£4.00	—
	25	Beauties Group 3 RB.118/29	£4.00	—
		Beauties Group 4 RB.118/36:		
	50	a Coloured	£4.00	£200.00
	? 50	b Sepia	£15.00	—
	52	Beauties PC Inset	£9.00	£470.00
	25	Beauties — Star Girls RB.118/76	£16.00	—
	25	Dancers RB.118/52	£13.00	—
	50	Dancing Women	£22.00	—
	50	Fancy Bathers	£22.00	—
	36	Japanese Girls RB.118/139	£60.00	—
	25	Military Uniforms RB.118/101	£15.00	—
	25	Military Uniforms RB.118/102	£13.00	—
	27	Military Uniforms RB.118/103	£9.00	—
	50	Musical Instruments	£16.00	—
	50	National Flag and Arms	£10.00	—
	25	National Flag and Flowers — Girls	£22.00	—
	50	Savage Chiefs and Rulers	£24.00	—

B NET DESIGN BACK IN GREEN

	25	Beauties Black background RB.118/62	£13.00	—
	25	Beauties Curtain background RB.118/65	£12.00	£300.00
	25	Beauties Flower Girls RB.118/67	£12.00	—
	25	Beauties Group 1 RB.118/1	£4.00	—
	27	Beauties Group 1 RB.118/2	£4.00	—
	25	Beauties Group 1 RB.118/3	£4.00	—
	24	Beauties Group 1 RB.118/4	£4.00	—
	25	Beauties Group 1 RB.118/5	£4.00	—

Size	Number in set		Price per card	Complete set

THE AMERICAN TOBACCO COMPANY, USA *(continued)*

Size	Number in set		Price per card	Complete set
	25	Beauties Group 1 RB.118/6	£4.00	—
	50	Beauties Group 1 RB.118/10	£4.00	—
	25	Beauties Group 2 RB.118/16	£4.00	—
	25	Beauties Group 2 RB.118/17	£4.00	—
	? 24	Beauties Group 2 RB.118/18	£4.00	—
	25	Beauties Group 2 RB.118/19	£4.00	—
	25	Beauties Group 2 RB.118/20	£4.00	—
	25	Beauties Group 2 RB.118/21	£5.00	—
	36	Beauties Group 2 RB.118/22	£6.00	—
	25	Beauties Group 3 RB.118/25	£4.00	—
	? 10	Beauties Group 3 RB.118/28	—	—
	25	Beauties Group 3 RB.118/30	£4.00	—
	25	Beauties Group 3 RB.118/31	£8.00	—
	25	Beauties Group 3 RB.118/32	£4.00	—
	50	Beauties Marine and Universe Girls RB.118/71	£30.00	—
	25	Beauties Palette Girls RB.118/74	£12.00	—
	25	Beauties Star Girls RB.118/76	£18.00	—
	25	Beauties — Stippled background RB.118/78	£12.00	—
	20	Beauties — thick border RB.118/79	£30.00	—
	52	Beauties with Playing Card inset Set 1 RB.118/85 (Head & Shoulder)	£12.00	—
	52	Beauties with Playing Card inset Set 2 RB.118/86 (Half Length)	£12.00	—
	25	Boer War Series II — Series A:		
		a) numbered	£6.00	£150.00
		b) unnumbered	£7.00	—
		c) unnumbered and untitled "series A"	£8.00	—
	22	Boer War Series II — Series B	£8.00	—
	25	Chinese Girls	£12.00	—
	25	Fish from American Waters	£9.00	—
	25	International Code Signals	£12.00	—
	27	Military Uniforms numbered RB.118/103	£9.00	—
	25	Military Uniforms unnumbered RB.118/104	£14.00	—
	50	National Flags and Arms	£10.00	—
	25	Old and Ancient Ships 1st Series RB.118/143	£6.00	£150.00
	25	Old and Ancient Ships 2nd Series RB.118/143	£10.00	£250.00
	25	Star Series — Beauties	£16.00	—

C NET DESIGN BACK IN BLUE

Size	Number in set		Price per card	Complete set
		Actresses RB.118-90:		
P	? 300	A Large Letter Back (word 'Brands' 29mm)	£4.00	—
P	? 300	B Small Letter Back (word 'Brands' 25mm)	£5.00	—
	25	Beauties blue frameline RB.118/64:		
		A Matt	£20.00	—
		B Varnished	£20.00	—
	28	Beauties — Domino Girls RB.118/66	£20.00	—
	25	Beauties Group 1 dull backgrounds RB.118/7.2	£12.00	—
	25	Beauties Group 1 vivid coloured backgrounds set 1 RB.118/7.3	£12.00	—
	25	Beauties Group 1 vivid coloured backgrounds set 2 RB.118/9	£12.00	—
	25	Beauties numbered RB.118/72:		
		A Front in black and white	£18.00	—
		B Front in mauve	£16.00	—
	24	Beauties — orange framelines RB.118/73	£30.00	—
		Beauties — playing cards RB.118/87:		
	52	A Inscribed 52 subjects	£10.00	—
	53	B Inscribed 53 subjects	£10.00	—
	32	Celebrities RB.118/94	£7.00	—
	25	Comic Scenes RB.118/113	£9.00	—
P	? 149	Views RB.118/96	£3.00	—

Size	Number in set		Price per card	Complete set

THE AMERICAN TOBACCO COMPANY, USA *(continued)*

Size	Number in set	Title	Price per card	Complete set
D	***"OLD GOLD" BACK***			
	25	Beauties Group 1 RB.118/1	£4.00	—
	27	Beauties Group 1 RB.118/2	£4.00	—
	25	Beauties Group 1 RB.118/3	£4.00	—
	24	Beauties Group 1 RB.118/4	£4.00	—
	25	Beauties Group 1 RB.118/5	£4.00	—
	25	Beauties Group 1 RB.118/6	£4.00	—
	? 47	Beauties Group 2 RB.118/16, 17, 18	£4.00	—
	25	Beauties Group 2 RB.118/22	£4.00	—
	25	Beauties Group 3 RB.118/25	£4.00	—
	27	Beauties Group 3 RB.118/26	£4.00	—
	25	Beauties Group 3 RB.118/27	£4.00	—
	25	Beauties Group 3 RB.118/28	£4.00	—
	25	Beauties Group 3 RB.118/30	£4.00	—
	25	Flowers Inset on Beauties RB.118/41	£10.00	£250.00
	25	International Code Signals:		
		A With series title RB.118/42	£10.00	£250.00
		B Without series title RB.118/43	£10.00	£250.00
E	***LABELS BACK***			
	35	Beauties Group 1 RB.118/2-3	£5.00	—
	25	Beauties Group 2 1st Set RB.118/15	£5.00	—
	25	Beauties Group 2 2nd Set RB.118/16	£5.00	—
		Beauties Group 3 RB.118/25-26:		
	27	A Old Gold Label	£5.00	—
	26	B Brands Label	£5.00	—
F	***OTHER BACKS WITH NAME OF FIRM***			
P	100	Actresses RB.118/91	£5.00	—
	44	Australian Parliament	£5.00	—
	25	Battle Scenes	£13.00	—
	1	Columbian and Other Postage Stamps (1892)	—	£13.00
	50	Congress of Beauty — Worlds Fair	£22.00	—
	25	Constellation Girls	£25.00	—
	50	Fish from American Waters	£12.00	—
	50	Flags of All Nations	£10.00	—
	25	Flower Inset on Beauties RB.118/41	£12.00	£300.00
	25	International Code Signals RB.118/42	£12.00	£300.00
	25	Songs A RB.118/46 (1896):		
		A Thicker board size 70 × 39mm	£15.00	—
		B Thinner board size 67 × 39mm	£15.00	—
	25	Songs B RB.118/47 (1898):		
		A Size 70 × 39mm	£15.00	—
		B Size 67 × 39mm	£15.00	—
	25	Songs C 1st series RB.118/48 (1900)	£10.00	—
	25	Songs C 2nd series RB.118/48 (1900)	£12.00	—
	25	Songs D RB.118/49 (1899)	£9.00	£225.00
	27	Songs E RB.118/50 (1901)	£12.00	—
	25	Songs F RB.118/51 (1897):		
		A Size 70 × 36mm, with scroll at base	£12.00	—
		B Size 67 × 38mm, without scroll at base	£12.00	—
	25	Songs G RB.118/53 (1899)	£12.00	—
	25	Songs H RB.118/54 (1901)	£18.00	—
	25	Songs I RB.118/55 (1895)	£22.00	—
ISSUES 1903-1940				
L	50	Actors	£6.50	—
	85	Actress Series	£7.00	—
L	50	Actresses	£10.00	—

Size	Number in set		Price per card	Complete set

THE AMERICAN TOBACCO COMPANY, USA *(continued)*

Size	Number in set		Price per card	Complete set
		Animals:		
L	40	A Descriptive back	£2.50	—
L	40	B Non descriptive back	£2.50	—
L	25	Arctic Scenes	£6.00	—
M	15	Art Gallery Pictures	£5.00	—
M	50	Art Reproductions	£5.00	—
	21	Art Series	£15.00	—
	18	Ask Dad	£12.00	—
L	50	Assorted Standard Bearers of Different Countries	£6.00	—
	25	Auto-drivers	£15.00	—
M	50	Automobile Series	£14.00	—
L	50	Baseball Folder series (T201) (1911)	£30.00	—
M	121	Baseball series (T204)	£40.00	—
	208	Baseball series (T205) (1911)	£20.00	—
	522	Baseball series (T206)	£20.00	—
	200	Baseball series (T207) (1910)	£30.00	—
	565	Baseball series (T210)	£30.00	—
	75	Baseball series (T211)	£30.00	—
	426	Baseball series (T212)	£30.00	—
	180	Baseball series (T213)	£30.00	—
	90	Baseball series (T214)	£100.00	—
	100	Baseball series (T215)	£30.00	—
L	76	Baseball Triple Folders (T202) (1912)	£40.00	—
		Bird series:		
	50	A With white borders	£2.50	—
	50	B With gold borders	£2.50	—
	30	Bird Series with Fancy Gold Frame	£3.00	—
M	360	Birthday Horoscopes	£2.00	—
M	24	British Buildings "Tareyton" issue	£3.00	—
M	42	British Sovereigns "Tareyton" issue	£3.00	—
M	50	Butterfly Series	£4.50	—
L	153	Champion Athlete & Prize Fighter series (size 73 × 64mm) (1911)	£7.50	—
L	50	Champion Athlete and Prize Fighter series (size 83 × 63 mm)	£12.00	—
L	50	Champion Pugilists	£20.00	—
EL	100	Champion Women Swimmers	£9.00	—
M	150	College series	£2.80	—
M	50	Costumes and Scenery for All Countries of the World	£3.50	—
L	49	Cowboy series	£7.00	—
M	38	Cross Stitch	£9.00	—
M	17	Embarrassing Moments or Emotional Moments	£30.00	—
M	50	Emblem Series	£3.50	—
L	100	Fable Series	£3.00	—
LP	53	Famous Baseball Players, American Athletic Champions and Photoplay Stars	£50.00	—
	50	Fish Series inscribed "1 to 50" — 1st 50 subjects	£2.50	—
	50	Fish Series inscribed "1 to 100" — 2nd 50 subjects	£2.50	—
	200	Flags of All Nations	£2.00	—
M	100	Flags of All Nations	£15.00	—
	50	Foreign Stamp Series	£6.50	—
L	505	Fortune Series	£2.20	—
M	79	Henry "Tareyton" issue	£2.50	—
L	50	Heroes of History	£8.00	—
M	50	Historic Homes	£5.00	—
L	25	Historical Events Series	£8.00	—
M	25	Hudson — Fulton Series	£7.00	—
L	50	Indian Life in the 60s (1910)	£8.00	—
L	221	Jig Saw Puzzle Pictures	£10.00	—

Size	Number in set		Price per card	Complete set

THE AMERICAN TOBACCO COMPANY, USA *(continued)*

Size	Number in set		Price per card	Complete set
L	50	Light House Series	£7.50	—
L	50	Men of History	£8.00	—
M	100	Military Series white borders	£5.00	—
	50	Military Series gilt borders	£6.00	—
	50	Military Series "Recruit" issue:		
		A Uncut cards	£6.00	—
		B Die-cut cards	£6.00	—
	50	Movie Stars	£5.00	—
L	100	Movie Stars	£5.00	—
	33	Moving Picture Stars	£20.00	—
EL	50	Murad Post Card Series	£8.50	—
	100	Mutt & Jeff Series (black and white)	£5.00	—
	100	Mutt & Jeff Series (coloured)	£5.00	—
EL	16	National League and American League Teams	£50.00	—
	50	Pugilistic Subjects	£24.00	—
EL	18	Puzzle Picture Cards	£16.00	—
M	200	Riddle Series	£2.80	—
EL	60	Royal Bengal Souvenir Cards	£9.00	—
M	150	Seals of the United States and Coats of Arms of the World	£2.00	—
L	25	Series of Champions	£28.00	—
L	50	Sights and Scenes of the World	£4.00	—
L	50	Silhouettes	£8.50	—
L	25	Song Bird Series	£35.00	—
	39	Sports Champions	£25.00	—
	45	Stage Stars	£8.00	—
	25	State Girl Series	£7.00	—
L	50	Theatres Old and New Series	£7.50	—
M	50	Toast Series	£8.50	—
M	550	Toast Series	£2.00	—
L	25	Toasts	£13.00	—
	50	Types of Nations:		
		A Without series title	£3.00	—
		B With series title	£3.00	—
		C Anonymous back	£3.00	—
L	25	Up to Date Baseball Comics	£25.00	—
L	25	Up to Date Comics	£8.50	—
P	340	World Scenes and Portraits	£3.00	—
	250	World War I Scenes	£2.25	—
L	50	World's Champion Athletes	£12.00	—
L	25	The World's Greatest Explorers	£6.00	—

THE AMERICAN TOBACCO CO. OF NEW SOUTH WALES LTD, Australia

Size	Number in set		Price per card	Complete set
	25	Beauties Group 1 RB.118/8 (c1900)	£12.00	—
	25	Beauties Group 2 (c1900)	£12.00	—

THE AMERICAN TOBACCO CO. OF VICTORIA LTD, Australia

Size	Number in set		Price per card	Complete set
	? 98	Beauties Group 2 (c1900)	£12.00	—

ASHEVILLE TOBACCO WORKS AND CIGARETTE CO., USA

Size	Number in set		Price per card	Complete set
	39	Actresses (c1890)	£70.00	—

ATLAM CIGARETTE FACTORY, Malta

Size	Number in set		Price per card	Complete set
M	65	Beauties back in blue (c1925)	£2.50	—
	150	Beauties back in brown (c1925)	£6.00	—
M	519	Celebrities (c1925)	£1.20	—

Size	Number in set		Price per card	Complete set

ATLAM CIGARETTE FACTORY, Malta *(continued)*

L	50	Views of Malta (c1925)	£5.00	—
M	128	Views of the World (c1925)	£5.00	—

BANNER TOBACCO CO., USA

L	? 41	Actors and Actresses (c1890)	£70.00	—
EL	25	Girls (c1890)	£35.00	—

THOMAS BEAR & SONS LTD

	50	Aeroplanes (1926)	£4.00	—
	50	Cinema Artistes Set 2 (c1935)	£3.50	—
	50	Cinema Artistes Set 4 (c1935)	£3.50	—
	50	Cinema Stars coloured (1930)	£2.80	£140.00
	50	Do You Know (1923)	£1.80	£90.00
	270	Javanese series 1 blue background (c1925)	£1.70	—
	100	Javanese series 4 yellow background (c1925)	£8.00	—
	50	Stage and Film Stars (1926)	£3.80	—

AUG BECK & CO. USA

	? 44	Picture Cards (c1890)	£60.00	—
	23	Presidents of U.S. (coloured) (c1890)	£70.00	—
	23	Presidents of U.S. (sepia) (c1890)	£70.00	—
	? 14	State Seals (c1890)	£75.00	—

BRITISH AMERICAN TOBACCO CO. LTD

A WITH MAKER'S NAME NET DESIGN IN GREEN (ISSUES 1902-05)

	25	Beauties Art series RB.118/61	£12.00	—
	25	Beauties — Black background RB.118/62	£11.00	—
	25	Beauties — Blossom Girls RB.118/63	£40.00	—
	25	Beauties — Flower Girls RB.118/67	£10.00	—
	25	Beauties — Fruit Girls RB.118/68	£14.00	—
	25	Beauties — Girls in Costumes RB.118/69	£14.00	—
	20	Beauties Group 1 RB.118/9	£11.00	—
	25	Beauties — Lantern Girls RB.118/70	£11.00	£275.00
	50	Beauties — Marine and Universe Girls RB.118/71	£12.00	—
	25	Beauties — Palette Girls RB.118/74:		
		A Plain border to front	£10.00	—
		B Red border to front	£14.00	—
	24	Beauties — Smoke Girls RB.118/75	£16.00	—
	25	Beauties — Star Girls RB.118/76	£16.00	—
	25	Beauties — Stippled background RB.118/78	£10.00	£250.00
	25	Beauties — Water Girls RB.118/80	£10.00	£250.00
	50	Buildings RB.118/131	£10.00	—
	25	Chinese Girls 'A' RB.118/111	£10.00	—
	25	Chinese Girls 'B' RB.118/112:		
		A Background plain	£10.00	—
		B Background with Chinese letters	£10.00	—
	25	Chinese Girls 'C' RB.118/113	£10.00	—
		Chinese Girls 'D' RB.118/114:		
	20	A Back design 53mm long	£10.00	—
	25	B Back design 60mm long	£10.00	—
	25	Chinese Girls 'E' RB.118/115	£10.00	—
	25	Chinese Girls 'F' Set 1 RB.118/116:		
		A Fronts reddish background	£10.00	—
		B Fronts sepia background	£10.00	—

Size	Number in set		Price per card	Complete set

BRITISH AMERICAN TOBACCO CO. LTD *(continued)*

	25	Chinese Girls 'F' Set 2 RB.118/116:		
		A Yellow border	£10.00	—
		B Gold border	£12.00	—
	50	Chinese Girls 'F' Set 3 RB.118/116:		
		A Plain background	£10.00	—
		B Chinese characters background	£11.00	—
	40	Chinese Trades RB.118/108	£8.00	—

B WITH MAKER'S NAME NET DESIGN IN BLUE (ISSUES 1902-05)

	25	Beauties — numbered	£18.00	—
	53	Beauties — Playing Cards	£10.00	—

C WITH MAKER'S NAME OTHER BACKS

MP	50	Beauties (1925)	£2.50	—
MP	40	Beauties (1926)	£2.50	—
M	50	Birds, Beasts and Fishes (1925)	£2.00	£100.00
	50	Danish Athletes (1905)	£15.00	—
	28	Dominoes (1905)	£6.00	—
	48	Fairy Tales (1926)	£4.00	—
	48	A Famous Picture — The Toast (c1930)	£3.00	—
	25	New York Views (c1908)	£12.00	—
	53	Playing Cards (1905)	£11.00	—
M	50	Wild Animals (c1930)	£2.50	—

D SERIES WITH BRAND NAMES

ALBERT CIGARETTES

M	50	Aeroplanes (Civils) (1935)	£12.00	—
	50	Artistes de Cinema Nd 1-50 (1932)	£3.00	—
	50	Artistes de Cinema Nd 51-100 (1933)	£3.00	—
	50	Artistes de Cinema Nd 101-150 (1934)	£3.00	—
MP	? 67	Beauties (c1928)	£4.50	—
M	75	Belles Vues de Belgique (c1930)	£3.00	—
M	50	Birds, Beasts & Fishes (c1930)	£4.00	—
M	50	Butterflies (Girls) (1926)	£6.00	—
M	50	Cinema Stars (brown photogravure) (c1927)	£3.00	—
M	100	Cinema Stars (numbered, coloured) (c1928)	£3.00	—
M	208	Cinema Stars (unnumbered, coloured) (c1929)	£3.00	—
M	100	Circus Scenes (c1930)	£3.50	—
M	100	Famous Beauties (1916)	£3.50	—
M	50	L'Afrique Equitoriale de l'Est a l'Ouest (c1930)	£2.50	—
M	100	La Faune Congolaise (c1930)	£1.50	—
M	50	Les Grandes Paquebots du Monde (1924)	£6.00	—
M	50	Merveilles du Monde (1927)	£3.50	—
M	50	Women of Nations (Flag Girls) (1922)	£4.00	—

ATLAS CIGARETTES

	50	Buildings (1907)	£5.00	—
	25	Chinese Beauties (1912)	£4.00	—
	50	Chinese Trades Set IV (1908)	£3.00	—
	85	Chinese Trades Set VI (1912)	£3.00	—

BATTLE AX CIGARETTES

M	100	Famous Beauties (1916)	£5.00	—
M	50	Women of Nations (Flag Girls) (1917)	£6.00	—

COPAIN CIGARETTES

	52	Birds of Brilliant Plumage (1927)	£5.50	—

DOMINO CIGARETTES

	25	Animaux et Reptiles (1961)	20p	£5.00
	25	Corsaires et Boucaniers (1960)	20p	£3.00
	25	Figures Historiques 1st series (1961)	50p	£12.50

Size	Number in set		Price per card	Complete set
BRITISH AMERICAN TOBACCO CO. LTD *(continued)*				
	25	Figures Historiques 2nd series (1961)	80p	£20.00
	25	Fleurs de Culture (1960)	20p	£2.50
	25	Les Oiseaux et l'Art Japonais (1961)	£1.00	—
	25	Les Produits du Monde (1960)	20p	£2.50
	50	Voitures Antiques (1961)	£1.30	—
EAGLE BIRD CIGARETTES				
	50	Animals and Birds (1909)	£2.00	—
	50	Aviation series (1912)	£4.00	—
	25	Birds of the East (1912)	£2.00	£50.00
	25	China's Famous Warriors (1911)	£4.00	—
	25	Chinese Beauties 1st series (1908):		
		A Vertical back	£3.00	—
		B Horizontal back	£3.00	—
	25	Chinese Beauties 2nd series (1909):		
		A Front without framelines	£2.60	—
		B Front with framelines	£2.60	—
	50	Chinese Trades (1908)	£2.50	—
	25	Cock Fighting (1911)	£12.00	—
	60	Flags and Pennons (1926)	£1.30	£80.00
	50	Romance of the Heavens (1929)	£2.50	—
	50	Siamese Alphabet (1922)	£1.50	£75.00
	50	Siamese Dreams and Their Meanings (1923)	£1.20	£60.00
	50	Siamese Horoscopes (c1915)	£1.20	£60.00
	50	Siamese Play-Inao (c1915)	£1.40	£70.00
	50	Siamese Play-Khun Chang Khun Phaen 1st series (c1915)	£1.40	£70.00
	50	Siamese Play-Khun Chang Khun Phaen 2nd series (c1915)	£1.40	£70.00
	36	Siamese Play-Phra Aphaiu 1st series (c1918)	£1.50	£55.00
	36	Siamese Play-Phra Aphaiu 2nd series (1919)	£1.50	£55.00
	150	Siamese Play — Ramakien I (c1913)	£1.40	—
	50	Siamese Play — Ramakien II (1914)	£1.40	£70.00
	50	Siamese Uniforms (1915)	£2.00	£100.00
	50	Views of Siam (1928)	£3.00	£150.00
	50	Views of Siam (Bangkok) (1928)	£4.00	£200.00
	30	War Weapons (1914)	£2.50	£75.00
KONG BENG CIGARETTES				
	60	Animals (cut-outs) (1912)	£7.00	—
MASCOT CIGARETTES				
	100	Cinema Stars (Nd 201-300) (1931)	£3.00	—
M	208	Cinema Stars unnumbered (1924)	£2.40	—
MILLBANK CIGARETTES				
	60	Animals (cut-outs):		
		A '1516' at base of back (1922)	£1.20	—
		B '3971' at base of back (1923)	£1.20	—
NASSA CIGARETTES				
M	50	Birds, Beasts and Fishes (1924)	£5.00	—
PEDRO CIGARETTES (see also Imperial Tobacco Co. of India)				
	50	Actors and Actresses (c1905)	£3.50	—
	40	Nautch Girls. Coloured (1905)	£2.50	—
	37	Nautch Girls. Red border (c1905)	£2.50	—
PINHEAD CIGARETTES				
	50	Chinese Modern Beauties (1912)	£4.00	—
	33	Chinese Heroes Set 1 (1912)	£4.00	—
	50	Chinese Heroes Set 2 (1913)	£4.00	—
	50	Chinese Trades Set III (1908)	£4.00	£200.00
	50	Chinese Trades Set IV (1909)	£4.00	£200.00

Size	*Number in set*		*Price per card*	*Complete set*

BRITISH AMERICAN TOBACCO CO. LTD *(continued)*

	50	Chinese Trades Set V (1910)	£4.00	£200.00
	50	Types of the British Army (1909)	£5.00	—
RAILWAY CIGARETTES (see also Imperial Tobacco Co. of India)				
	37	Nautch Girls series (1907)	£2.75	—
TEAL CIGARETTES				
	30	Chinese Beauties (c1915)	£5.00	—
	50	Cinema Stars (1930):		
		A Back in blue	£2.00	—
		B Back in red brown	£2.00	—
	30	Fish series (1916)	£3.50	—
	50	War Incidents (1916)	£2.50	£125.00
TIGER CIGARETTES				
	52	Nautch Girls series (1911):		
		A Without frameline to front	£2.75	—
		B With frameline to front:		
		i With crossed cigarettes on back	£2.75	—
		ii Without crossed cigarettes on back	£2.75	—
NO BRAND NAME BLUE FLAG PACKET WITH SIAMESE TEXT				
	50	Puzzle Sectional Series (c1915)	£2.00	—
	50	Siamese Dancers (c1915)	£1.50	£75.00
	50	Siamese Life (c1915)	£1.50	£75.00
	50	Siamese Proverbs (c1915)	£1.60	£80.00
	50	Types of the British Army (c1916)	£4.00	—
E PRINTED ON BACK NO MAKER'S NAME OR BRAND				
(See also Imperial Tobacco Co. of Canada Ltd and United Tobacco Companies (South) Ltd)				
		Actresses 'ALWICS' (c1905):		
	175	A Portrait in black	£3.75	—
	50	B Portrait in red	£4.00	—
	50	Aeroplanes (1926)	£3.00	£150.00
	50	Aeroplanes of Today (1936)	£1.20	£60.00
	25	Angling (1930)	£5.00	—
	50	Arms and Armour (1910)	£6.00	—
	25	Army Life (c1910)	£6.40	—
	50	Art Photogravures (1913)	£1.10	—
	1	Australia Day (1915)	—	£15.00
	22	Automobielen (c1925)	£7.50	—
	75	Aviation (1910)	£4.50	—
	50	Aviation series (1911):		
		A With album clause	£4.00	—
		B Without album clause	£4.00	—
		Beauties Set I (1925):		
P	50	A Black and white	£2.30	£115.00
MP	50	B Coloured	£2.00	—
P	50	Beauties 2nd series (1925):		
		A Black and white	£2.30	£115.00
		B Coloured	£2.00	—
P	50	Beauties 3rd series (1926)	£1.50	£75.00
	50	Beauties red tinted (c1906)	£3.00	—
		Beauties tobacco leaf back (c1908):		
	52	A With PC inset	£3.50	£175.00
	50	B Without PC inset	£4.00	£200.00
P	50	Beauties of Great Britain (1930):		
		A Non-stereoscopic	70p	£35.00
		B Stereoscopic	£2.50	—
P	50	Beautiful England (1928)	50p	£25.00

Size	Number in set		Price per card	Complete set

BRITISH AMERICAN TOBACCO CO. LTD *(continued)*

MP	60	La Belgique Monumentale et Pittoresque (c1925)	£3.25	—
	50	Best Dogs of Their Breed (1916)	£4.20	—
	50	Billiards (1929)	£2.20	—
	50	Birds, Beasts and Fishes (1937)	70p	£35.00
M	50	Birds, Beasts and Fishes (1929)	£1.20	£60.00
	24	Birds of England (1924)	£2.60	£65.00
	50	Boy Scouts (1930) — without album clause	£2.50	£125.00
	50	Britain's Defenders (1915):		
		A Blue grey fronts	£2.00	—
		B Mauve fronts	£1.80	£90.00
	50	British Butterflies (1930)	£1.10	£55.00
	50	British Empire series (1913)	£2.50	—
	25	British Trees and Their Uses (1930)	£2.00	£50.00
	50	British Warships and Admirals (1915)	£4.00	—
	50	Butterflies and Moths (1911):		
		A With album clause	£3.00	—
		B Without album clause	£2.00	—
	50	Butterflies (Girls) (1928)	£6.00	£300.00
M	50	Butterflies (Girls) (1928)	£7.50	£375.00
M	50	Celebrities of Film and Stage (1930):		
		A Title on back in box	£2.00	£100.00
		B Title on back not in box	£2.00	£100.00
LP	48	Channel Islands Past and Present (1939):		
		A Without '3rd Series'	£1.20	—
		B With '3rd Series'	40p	£20.00
	40	Characters from the Works of Charles Dickens (1919):		
		A Complete set	—	£50.00
		B 38 different (— Nos 33, 39)	70p	£27.00
	50	Cinema Artistes, black and white set 1 (Nd 1-50) (c1928)	£1.80	£90.00
	50	Cinema Artistes black and white set 4 (Nd 101-150) (c1928)	£1.80	£90.00
		Cinema Artistes brown set 1 (c1930):		
	60	A With 'Metro Golden Mayer'	£2.50	—
	50	B Without 'Metro Golden Mayer'	£2.50	—
	50	Cinema Artistes brown set 2 (c1931):		
		A Oblong panel at top back	£2.00	£100.00
		B Oval panel at top back	£2.00	£100.00
L	48	Cinema Artistes set 3 (c1931)	£2.00	£100.00
	48	Cinema Celebrities (C) (1935)	£1.20	£60.00
L	48	Cinema Celebrities (C) (1935)	£1.50	£75.00
L	56	Cinema Celebrities (D) (1936)	£2.70	—
	50	Cinema Favourites (1929)	£2.20	£110.00
	50	Cinema Stars Set 2 (Nd 1-50) (1928)	£1.20	£60.00
	50	Cinema Stars Set 3 (Nd 51-100) (1929)	£3.00	—
	50	Cinema Stars Set 4 (Nd 101-150) (1930)	£1.20	—
	100	Cinema Stars 'BAMT' (coloured) (1931)	£2.30	—
P	50	Cinema Stars Set 1 (c1928)	£1.50	—
P	50	Cinema Stars Set 2 (c1928)	£1.20	£60.00
P	50	Cinema Stars Set 3 (c1928)	£1.50	—
MP	52	Cinema Stars Set 4 (c1928)	£1.80	—
MP	52	Cinema Stars Set 5 (c1928)	£1.80	—
MP	52	Cinema Stars Set 6 (c1928)	£2.50	—
LP	48	Cinema Stars Set 7 (c1928)	£3.00	—
P	50	Cinema Stars Set 8 (Nd 1-50) (c1928)	£1.20	£60.00
P	50	Cinema Stars Set 9 (Nd 51-100) (c1928)	£2.50	—
P	50	Cinema Stars Set 10 (Nd 101-150) (c1928)	£2.50	—
P	50	Cinema Stars Set 11 (Nd 151-200) (c1928)	£2.50	—
	25	Derby Day series (1914)	£9.00	—

Size	*Number in set*		*Price per card*	*Complete set*

BRITISH AMERICAN TOBACCO CO. LTD *(continued)*

Size	Number in set		Price per card	Complete set
	50	Do You Know? (1923)	50p	£25.00
	50	Do You Know? 2nd series (1931)	50p	£25.00
	25	Dracones Posthistorici (c1930)	£9.00	—
	25	Dutch Scenes (1928)	£3.20	£80.00
	50	Engineering Wonders (1930)	70p	£35.00
	40	English Costumes of Ten Centuries (1919)	£1.50	£60.00
P	25	English Cricketers (1926)	£3.00	£75.00
	26	Etchings (of Dogs) (1926)	£2.50	£65.00
P	50	Famous Bridges (1935)	£1.00	£50.00
	50	Famous Footballers Set 1 (1923)	£4.00	—
	50	Famous Footballers Set 2 (1924)	£4.00	—
	50	Famous Footballers Set 3 (1925)	£4.00	—
	25	Famous Racehorses (1926)	£3.00	£75.00
	25	Famous Railway Trains (1929)	£2.40	£60.00
	50	Favourite Flowers (c1925)	80p	£40.00
	50	Film and Stage Favourites (c1925)	£1.80	£90.00
	75	Film Favourites (1928)	£1.50	£115.00
	50	Flags of the Empire (1928)	80p	£40.00
	50	Foreign Birds (1930)	80p	£40.00
	50	Game Birds and Wild Fowl (1929)	£1.40	£70.00
LP	45	Grace and Beauty (Nos 1-45) (1938)	50p	£22.50
LP	45	Grace and Beauty (Nos 46-90) (1939)	30p	£13.50
LP	48	Guernsey, Alderney and Sark Past and Present 1st series (1937)	40p	£20.00
LP	48	Guernsey, Alderney and Sark Past and Present 2nd series (1938)	35p	£17.50
L	80	Guernsey Footballers Priaulx League (1938)	60p	£50.00
P	52	Here There and Everywhere:		
		A Non stereoscopic (1929)	40p	£20.00
		B Stereoscopic (1930)	80p	£40.00
	25	Hints and Tips for Motorists (1929)	£2.60	£65.00
P	50	Homeland Events (1928)	80p	£40.00
	50	Horses of Today (1906)	£5.00	—
	32	Houses of Parliament (red back) (1912)	£1.75	—
	32	Houses of Parliament (brown backs with verse) (1912)	£9.00	—
	50	Indian Chiefs (1930)	£9.00	—
	50	Indian Regiment series (1912)	£9.00	—
	50	International Air Liners (1937)	80p	£40.00
	25	Java Scenes (1929)	£9.00	—
LP	48	Jersey Then and Now 1st series (1935)	£1.00	£50.00
LP	48	Jersey Then and Now 2nd series (1937)	80p	£40.00
	50	Jiu Jitsu (1911)	£3.50	—
	50	Keep Fit (1939)	90p	£45.00
	50	Leaders of Men (1929)	£3.50	—
	50	Life in the Tree Tops (1931)	50p	£25.00
	50	Lighthouses (1926)	£1.80	£90.00
	40	London Ceremonials (1929)	£1.50	£60.00
P	50	London Zoo (1927)	70p	£35.00
	50	Lucky Charms (1930)	£1.50	£75.00
	25	Marvels of the Universe series (c1925)	£2.60	£65.00
	45	Melbourne Cup Winners (1906)	£7.50	—
	50	Merchant Ships of the World (1925)	£5.00	—
	25	Merchant Ships of the World (1925)	£3.50	—
	25	Military Portraits (1917)	£3.00	—
	36	Modern Beauties 1st series (1938)	£1.10	£40.00
	36	Modern Beauties 2nd series (1939)	60p	£22.00
MP	54	Modern Beauties 1st series (1937)	£1.00	£55.00
MP	54	Modern Beauties 2nd series (1938)	£1.00	£55.00
MP	36	Modern Beauties 3rd series (1938)	£1.50	£55.00

Size	Number in set		Price per card	Complete set

BRITISH AMERICAN TOBACCO CO. LTD *(continued)*

MP	36	Modern Beauties 4th series (1939)	£1.00	£36.00
ELP	36	Modern Beauties 1st series (1936)	£1.10	£40.00
ELP	36	Modern Beauties 2nd series (1936)	75p	£27.00
ELP	36	Modern Beauties 3rd series (1937)	85p	£30.00
ELP	36	Modern Beauties 4th series (1937)	£1.50	£55.00
ELP	36	Modern Beauties 5th series (1938)	£1.00	£36.00
ELP	36	Modern Beauties 6th series (1938)	85p	£30.00
ELP	36	Modern Beauties 7th series (1938)	£1.25	£45.00
LP	36	Modern Beauties 8th series (1939)	£1.50	£55.00
LP	36	Modern Beauties 9th Series (1939)	£1.50	£55.00
LP	36	Modern Beauties (1939)	£1.25	£45.00
	50	Modern Warfare (1936)	£1.40	£70.00
M	48	Modern Wonders (1938)	£3.00	—
	25	Modes of Conveyance (1928)	£2.20	£55.00
	48	Motor Cars green back (1926)	£4.00	—
	36	Motor Cars brown back (1929)	£6.00	—
	50	Motorcycles (1927)	£3.50	—
P	50	Native Life in Many Lands (1932)	£1.50	£75.00
P	50	Natural and Man Made Wonders of the World (1937)	60p	£30.00
P	50	Nature Studies stereoscopic (1928)	60p	£30.00
P	48	Nature Studies stereoscopic (1930)	80p	£40.00
	50	Naval Portraits (1917)	£2.60	—
	25	Notabilities (1917)	£2.60	£65.00
	25	Past and Present (1929)	£1.80	£45.00
P	48	Pictures of the East (1930):		
		A 'A Series of 48' 17mm long	£1.50	£75.00
		B 'A Series of 48' 14mm long	£1.50	£75.00
M	48	Picturesque China (c1925):		
		A With 'P' at left of base	£1.50	£75.00
		B Without 'P' at left of base	£1.50	£75.00
M	53	Playing Cards Ace of Hearts Back (c1935)	30p	£15.00
K	53	Playing Cards designed back (c1935):		
		A Blue back	£1.00	—
		B Red back	£1.00	—
	36	Popular Stage, Cinema and Society Celebrities (c1928)	£3.50	—
	25	Prehistoric Animals (1931)	£3.00	£75.00
	50	Prominent Australian and English Cricketers (1911)	£40.00	—
	25	Puzzle series (1916)	£6.00	—
	50	Railway Working (1927)	£1.80	£90.00
	10	Recruiting Posters (1915)	£7.00	—
	33	Regimental Pets (1911)	£6.50	—
	50	Regimental Uniforms (1936)	£1.60	£80.00
	50	Romance of the Heavens (1929)	90p	£45.00
P	50	Round the World in Pictures stereoscopic (1931)	£1.20	£60.00
	50	Royal Mail (1912)	£4.00	—
P	50	Royal Navy (1930)	£2.00	—
	27	Rulers of the World (1911)	£8.00	—
	40	Safety First (1931)	£2.00	£80.00
	25	Ships' Flags and Cap Badges 1st series (1930)	£3.00	£75.00
	25	Ships' Flags and Cap Badges 2nd series (1930)	£3.00	£75.00
P	50	Ships and Shipping (1928)	80p	£40.00
	50	Signalling series (1913)	£3.50	—
	100	Soldiers of the World (tobacco leaf back) (c1902)	£12.00	—
	50	Speed (1938)	70p	£35.00
	25	Sports and Games in Many Lands (1930)	£5.00	£125.00
	50	Stage and Film Stars (1926)	£1.60	—
M	50	Stars of Filmland (1927)	£2.50	—

Size	Number in set		Price per card	Complete set

BRITISH AMERICAN TOBACCO CO. LTD *(continued)*

Size	Number in set	Title	Price per card	Complete set
	48	Transport Then and Now (1940)	50p	£25.00
	32	Transport of the World (1917)	£9.00	—
	20	Types of North American Indians (c1930)	£14.00	—
P	50	Types of the World (1936)	70p	£35.00
P	270	Views of the World stereoscopic (1908)	£3.00	—
	50	War Incidents (brown back) (1915)	£1.80	£90.00
	50	War Incidents (blue back) (1916)	£1.80	£90.00
	25	Warriors of All Nations (gold panel) (1937)	£1.60	£40.00
	50	Warships (1926)	£5.00	—
	25	Whaling (1930)	£2.40	£60.00
P	50	Who's Who in Sport (1926)	£2.50	£125.00
	50	Wild Animals of the World (tobacco leaf back) (1902)	£8.00	—
	25	Wireless (1923)	£4.40	—
	50	Wonders of the Past (1930)	80p	£40.00
	50	Wonders of the Sea (1929)	70p	£35.00
	25	Wonders of the World (c1928)	80p	£20.00
	40	World Famous Cinema Artistes (1933)	£1.50	£60.00
M	40	World Famous Cinema Artistes (1933)	£1.50	£60.00
	50	World's Products (1929)	50p	£25.00
P	50	The World of Sport (1927)	£2.00	£100.00
P	50	Zoo (1935)	60p	£30.00
	50	Zoological Studies (1928):		
		A Brown back	50p	£25.00
		B Black back	£1.50	—

F PLAIN BACKS

Size	Number in set	Title	Price per card	Complete set
	50	Actors and Actresses 'WALP' (c1905):		
		A Portraits in black and white, glossy	£2.40	£120.00
		B Portraits flesh tinted, matt	£2.40	£120.00
	50	Actresses 'ALWICS' (c1905)	£2.40	—
	50	Actresses, four colours surround (c1905)	£2.40	£120.00
	30	Actresses unicoloured (c1910):		
		A Fronts in purple brown	£1.00	£30.00
		B Fronts in light brown	£1.00	£30.00
	50	Animals and Birds (1912)	£2.00	—
	60	Animals — cut-outs (1912)	£1.10	—
	50	Art Photogravures (1912)	£2.00	—
	50	Aviation series (1911)	£4.00	—
	40	Beauties — brown tinted (1913)	£2.20	—
	50	Beauties with backgrounds (1911)	£2.50	—
	32	Beauties Picture Hats I with borders (1914)	£3.00	—
	45	Beauties Picture Hats II without borders (1914)	£3.00	—
	30	Beauties and Children (c1910)	£5.00	—
	30	Beauties 'Celebrated Actresses' (c1910)	£3.00	—
	52	Birds of Brilliant Plumage — PC inset (1914)	£2.80	—
	25	Bonzo series (1923):		
		A With series title	£3.80	—
		B Without series title	£3.80	—
	30	Boy Scouts Signalling (c1920):		
		A Captions in English	£3.50	£105.00
		B Captions in Siamese	£3.50	£105.00
	50	British Man of War series (1910)	£10.00	—
	50	Butterflies and Moths (1910)	£1.60	—
	50	Cinema Artistes (c1928)	£2.50	—
	50	Cinema Stars RB.21/259 (c1930):		
		A Front matt	£1.50	£75.00
		B Front glossy	£1.50	—

Size	Number in set		Price per card	Complete set

BRITISH AMERICAN TOBACCO CO. LTD *(continued)*

	50	Cinema Stars RB.21/260 (Nd 1-50) (c1930)	£1.50	—
	50	Cinema Stars RB.21/260 (Nd 51-100) (c1930)	£1.50	—
	50	Cinema Stars RB.21/260 (Nd 101-150) (c1930)	£1.50	—
	100	Cinema Stars RB.21/260 (Nd 201-300) (c1930)	£1.20	£120.00
	50	Cinema Stars 'FLAG' (c1930)	£1.50	—
	27	Dancing Girls (1913)	£1.70	—
	32	Drum Horses (1910)	£5.00	—
	50	English Period Costumes	80p	£40.00
	50	Flag Girls of All Nations (1911)	£2.00	—
		Flags, Pennons and Signals (c1910):		
	70	A Numbered 1-70	£1.00	—
	70	B Unnumbered	£1.00	—
	50	C Numbered 71-120	£1.00	—
	45	D Numbered 121-165	£1.00	—
	20	Flowers (1915)	£1.50	£30.00
	50	Girls of All Nations (1908)	£2.00	—
	30	Heroic Deeds (1913)	£2.20	—
	25	Hindou Gods (1909)	£8.50	—
	32	Houses of Parliament (1914)	£3.00	—
	25	Indian Mogul Paintings (1909)	£10.00	—
LP	48	Jersey Then and Now 3rd series (c1940)	£2.00	—
	53	Jockeys and Owners Colours — PC inset (c1914)	£3.00	—
	30	Merrie England Female Studies (1922)	£5.00	—
K	36	Modern Beauties 1st series (1938)	£3.00	—
	36	Modern Beauties 2nd series (1939)	£3.00	—
P	48	Movie Stars (c1930)	£1.50	—
	50	Music Hall Celebrities (1911):		
		A Blue border	£2.50	—
		B Gilt border	£2.50	—
		C Red border	£2.50	—
		D Yellow border	£4.00	—
P	50	New Zealand, Early Scenes and Maori Life (c1928)	£1.60	—
	50	Poultry and Pidgeons (c1926)	£6.00	—
	25	Products of the World (1914)	£1.00	£25.00
	25	Roses (1912) W.373	£8.00	—
	50	Royal Mail (1912)	£5.00	—
	36	Ships and Their Pennants (1913)	£2.50	—
	75	Soldiers of the World (c1902)	£8.00	—
	30	Sporting Girls (1913)	£6.00	—
	50	Sports of the World (1917):		
		A Brown front	£4.00	—
		B Coloured front	£4.00	—
M	50	Stars of Filmland (1927)	£2.00	—
	32	Transport of the World (1917)	£1.50	—
	50	Types of the British Army (1908):		
		A Numbered	£3.20	—
		B Unnumbered	£3.20	—
P	50	Types of the World (1936)	£2.50	—
P	50	Units of the British Army and RAF (c1930)	£2.00	—
M	50	Women of Nations (Flag Girls) (1922)	£3.00	—
G		***PAPER BACKED SILKS ISSUED 1910-1917***		
M	25	Arabic Proverbs	£13.00	—
M	50	Arms of the British Empire:		
		A Back in blue	£3.00	—
		B Back in brown	£4.00	—
M	50	Australian Wild Flowers	£3.50	—

Size	Number in set		Price per card	Complete set

BRITISH AMERICAN TOBACCO CO. LTD *(continued)*

M	50	Best Dogs of Their Breed	£6.00	—
	110	Crests and Badges of the British Army	£2.50	—
M	108	Crests and Badges of the British Army	£2.50	—
M	50	Crests and Colours of Australian Universities, Colleges and Schools	£2.50	—

BRITISH AMERICAN TOBACCO COMPANY (CHINA) LTD

	32	Sectional Picture — 'Beauties of Old China' (1934)	£5.00	—

BRITISH AMERICAN TOBACCO CO. LTD, Switzerland

	30	Series Actrices (1921)	£6.00	—

BRITISH CIGARETTE CO. LTD, China

	25	British and Foreign Actresses and Beauties (c1900)	£75.00	—
	25	South African War Scenes (c1900)	£32.00	—

BROWN & WILLIAMSON TOBACCO CORP, USA (Wings Cigarettes)

M	50	Modern American Airplanes (c1938):		
		A Inscribed 'Series A'	£4.00	—
		B Without 'Series A'	£3.00	—
M	50	Modern American Airplanes 'Series B' (c1938)	£3.00	—
M	50	Modern American Airplanes 'Series C' (c1938)	£3.00	—
	50	Movie Stars (1940) (Golden Grain Tobacco)	£5.00	—

D. BUCHNER & CO., USA

	48	Actors (1887)	£30.00	—
L	50	Actresses (1891)	£28.00	—
L	? 61	American Scenes with a Policeman (c1890)	£70.00	—
	144	Baseball Players (c1890)	£150.00	—
L	28	Butterflies and Bugs (c1890)	£65.00	—
L	51	Morning Glory Maidens (c1890)	£50.00	—
L	23	Musical Instruments (c1890)	£60.00	—
L	21	Yacht Club Colours (c1890)	£60.00	—

BUCKTROUT & CO. LTD, Guernsey, Channel Islands

M	416	Around the World (1926):		
		A Inscribed 'Places of Interest' Nd. 1-104	50p	£52.00
		B Inscribed 'Around the World' Nd. 105-208	50p	£52.00
		C Inscribed 'Around the World' Nd. 209-312	50p	£52.00
		D Inscribed 'Around the World' Nd. 313-416	50p	£52.00
	24	Birds of England (1923)	£3.25	£80.00
	50	Cinema Stars, 1st series (1921)	£2.00	£100.00
	50	Cinema Stars, 2nd series (1922)	£2.20	£110.00
M	50	Football Teams (1924)	£3.20	—
M	22	Football Teams of the Bailiwick (1924)	£1.00	£22.00
	123	Guernsey Footballers (c1925)	£4.00	—
	20	Inventors Series (1924)	£1.25	£25.00
	25	Marvels of the Universe Series (1923)	£2.60	£65.00
M	54	Playing Cards (1928)	80p	£42.00
	25	Sports and Pastimes (1925)	£5.00	—

Size	*Number in set*		*Price per card*	*Complete set*

BUKHSH ELLAHIE & CO., India

	53	Indian Girl Playing Card inset:		
		A Full length girl seated	£25.00	—
		B Full length girl standing	£25.00	—
		C Bust length	£25.00	—
	2	Indian Series Ref W.240 (1900)	£300.00	—

CALCUTTA CIGARETTE CO., India

	25	Actresses — 'ALWICS' (c1905):		
		A Fronts in blue	£25.00	—
		B Fronts in chocolate	£30.00	—

A. G. CAMERON & SIZER, USA (including Cameron & Cameron)

	25	The New Discovery (1889):		
		A Without overprint	£34.00	—
		B With overprint	£34.00	—
	24	Occupations for Women (1895)	£50.00	—
		Photographic Cards (c1895):		
	? 230	Actresses	£18.00	—
L	? 6	Actresses	£22.00	—
	75	Framed Paintings	£15.00	—

V. CAMILLERI, Malta

MP	104	Popes of Rome (1922):		
		A Nd. 1-52	£1.70	£85.00
		B Nd. 53-104	£1.70	£85.00

CAMLER TOBACCO COY, Malta

P	250	Footballers (c1925)	£9.00	—
M	96	Maltese Families Coats of Arms:		
		A Thick board (c1925)	£1.20	—
		B Thin board (1958)	£1.20	—

CHING & CO., Jersey, Channel Islands

L	24	Around and About in Jersey, 1st series (1963)	30p	£7.50
L	24	Around and About in Jersey, 2nd series (1964)	80p	£20.00
	25	Do You Know? (1962)	20p	£2.50
	48	Flowers (1962)	£1.00	£50.00
L	24	Jersey Past and Present, 1st series (1960)	25p	£6.00
L	24	Jersey Past and Present, 2nd series (1961)	60p	£15.00
L	24	Jersey Past and Present, 3rd series (1961)	20p	£5.00
	25	Ships and Their Workings (1961)	20p	£2.50
	50	Veteran and Vintage Cars (1960)	40p	£20.00

THE CIGARETTE COMPANY, Jersey, Channel Islands

	72	Jersey Footballers (c1910)	£7.00	—

LA CIGARETTE ORIENTAL DE BELGIQUE, Belgium

L	100	Famous Men Throughout the Ages (c1940)	50p	—

C. COLOMBOS, Malta

MP	200	Actresses (c1900)	£3.50	—
MP	59	Actresses (c1900)	£15.00	—
	50	Actresses (coloured) (c1900)	£15.00	—

Size	Number in set		Price per card	Complete set

C. COLOMBOS, Malta *(continued)*

MP	57	Celebrities (c1900)	£17.00	—
P	136	Dante's Divine Comedy (c1914)	£2.40	—
		Famous Oil Paintings (c1910):		
MP	72	1 Series A	£1.00	—
MP	108	2 Series B	£1.00	—
MP	240	3 Series C	£1.00	—
MP	100	4 Series D	£1.00	—
LP	91	5 Large size	£7.00	—
MP	100	Life of Napoleon Bonaparte (c1914)	£3.00	—
MP	70	Life of Nelson (c1914)	£3.00	—
MP	70	Life of Wellington (c1914)	£3.00	—
MP	100	National Types and Costumes (c1910)	£3.00	—
MP	30	Opera Singers (c1900)	£32.00	—
	120	Paintings and Statues (c1912)	£1.00	—
M	112	Royalty and Celebrities (c1910)	£3.20	—

COLONIAL TOBACCOS (PTY) LTD, South Africa

EL	150	World's Fairy Tales (c1930)	£4.00	—

D. CONDACHI & SON, Malta

	? 15	Artistes & Beauties (c1905)	£22.00	—

CONSOLIDATED CIGARETTE CO., USA

		Ladies of the White House (c1895):		
	14	A Size 73 × 43mm, white borders	£37.00	—
	25	B Size 70 × 38mm, no borders	£32.00	—

A.G. COUSIS & CO., Malta

		Actors and Actresses (c1910):		
P	100	A Back with framework	£2.25	—
KP	100	B Back without framework	£2.25	—
K	254	Actors and Actresses (c1925)	£1.25	—
KP	100	Actresses Series I (c1910)	£2.00	—
KP	80	Actresses Series II (c1910)	£2.00	—
P	100	Actresses (c1910):		
		A Series I	£2.00	—
		B Series II	£2.00	—
		C Series III	£2.00	—
		D Series IV	£2.00	—
		E Series V	£2.00	—
		F Series VI	£2.00	—
		G Series VII	£2.00	—
		H Series VIII	£2.00	—
		I Series IX	£2.00	—
		J Series X	£2.00	—
		K Series XI	£2.00	—
		L Series XII	£2.00	—
		M Series XIII	£2.00	—
		N Series XIV	£2.00	—
		O Series XV	£2.00	—
		P Series XVI	£2.00	—
		Q Series XVII	£2.00	—
		R Series XVIII	£2.00	—
		S Series XIX	£2.00	—

Size	Number in set		Price per card	Complete set

A.G. COUSIS & CO., Malta *(continued)*

		Actresses (c1910):		
KP	2281	A Miniature size 50 × 30mm	£1.25	—
P	1283	B Small size 58 × 39mm	£1.25	—
MP	325	Actresses, Celebrities and Warships (c1910)	£10.00	—
		Actresses, Partners and National Costumes (c1910):		
KP	200	A Miniature size 50 × 30mm	£2.25	—
P	100	B Small size 60 × 39mm	£2.50	—
MP	50	Beauties, Couples and Children (c1908):		
		A Back inscribed 'Collection No. 1'	£3.50	—
		B Back inscribed 'Collection No. 2'	£3.50	—
		C Back inscribed 'Collection No. 3'	£3.50	—
K	50	Beauties, Couples and Children (red back) (c1925)	£2.50	—
P	402	Celebrities numbered matt (c1910):		
		A Front inscribed 'Cousis' Dubec Cigarettes', Nd. 1-300	£1.80	—
		B Front inscribed 'Cousis' Cigarettes', Nd. 301-402	£1.80	—
P	2162	Celebrities unnumbered (c1910):		
		A Miniature size 50 × 30mm	£1.25	—
		B Small size 59 × 39mm	£1.25	—
MP	72	Grand Masters of the Order of Jerusalem (c1910)	£3.50	—
P	100	National Costumes (c1910)	£2.75	—
MP	? 57	Paris Exhibition 1900 (c1901)	£28.00	—
MP	102	Paris Series (1902)	£28.00	—
		Popes of Rome (c1910):		
MP	182	A Back inscribed 'A.G. Cousis & Co'	£2.00	—
MP	81	B Back inscribed 'Cousis' Dubec Cigarettes'	£3.20	—
P	100	Statues and Monuments (c1910):		
		A Numbered	£2.00	—
		B Unnumbered	£2.00	—
KP	127	Views of Malta (c1910)	£2.50	—
P	115	Views of Malta numbered (c1910)	£1.50	—
MP	127	Views of Malta numbered (c1910)	£1.50	—
MP	? 65	Views of Malta unnumbered (c1910)	£1.50	—
P	559	Views of the World (c1910):		
		A Small size 59 × 39mm	£1.50	—
		B Medium size 65 × 45mm	£1.50	—
P	99	Warships, white border (c1910)	£3.50	—
		Warships, Liners and Other Vessels (c1904):		
MP	105	A 'Cousis' Dubec Cigarettes'	£7.00	—
MP	22	B 'Cousis' Excelsior Cigarettes'	£7.00	—
MP	40	C 'Cousis' Superior Cigarettes'	£7.00	—
MP	851	D 'Cousis' Cigarettes'	£2.00	—
KP	851	E 'Cousis' Cigarettes'	£2.00	—

CROWN TOBACCO CO., India

		National Types, Costumes and Flags (c1900):		
	? 19	A Size 70 × 40mm	£40.00	—
	? 14	B Size 88 × 49mm	£45.00	—

DIXSON, Australia

	50	Australian MPs and Celebrities (c1900)	£18.00	—

DOMINION TOBACCO CO., Canada

	50	The Smokers of the World (c1905)	£60.00	—

Size	Number in set		Price per card	Complete set

DOMINION TOBACCO CO. LTD, New Zealand

	50	Coaches and Coaching Days (c1928)	£2.50	—
	50	People and Places Famous in New Zealand History (c1928)	£1.80	—
	50	Products of the World (c1928)	£1.00	£50.00
	50	USS Co's Steamers (c1928)	£3.00	—

DUDGEON & ARNELL, Australia

K	16	1934 Australian Test Team (1934)	£8.50	—
K	55	Famous Ships (1933)	£4.00	—

W. DUKE, SONS & CO., USA

ALL SERIES ISSUED 1885-95

	50	Actors and Actresses Series No. 1	£17.00	—
M	50	Actors and Actresses Series No. 1	£36.00	—
	50	Actors and Actresses Series No. 2	£17.00	—
M	50	Actors and Actresses Series No. 2	£36.00	—
EL	30	Actors and Actresses (3 subjects per card)	£36.00	—
	25	Actresses RB.118/27	£11.00	—
EL	25	Actresses (black border)	£40.00	—
EL	25	Actresses (Folders)	£50.00	—
EL	25	Albums of American Stars:		
		A Folder with card	£50.00	—
		B Card only without folder	£40.00	—
EL	25	Battle Scenes	£40.00	—
EL	25	Bicycle and Trick Riders	£40.00	—
EL	25	Breeds of Horses	£36.00	—
EL	25	Bridges	£28.00	—
EL	25	Burlesque Scenes	£40.00	—
	50	Coins of All Nations:		
		A White background	£17.00	—
		B Shaded background	£17.00	—
EL	25	Comic Characters	£28.00	—
EL	25	Cowboys Scenes	£40.00	—
EL	50	Fairest Flowers in the World	£26.00	—
	50	Fancy Dress Ball Costumes	£17.00	—
M	50	Fancy Dress Ball Costumes	£36.00	—
EL	50	Fancy Dress Ball Costumes	£28.00	—
	50	Fishers and Fish	£17.00	—
EL	25	Fishes and Fishing (2 subjects per card)	£36.00	—
EL	25	Flags and Costumes	£32.00	—
	50	Floral Beauties and Language of Flowers	£16.00	—
EL	25	French Novelties	£30.00	—
EL	25	Gems of Beauty:		
		A Back 'Fair Play Long Cut'	£30.00	—
		B Back 'Honest Long Cut'	£30.00	—
	50	Great Americans	£25.00	—
EL	16	Great Americans (3 subjects per card)	£40.00	—
	25	Gymnastic Exercises	£30.00	—
EL	25	Habitations of Man	£28.00	—
	50	Histories of Generals (Booklets) (1888)	£40.00	—
EL	50	Histories of Generals (Cards)	£40.00	—
	50	Histories of Poor Boys who have become rich and other famous people (Booklets)	£30.00	—
	50	Holidays	£16.00	£800.00
EL	25	Illustrated Songs	£28.00	—
EL	25	Industries of the States	£36.00	—

Size	Number in set		Price per card	Complete set

W. DUKE, SONS & CO., USA *(continued)*

Size	Number in set		Price per card	Complete set
	50	Jokes:		
		A With A.T.C. name	£17.00	—
		B Without A.T.C. name	£17.00	—
EL	25	Jokes (2 subjects per card)	£36.00	—
EL	25	Lighthouses (die cut)	£28.00	—
EL	25	Miniature Novelties	£28.00	—
	50	Musical Instruments	£22.00	—
EL	25	Musical Instruments of the World (2 subjects per card)	£36.00	—
	36	Ocean and River Steamers	£27.00	—
M	240	Photographs from Life RB.23/D76-84	£6.00	—
	53	Playing Cards	£12.00	—
	50	Popular Songs and Dancers	£23.00	—
	50	Postage Stamps	£16.00	—
EL	25	Presidential Possibilities	£36.00	—
		Rulers, Flags and Coats of Arms (1888):		
EL	50	A Thick card type	£25.00	—
EL	50	B Thin folders (titled Rulers, Coats of Arms & Flags)	£16.00	—
	50	Scenes of Perilous Occupations	£24.00	—
EL	25	Sea Captains	£34.00	—
	50	Shadows	£17.00	£850.00
EL	25	Snap Shots from Puck	£27.00	—
EL	25	Stars of the Stage, 1st series (bust poses, white edge):		
		A With 'Duke'	£30.00	£750.00
		B Inscribed 'Third Series'	£30.00	—
EL	25	Stars of the Stage, 2nd series (full length poses)	£30.00	—
EL	25	Stars of the Stage, 3rd series (bust poses, black edge)	£30.00	£750.00
EL	25	Stars of the Stage, 4th series (die cut)	£30.00	—
EL	48	State Governors' Coats of Arms	£27.00	—
EL	48	State Governors' Coats of Arms (Folders)	£16.00	—
EL	25	Talk of the Diamond	£90.00	—
	50	The Terrors of America and Their Doings	£17.00	—
M	50	The Terrors of America and Their Doings	£36.00	—
EL	50	The Terrors of America and Their Doings	£30.00	—
	50	Tinted Photos:		
		A Standard size	£23.00	—
		B Die cut to shape	£17.00	—
EL	24	Tricks With Cards	£50.00	—
EL	25	Types of Vessels (die cut)	£28.00	—
	50	Vehicles of the World	£24.00	—
	50	Yacht Colors of the World	£18.00	—
M	50	Yacht Colours of the World	£36.00	—
EL	50	Yacht Colours of the World	£36.00	—

PHOTOGRAPHIC CARDS

Size	Number in set		Price per card	Complete set
	340	Actors and Actresses, 'Cross-Cut Cigarettes' with number and caption in design, Group 1	£4.00	—
	260	Actors and Actresses, 'Cross-Cut Cigarettes' in design, number and caption at base, Group 2	£4.00	—
	?	Actors and Actresses, 'Cross-Cut Cigarettes' and all wording at base, Group	£4.00	—
	148	Actors and Actresses, 'Dukes Cameo Cigarettes' in design, number and caption at base, Group 4	£4.00	—
	?	Actors and Actresses, 'Dukes Cameo Cigarettes', number and caption at base, Group 5	£4.00	—
	?	Actors and Actresses, 'Dukes Cigarettes' in design, number and caption at base, Group 6	£4.00	—
	?	Actors and Actresses, 'Dukes Cigarettes' and all wording at base, Group 7	£4.00	—

Size	Number in set		Price per card	Complete set

W. DUKE, SONS & CO., USA *(continued)*

	?	Actors, Actresses and Celebrities, printed back:		
		1 Horizontal 'Dukes Cameo Cigarettes' back	£4.00	—
		2 Vertical 'Sales 1858' back	£4.00	—
		3 Horizontal 'Dukes Cigarettes' back	£4.00	—
EL	?	Actors, Actresses, Celebrities etc	£6.00	—

H. ELLIS & CO., USA

	25	Breeds of Dogs (c1890):		
		A 'Bengal Cheroots'	£45.00	—
		B 'Tiger Cigarettes'	£45.00	—
		C 'Triplex Cigarettes'	£45.00	—
	25	Costumes of Women (c1890)	£65.00	—
	25	Generals of the Late Civil War (c1890)	£80.00	—
	25	Photographic Cards — Actresses (c1887)	£15.00	—

JOHN FINZER & BROS., USA

L	10	Inventors and Inventions (c1891)	£50.00	—

FOH CHONG, China

M	10	Chinese Series (c1930)	—	£20.00

G.W. GAIL & AX., USA

EL	25	Battle Scenes (c1890)	£40.00	—
EL	25	Bicycle and Trick Riders (c1890)	£40.00	—
EL	25	French Novelties (c1890)	£36.00	—
EL	25	Industries of the States (c1890)	£36.00	—
EL	25	Lighthouses (die cut) (c1890)	£32.00	—
EL	25	Novelties (die cut) (c1890)	£32.00	—
EL	?	Photographic Cards (c1890)	£6.00	—
EL	25	Stars of the Stage (c1890)	£32.00	—

GENERAL CIGAR COMPANY, Montreal, Canada

		Northern Birds:		
EL	24	A With series title Nd. 1-24 (1968)	£1.20	—
EL	12	B Without series title, Nd. 25-36 (1977)	£1.40	—

G.G. GOODE LTD, Australia

	17	Prominent Cricketers Series 1924	£100.00	—

GOODWIN & CO., USA

	15	Beauties — 'PAC' (c1888)	£60.00	—
	50	Champions (c1888)	£50.00	—
	50	Dogs of the World (c1888):		
		A Captions front and back	£25.00	—
		B Captions front only	£25.00	—
		C Captions back only	£25.00	—
	50	Flowers (c1888)	£24.00	—
	50	Games and Sports Series (c1888)	£32.00	—
	50	Holidays (c1888)	£30.00	—
	50	Occupations for Women (c1888)	£55.00	—
	10	Old Judge Actresses (thick card) (c1888)	£90.00	—

Size	Number in set		Price per card	Complete set

GOODWIN & CO., USA *(continued)*

		Photographic Cards (c1888):		
	?	Actors and Actresses	£7.00	—
	?	Baseball Players	£55.00	—
	?	Celebrities and Prizefighters	£30.00	—
	50	Vehicles of the World (c1888)	£30.00	—
	50	Wild Animals of the World (c1888)	£30.00	—

GUERNSEY TOBACCO CO., Channel Islands

		A Famous Picture:		
	49	A And When Did You Last See Your Father? (1934)	£2.30	—
	48	B The Laughing Cavalier (1935)	£2.30	—
	48	C The Toast (1936)	£2.30	—
K	52	Miniature Playing Cards (1933)	£1.20	—

THOS. H. HALL, USA

	4	Actresses RB.23/-H6-1 (1880)	£70.00	—
	14	Actresses RB.23/-H6-2, multi-backed (c1885)	£18.00	—
	140	Actors and Actresses RB.23/-H6-3, multi-backed (c1885)	£18.00	—
	112	Actresses and Actors RB.23/-H6-4, multi-backed (c1885)	£18.00	—
	? 196	Actresses and Actors RB.23/-H6-5, multi-backed (c1885)	£18.00	—
	? 158	Actresses and Actors RB.23/-H6-6, multi-backed (c1885)	£18.00	—
	52	Actresses RB.23/-H6-7 (c1885)	£20.00	—
	12	Actresses RB.23/-H6-8 (c1885)	£36.00	—
	25	Actresses RB.23/-H6-9 (c1885)	£30.00	—
	11	Actresses RB.23/-H6-10 (c1885)	£80.00	—
	12	Athletes RB.23/-H6-3 (1881)	£70.00	—
	4	Presidential Candidates RB.23/-H6-1 (1880)	£70.00	—
	22	Presidents of the United States RB.23/-H6-11 (c1888)	£37.00	—
	25	Theatrical Types RB.23/-H6-12 (c1890)	£36.00	—

HARTLEY'S TOBACCO CO., South Africa

L	19	South African English Cricket Tour 1929	£80.00	—

THE HILSON CO., USA

L	25	National Types (1900)	£26.00	—

IMPERIAL CIGARETTE & TOBACCO CO., Canada

	? 24	Actresses (c1900)	£60.00	—

IMPERIAL TOBACCO COMPANY OF CANADA LTD, Canada

A WITH FIRM'S NAME

	25	Beauties — Girls in Costume (c1903)	£55.00	—
	24	Beauties — Smoke Girls (c1903)	£55.00	—
M	50	Birds, Beasts and Fishes (1923)	£1.60	£80.00
L	100	Birds of Canada (1924)	£3.50	—
L	100	Birds of Canada (Western Canada) (1925)	£5.50	—
	50	British Birds (1923)	£1.00	£50.00
	48	Canadian History Series (1926)	£1.80	—
	50	Children of All Nations (1924)	£1.00	£50.00
	23	Dogs Series (1924)	£2.00	£45.00
	50	Dogs, 2nd series (1925)	£1.50	£75.00

Size	Number in set		Price per card	Complete set

IMPERIAL TOBACCO COMPANY OF CANADA LTD, Canada *(continued)*

Size	Number in set		Price per card	Complete set
	50	Famous English Actresses (1924)	£1.00	£50.00
	50	Film Favourites (1925):		
		A English Issue:		
		i Numbered	£3.00	—
		ii Unnumbered	£3.20	—
		B French Issue:		
		i Numbered	£6.00	—
		ii Unnumbered	£6.00	—
	50	Fish and Bait (1924)	£1.60	£80.00
	50	Fishes of the World (1924)	£2.20	£110.00
	50	Flower Culture in Pots (1925)	70p	£35.00
	30	Game Bird Series (1925)	£2.00	£60.00
	50	Gardening Hints (1923)	70p	£35.00
M	25	Heraldic Signs and Their Origins (1925)	£1.40	£35.00
	50	How to Play Golf (1925)	£8.00	—
	50	Infantry Training (1915):		
		A Glossy card	£2.50	—
		B Matt card	£2.50	—
L	48	Mail Carriers and Stamps (1903)	£27.00	—
	50	Merchant Ships of the World (1924)	£1.20	£60.00
	25	Military Portraits (1914)	£2.60	—
	50	Modern War Weapons, 'Sweet Caporal' issue (1914)	£3.50	—
	56	Motor Cars (1924)	£2.00	—
	50	Naval Portraits (1914)	£2.40	—
	25	Notabilities (1914)	£2.40	—
	53	Poker Hands (1924)	£1.50	—
	53	Poker Hands, New Series (1925)	£1.50	—
	25	Poultry Alphabet (1924)	£2.80	—
	50	Railway Engines (1924):		
		A With 'Wills' blanked out	£1.30	—
		B Without 'Wills'	£1.20	£60.00
	50	The Reason Why (1924)	£1.00	£50.00
	127	Smokers Golf Cards (1925)	£5.00	—
B	***WITHOUT FIRM'S NAME***			
	50	Arms of the British Empire (1911)	£2.50	—
	50	Around the World (c1910):		
		A Numbered	£3.50	—
		B Unnumbered	£6.00	—
	90	Baseball Series (1912)	£35.00	—
	30	Bird Series (c1910)	£2.50	—
	50	Boy Scouts (1911) — with album clause	£5.50	—
	50	Canadian Historical Portraits (1913)	£6.00	—
	50	Canadian History Series (1914)	£2.00	—
	50	Fish Series (c1910)	£2.40	—
	50	Fowls, Pigeons and Dogs (1911)	£3.50	—
	45	Hockey Players (1912)	£20.00	—
	36	Hockey Series (coloured) (1911)	£20.00	—
	50	How To Do It (c1910)	£3.00	—
	100	Lacrosse Series (coloured), Leading Players (c1910)	£7.00	—
	100	Lacrosse Series (coloured) (c1910)	£7.00	—
	50	Lacrosse Series (black and white) (c1910)	£7.00	—
	50	L'Historie du Canada (1926)	£1.50	—
	50	Movie Stars (c1930)	£2.00	—
L	50	Pictures of Canadian Life (c1910):		
		A Brown front	£7.00	—
		B Green front	£7.00	—

Size	Number in set		Price per card	Complete set

IMPERIAL TOBACCO COMPANY OF CANADA LTD, Canada *(continued)*

	50	Prominent Men of Canada (c1910)	£3.50	—
	50	Tricks and Puzzles (c1910)	£7.00	—
	50	Types of Nations (c1910)	£3.00	—
	25	Victoria Cross Heroes (blue back) (1915)	£3.20	£80.00
L	45	Views of the World (c1910)	£6.00	—
	25	The World's Dreadnoughts (1910)	£4.00	—
C		***SILKS ISSUED 1910-25***		
M	55	Animals with Flags	£4.00	—
EL	50	Canadian History Series	£11.00	—
M	121	Canadian Miscellany	£4.50	—
M	55	Garden Flowers of the World	£2.50	—
M	55	Orders and Military Medals	£3.50	—
M	55	Regimental Uniforms of Canada	£3.50	—
L	50	Yachts, Pennants and Views	£7.00	—

THE IMPERIAL TOBACCO CO. OF INDIA LTD, India

	25	Indian Historical Views (1915):		
		A Set 1, First Arrangement	£2.20	—
		B Set 2, Second Arrangement	£2.20	—
	40	Nautch Girl Series:		
		A 'Pedro Cigarettes' (c1905)	£3.00	—
		B 'Railway Cigarettes' (c1907)	£2.50	—
	52	Nautch Girl Series, PC inset:		
		A 'Pedro Cigarettes' (c1905)	£3.00	—
		B 'Railway Cigarettes' (c1907)	£2.50	—
K	53	Playing Cards, red back (1919)	£1.50	—
K	52	Playing Cards, blue back (1933)	£1.50	—

THE JERSEY TOBACCO CO. LTD, Channel Islands

K	53	Miniature Playing Cards (1933)	£1.00	—

JUST SO, USA

EL	?	Actresses (c1890)	£10.00	—

KENTUCKY TOBACCO PTY. LTD, South Africa

L	120	The March of Mankind (1940)	£2.25	—

KHEDIVIAL CO., USA

M	10	Aeroplane Series (c1910):		
		A Back 'Duke of York Cigarettes'	£25.00	—
		B Back 'Oxford Cigarettes'	£25.00	—
M	10	Prize Dog Series (c1910):		
		A Back 'Duke of York Cigarettes'	£25.00	—
		B Back 'Oxford Cigarettes'	£25.00	—
M	25	Prize Fight Series No. 101 (c1910):		
		A Back with Fight Details	£30.00	—
		B Back without Fight Details	£30.00	—
M	25	Prize Fight Series No. 102 (c1910)	£30.00	—

WM. S. KIMBALL & CO., USA

ALL SERIES ISSUED 1885-95

	? 42	Actresses	£75.00	—

Size	*Number in set*		*Price per card*	*Complete set*

WM. S. KIMBALL & CO., USA *(continued)*

	72	Ancient Coins:		
		A Title Ancient Coins	£30.00	—
		B Title Facsimile of Ancient Coins	£30.00	—
	48	Arms of Dominions	£22.00	—
	50	Ballet Queens	£24.00	—
	52	Beauties with Playing Card Insets	£24.00	—
EL	20	Beautiful Bathers	£45.00	—
	50	Butterflies	£24.00	—
		Champions of Games and Sports:		
	25	A Front with Firm's name	£55.00	—
	50	B Front without Firm's name	£55.00	—
	50	Dancing Girls of the World	£23.00	—
	50	Dancing Women	£23.00	—
	50	Fancy Bathers	£23.00	—
EL	25	French Novelties	£40.00	—
EL	25	Gems of Beauty	£40.00	—
	50	Goddesses of the Greeks & Romans	£30.00	—
EL	25	Household Pets	£35.00	—
	?	Photographic Actresses RB.23/K26-15-2	£7.00	—
EL	20	Pretty Athletes	£40.00	—
	50	Savage and Semi Barbarous Chiefs and Rulers	£30.00	—

KINNEY BROS., USA

ALL SERIES ISSUED 1885-95

	25	Actresses Group 1 Set 1 RB.118/1	£8.00	—
	25	Actresses Group 1 Set 2 RB.118/2	£12.00	—
	25	Actresses Group 1 Set 3 RB.118/3	£13.00	—
	25	Actresses Group 1 Set 4 RB.118/4	£15.00	—
	25	Actresses Group 1 Set 5 RB.118/5	£15.00	—
	25	Actresses Group 2 RB.118/15	£7.00	—
	25	Actresses Group 2 RB.118/16:		
		A Subjects named	£7.00	—
		B Subjects unnamed	£7.00	—
	25	Actresses Group 3 RB.118/26	£7.00	—
	25	Actresses Group 3 RB.118/29	£7.00	—
	50	Actresses Group 4 RB.118/36	£7.00	—
	129	Actresses Group 4 RB.118/37	£6.50	—
	25	Animals	£20.00	—
	10	Butterflies of the World. Light background	£22.00	—
	50	Butterflies of the World. Gold background	£20.00	—
	25	Famous Gems of the World	£22.00	—
	52	Harlequin Cards 1st series	£24.00	—
	53	Harlequin Cards 2nd series (1889)	£24.00	—
L	50	International Cards	£40.00	—
K	24	Jocular Oculars	£40.00	—
	25	Leaders:		
		A Standard size	£24.00	£600.00
		B Narrow card — officially cut	£24.00	£600.00
	50	Magic Changing Cards (1881)	£24.00	—
	622	Military Series:		
		A Coloured background:		
	50	1 Inscribed '7' on front	£7.00	—
	50	2 Inscribed '8' on front	£7.00	—
	30	3 Inscribed '9' on front	£7.00	—
	50	4 Without numeral	£7.00	—
	50	5 Foreign 1886 Types	£7.00	—

Size	Number in set		Price per card	Complete set

KINNEY BROS., USA *(continued)*

Size	Number in set		Price per card	Complete set
	622	Military Series, A Coloured background *continued*:		
		6 Other coloured background:		
	18	A U.S. Continental	£7.00	—
	3	B Vatican	£60.00	—
	5	C Decorations	£50.00	—
		B Plain white or lightly coloured background:		
	51	1 U.S Army and Navy	£7.00	—
	85	2 U.S. State Types	£7.00	—
	60	3 U.S and Foreign Types	£10.00	—
	50	4 England and N.G.S.N.Y.	£15.00	—
	50	5 Foreign 1853 Types	£10.00	—
	50	6 Foreign Types 1886	£7.00	—
	15	7 French Army and Navy	£7.00	—
	5	8 State Seals	£50.00	—
		National Dances:		
	50	A Front with white border	£20.00	—
	26	B Front without border	£22.00	—
	25	Naval Vessels of the World	£22.00	—
	50	New Year 1890 (1889)	£24.00	—
	25	Novelties Type 1. Thick circular, no border	£25.00	—
	50	Novelties Type 2. Thin circular with border	£13.00	—
		Novelties Type 3. Die cut:		
	25	A Inscribed '25 Styles'	£9.00	—
	50	B Inscribed '50 Styles'	£9.00	—
	75	C Inscribed '75 Styles'	£9.00	—
	50	Novelties Type 5. Standard size cards	£12.00	—
	14	Novelties Type 6. Oval	£28.00	—
		Photographic Cards:		
	?	A Actors and Actresses. Horizontal back with Kinney's name	£4.00	—
	?	B Actors and Actresses. Vertical, Sweet Caporal backs	£4.00	—
	45	C Famous Ships	£12.00	—
		Racehorses (1889):		
	25	1 American Horses:		
		A Back with series title 'Famous Running Horses'	£26.00	—
		B Back 'Return 25 of these small cards' 11 lines of text	£24.00	—
	25	2 English Horses 'Return 25 of these cards' with 6 lines of text	£24.00	—
	25	3 Great American Trotters	£26.00	—
	50	Surf Beauties	£24.00	—
	52	Transparent Playing Cards	£15.00	—
	25	Types of Nationalities (folders)	£26.00	—

KRAMERS TOBACCO CO. (PTY) LTD, South Africa

Size	Number in set		Price per card	Complete set
	50	Badges of South African Rugby Football Clubs (1933)	£8.00	—

LEWIS & ALLEN CO. USA

Size	Number in set		Price per card	Complete set
L	? 120	Views and Art Studies (c1910)	£6.00	—

LONE JACK CIGARETTE CO. USA

Size	Number in set		Price per card	Complete set
	25	Inventors and Inventions (c1888)	£70.00	—
	50	Language of Flowers (1888):		
		A Front 'Lone Jack Cigarettes'	£30.00	—
		B Front 'Ruby Cigarettes'	£30.00	—
		C Front 'Unknown Cigarettes'	£30.00	—

Size	Number in set		Price per card	Complete set

P. LORILLARD CO., USA

ALL SERIES ISSUED 1885-98

M	25	Actresses RB.23/L70-4-3	£30.00	—
M	25	Actresses RB.23/L70-5	£30.00	—
EL	25	Actresses RB.23/L70-6:		
		A 'Red Cross' long cut	£30.00	—
		B 'Sensation Cut Plug' front and back	£30.00	—
		C 'Sensation Cut Plug' front only	£30.00	—
EL	25	Actresses RB.23/L70-8	£30.00	—
EL	25	Actresses in Opera Roles RB.23/L70-9	£40.00	—
M	25	Ancient Mythology Burlesqued RB.23/L70-10	£28.00	—
M	50	Beautiful Women RB.23/L70-11:		
		A '5c Ante' front and back	£26.00	—
		B 'Lorillard's Snuff' front and back	£26.00	—
		C 'Tiger' front and back	£26.00	—
EL	25	Circus Scenes	£80.00	—
	25	National Flags	£30.00	—
EL	50	Prizefighters	£120.00	—
M	25	Types of the Stage	£28.00	—

W.C. MACDONALD INC., Canada

	?	Aeroplanes and Warships (c1940)	£1.30	—
M	53	Playing Cards (different designs) (1926-47)	70p	—

B. & J.B. MACHADO, Jamaica

	25	British Naval series (1916)	£22.00	—
	50	The Great War — Victoria Cross Heroes (1916)	£24.00	—
P	50	Popular Film Stars (1926)	£6.00	—
P	50	The Royal Family at Home and Abroad (1927)	£5.00	—
P	52	Stars of the Cinema (1926)	£6.00	—
P	50	The World of Sport (1928)	£8.00	—

MACLIN-ZIMMER-MCGILL TOB. CO., USA

EL	53	Playing Cards — Actresses (c1890)	£23.00	—

MALTA CIGARETTE CO., Malta

	135	Dante's Divine Comedy (c1905)	£15.00	—
	M40	Maltese Families Arms & Letters (c1905)	£7.00	—
	? 44	Prominent People (c1905)	£15.00	—

H. MANDELBAUM, USA

	36	Flags of Nations (c1890)	£40.00	—
	20	Types of People (c1890)	£60.00	—

MARBURG BROS., USA

	50	National Costume Cards (c1890):		
		A Front 'Greenback Smoking Mixture'	£60.00	—
		B Front 'Seal of Virginia Smoking Mixture'	£60.00	—
	50	Typical Ships (c1890)	£60.00	—

MASPERO FRERES LTD, Palestine

	50	Birds, Beasts and Fishes (1925)	£4.00	—

Size	*Number in set*		*Price per card*	*Complete set*

P.H. MAYO & BROTHER, USA

	25	Actresses RB.23/M80-1 (c1890)	£30.00	—
M	25	Actresses RB.23/M80-3 (c1890)	£30.00	—
L	12	Actresses RB.23/M80-4 (c1890)	£75.00	—
	? 39	Actresses RB.23/M80-5 (c1890)	£30.00	—
	40	Baseball Players (c1890)	£120.00	—
	20	Costumes and Flowers (c1890)	£32.00	—
	25	Head Dresses of Various Nations (c1890)	£34.00	—
M	25	National Flowers (Girl and Scene) (c1890)	£34.00	—
	20	Naval Uniforms (c1890)	£32.00	—
	35	Prizefighters (c1890)	£65.00	—
	20	Shakespeare Characters (c1890)	£32.00	—

M. MELACHRINO & CO., Switzerland

	52	Peuples Exotiques 1st series (c1925)	£1.00	—
	52	Peuples Exotiques 2nd series (c1925)	£1.00	—
	52	Peuples Exotiques 3rd series (c1925)	£1.00	—

MIFSUD & AZZOPARDI, Malta

KP	59	First Maltese Parliament (1922)	£8.00	—

L. MILLER & SONS, USA

M	25	Battleships (c1900)	£30.00	—
M	25	Generals and Admirals (Spanish War) (c1900)	£30.00	—
M	24	Presidents of US (c1900)	£26.00	—
M	50	Rulers of the World (c1900)	£24.00	—

CHAS. J. MITCHELL & CO., Canada

	26	Actresses — 'FROGA A' (1900):		
		A Backs in brown	£36.00	—
		B Backs in green	£34.00	—
	26	Actresses – 'FROGA B' with Playing Card inset (1900)	£60.00	—

MITSUI & CO., Japan

	?	Japanese Women (c1908)	£9.00	—

MOORE & CALVI, USA

EL	53	Playing Cards — Actresses (c1890):		
		A 'Trumps Long Cut' back	£25.00	—
		B 'Hard-A-Port' with maker's name	£23.00	—
		C 'Hard-A-Port' without maker's name	£23.00	—

MURAI BROS. & CO., Japan

	150	Actresses — 'ALWICS' (c1905)	£10.00	—
	100	Beauties — 'THIBS' (c1900)	£32.00	—
	50	Beauties Group 1 (c1902)	£14.00	—
	25	Chinese Beauties 1st series Peacock issue (c1910)	£3.60	£90.00
	25	Chinese Beauties 3rd series Peacock issue (c1910)	£4.50	—
	50	Chinese Beauties, back in red (c1908)	£6.00	—
	50	Chinese Children's Games without border Peacock issue (c1910)	£3.20	£160.00
	20	Chinese Children's Games with border Peacock issue (c1910)	£3.20	—
	54	Chinese Girls Set 3 (c1905)	£7.50	—
	50	Chinese Pagodas Peacock issue (c1910)	£4.00	—

Size	Number in set		Price per card	Complete set

MURAI BROS. & CO., Japan *(continued)*

	30	Chinese Series Peacock issue (c1910)	£3.50	—
	40	Chinese Trades I, back in black (c1905)	£25.00	—
	40	Chinese Trades II, back in olive, Peacock issue (c1910)	£5.00	—
	50	Dancing Girls of the World (c1900)	£40.00	—

NATIONAL CIGARETTE CO., Australia

	13	English Cricket Team 1897-8:		
		A Front black and white	£400.00	—
		B Front yellow-brown	£400.00	—

NATIONAL CIGARETTE AND TOBACCO CO., USA

	25	National Types (c1890)	£28.00	—
	44	National Types (c1890)	£26.00	—

PHOTOGRAPHIC CARDS

	?	Actresses (c1888):		
		A Plain back	£8.00	—
		B Printed back	£9.00	—

NATIONAL TOBACCO WORKS, USA

EL	13	Art Miniatures (1892)	£25.00	—
EL	?	Cabinet Pictures (c1890)	£25.00	—

OLD FASHION, USA

L	? 200	Photographic Cards — Actresses (c1890)	£15.00	—

PENINSULAR TOBACCO CO. LTD, India

	50	Animals and Birds (1910)	£2.70	—
	52	Birds of Brilliant Plumage (1916):		
		A Back with single large packings	£3.20	—
		B Back with two small packings	£3.20	—
	25	Birds of the East, 1st series (1912)	£2.60	—
	25	Birds of the East, 2nd series (1912)	£2.60	£65.00
	25	China's Famous Warriors:		
		A Back 'Monchyr India'	£3.60	£90.00
		B Back 'India' only	£3.60	£90.00
	25	Chinese Heroes (1913)	£3.20	£80.00
	50	Chinese Modern Beauties (1912)	£6.50	—
	50	Chinese Trades (1908):		
		A Back with 'Monchyr'	£3.20	—
		B Back without 'Monchyr'	£3.20	—
	30	Fish series (1916)	£2.70	—
	25	Hindoo Gods (1909)	£3.20	£80.00
	37	Nautch Girl series (1910)	£7.00	—
	25	Products of the World (1915)	£2.40	60.00

PIZZUTO, Malta

	50	Milton's Paradise Lost (c1910)	£18.00	—

PLANTERS' STORES & AGENCY CO. LTD, India

	? 47	Actresses — 'FROGA' (1900)	£38.00	—
	25	Beauties 'FECKSA' (1900)	£40.00	—

Size	Number in set		Price per card	Complete set

POLICANSKY BROS., South Africa

	50	Beautiful Illustrations of South African Fauna (1925):		
		A Back 'Mast Cigarettes'	£10.00	—
		B Back 'Mignon Cigarettes'	£10.00	—

R.J. REYNOLDS (Doral), USA

		America's Backyard (plants) (2006):		
	23	A Set of 23	£1.25	—
	1	B Limited Edition Holographic Card	—	£5.00
		America On The Road (2004):		
	25	A Set of 24 plus List Card	£1.25	—
	1	B Limited Edition Card	—	—
		American Treasures (2005):		
	25	A Set of 24 plus List Card	£1.25	—
	1	B Limited Edition Card	—	—
	4	Doral's Employees (2006)	£1.25	£5.00
	52	The 50 States (2000) plus 2 List Cards	£1.25	—
		Great American Festivals (2003):		
	31	A Set of 30 plus List Card	£1.25	—
	1	B Limited Edition Card	—	—
		Smoking Moments (2007):		
	24	A Set of 24	£1.25	—
	1	B Limited Edition Card — At The Drive In	—	—
		Snapshots of The Century (2001):		
	36	A Set of 35 plus Title Card	£1.25	—
	1	B Limited Edition Card	—	£3.00
	1	C Special Edition Card	—	£6.00

D. RITCHIE & CO., Canada

	52	Beauties Playing Card inset, multi-backed (c1890)	£35.00	—
	52	Playing Cards, mutli-backed (c1890)	£35.00	—

RUGGIER BROS., Malta

M	50	Story of the Knights of Malta (c1925)	£6.50	—

SANTA FE NATURAL TOBACCO CO., USA

	36	A Tribute To The Endangered Set 1 (2001)	£1.25	—
	36	A Tribute To The Endangered Set 2 (2001)	£1.25	—
	36	Century of The Great American Spirit Set 1 (2000)	£1.25	—
	36	Century of The Great American Spirit Set 2 (2000)	£1.25	—
	36	Music of America (2003)	£1.25	—
	36	Spirit of The Old West Series 1 (1999)	£1.25	—
	36	Spirit of The Old West Series 2 (1999)	£1.25	—

SCERRI, Malta

		Beauties and Children (c1930):		
	150	A Black and white, no borders	£1.20	—
	? 86	B Black and white, white border	£14.00	—
	45	C Coloured	£1.70	—
MP	50	Beautiful Women (c1935)	£3.20	£160.00
MP	480	Cinema Artists (c1935)	£2.40	—
MP	180	Cinema Stars (c1935)	£2.70	—
MP	50	Famous London Buildings (c1935)	£4.00	—
MP	60	Film Stars 1st series Nos 1-60 (c1935)	£3.20	—
MP	60	Film Stars 2nd series Nos 61-120 (c1935)	£3.20	—
	52	Interesting Places of the World (c1936)	50p	£26.00

Size	*Number in set*		*Price per card*	*Complete set*

SCERRI, Malta *(continued)*

P	25	International Footballers (c1935)	£30.00	—
M	401	Malta Views (c1930)	80p	—
M	51	Members of Parliament — Malta (c1930)	44p	£22.00
	146	Prominent People (c1930)	£1.50	—
MP	100	Scenes from Films (c1935)	£3.00	—
LP	100	Talkie Stars (c1930)	£3.00	—
M	100	World's Famous Buildings (c1930)	55p	£55.00

J.J. SCHUH TOBACCO CO. PTY LTD, Australia

ALL SERIES ISSUED 1920-25

	60	Australian Footballers series A (half-full length)	£11.00	—
	40	Australian Footballers series B (Rays)	£11.00	—
	59	Australian Footballers series C (oval frame)	£20.00	—
		Australian Jockeys:		
	30	A Numbered	£6.50	—
	30	B Unnumbered	£6.50	—
P	72	Cinema Stars	£2.50	—
	60	Cinema Stars	£2.75	—
L	12	Maxims of Success	£40.00	—
P	72	Official War Photographs	£3.50	—
P	96	Portraits of Our Leading Footballers	£5.00	—

G. SCLIVAGNOTI, Malta

	50	Actresses and Cinema Stars (1923)	£3.00	—
MP	71	Grand Masters of the Orders of Jerusalem (1897)	£11.00	—
P	102	Opera Singers (1897)	£15.00	—
M	100	Opera Singers (1897)	£15.00	—

SIMONETS LTD, Jersey, Channel Islands

MP	36	Beautiful Women (c1925)	£6.00	—
P	24	Cinema Scenes series (c1925)	£7.50	—
P	27	Famous Actors and Actresses (c1925)	£6.50	—
	50	Local Footballers (c1914)	£6.50	—
	25	Picture Series (c1920)	£5.00	—
P	27	Sporting Celebrities (c1930)	£10.00	—
LP	50	Views of Jersey (plain back) (c1940)	£2.50	—

THE SINSOCK & CO., Korea

	20	Korean Girls (c1905)	£20.00	—

SNIDERS & ABRAHAMS PTY LTD, Australia

		Actresses (c1905):		
	30	A Gold background	£7.00	—
	14	B White Borders	£7.00	—
	20	Admirals and Warships of USA (1908)	£8.00	—
	60	Animals (c1912)	£3.75	—
	60	Animals and Birds (c1912):		
		A 'Advertising Gifts' issue	£2.75	—
		B 'Peter Pan' issue	£3.20	—
	15	Australian Cricket Team (1905)	£45.00	—
	16	Australian Football Incidents in Play (c1906)	£15.00	—
	24	Australian Footballers (full length) series AI, back with 'O & A' (1905)	£20.00	—
	50	Australian Footballers (full length) series AII, back without 'O & A' (1905)	£20.00	—
	76	Australian Footballers (½ length) series B (1906)	£20.00	—

Size	Number in set		Price per card	Complete set

SNIDERS & ABRAHAMS PTY LTD, Australia *(continued)*

	76	Australian Footballers (½ length) series C (1907)	£20.00	—
	140	Australian Footballers (head and shoulders) series D (1908)	£18.00	—
	60	Australian Footballers (head in oval) series E (1910)	£18.00	—
	60	Australian Footballers (head in rays) series F (1911)	£18.00	—
	60	Australian Footballers (with pennant) series G (1912)	£18.00	—
	60	Australian Footballers (head in star) series H (1913)	£18.00	—
	60	Australian Footballers (head in shield) series I (1914)	£18.00	—
	56	Australian Footballers (½-¾ length) series J (1910)	£18.00	—
	48	Australian Jockeys, back in blue (1907)	£5.00	—
	83	Australian Jockeys, back in brown (1908)	£5.50	—
	56	Australian Racehorses, horizontal back (1906)	£6.00	—
	56	Australian Racehorses, vertical back (1907)	£6.00	—
	40	Australian Racing Scenes (1911)	£6.00	—
	? 133	Australian VCs and Officers (1917)	£6.50	—
	12	Billiard Tricks (c1910)	£20.00	—
	60	Butterflies and Moths, captions in small letters (c1912)	£2.00	—
	60	Butterflies and Moths, captions in block letters (c1912)	£2.00	—
	60	Cartoons and Caricatures (c1908):		
		A Front with border	£6.50	—
		B Front without border	£6.50	—
	12	Coin Tricks (c1910)	£15.00	—
	64	Crests of British Warships (1915):		
		A Back in blue	£5.00	—
		B Back in green	£5.00	—
	40	Cricketers in Action (1906)	£60.00	—
	12	Cricket Terms (c1906)	£30.00	—
	32	Dickens series (c1910)	£5.00	—
	16	Dogs (c1910):		
		A 'Standard' issue	£10.00	—
		B 'Peter Pan' issue:		
		1 White panel	£10.00	—
		2 Gilt panel	£10.00	—
		C 'Coronet' issue	£10.00	—
	6	Flags (shaped metal) (c1910)	£6.00	—
	6	Flags (shaped card) (c1910)	£6.00	—
	60	Great War Leaders and Warships (c1915):		
		A Front in green	£4.50	—
		B Front in sepia brown	£4.50	—
	30	How to Keep Fit (c1908)	£6.50	—
	60	Jokes (c1906):		
		A 'Aristocratica' back in brown	£4.00	—
		B 'Standard' back in blue	£4.00	—
		C 'Milo' back in green	£4.00	—
	12	Match Puzzles (c1910)	£15.00	—
	48	Medals and Decorations (c1915)	£6.00	—
M	48	Melbourne Buildings (c1915)	£8.00	—
	25	Natives of the World (c1906)	£18.00	—
	12	Naval Terms (c1906)	£9.00	—
	29	Oscar Ashe, Lily Brayton and Lady Smokers (1911)	£6.00	—
	40	Shakespeare Characters (c1908)	£5.50	—
	30	Signalling — Semaphore and Morse (c1916)	£7.00	—
	14	Statuary (c1906)	£9.00	—
	60	Street Criers in London, 1707 (c1916)	£8.00	—
	32	Views of Victoria in 1857 (c1908):		
		A Green back	£10.00	—
		B Brown back	£10.00	—
P	250	Views of the World 1908	£3.50	—

Size	Number in set		Price per card	Complete set

STAR TOBACCO CO., India

	52	Beauties (PC inset), multi-backed (c1898)	£28.00	–
	52	Indian Native Types (PC inset) (c1898)	£28.00	–

SUM MUYE & CO., Siam

	50	Siamese Royalty (c1912)	£8.00	–

TOBACCO PRODUCTS CORPORATION, USA

	220	Movie Stars (1915)	£3.00	–
	100	Movie Stars (sepia) (c1915)	£4.00	–
	120	Movie Stars (portrait in oval) (c1915)	£4.00	–

TOBACCO PRODUCTS CORPORATION OF CANADA LTD

	? 45	Canadian Sports Champions (c1920)	£18.00	–
	60	Do You Know (1924)	£6.00	–
	60	Hockey Players (1926)	£30.00	–
	120	Movie Stars (c1920)	£2.50	–
	100	Movie Stars (sepia) (c1920)	£4.00	–
	L20	Movie Stars Series 3 (Mack Sennett Girls)	£5.00	–
	? 120	Movie Stars Set 4 (c1920)	£3.50	–
	? L67	Movie Stars Series 5 (c1920)	£5.00	–
	L100	Movie Stars (sepia) (c1920)	£5.00	–

TUCKETT LIMITED, Canada

	25	Autograph Series (c1913)	£30.00	–
	? 210	Beauties and Scenes (c1910)	£8.00	–
	25	Boy Scout Series (c1915)	£25.00	–
P	100	British Views without Tucketts on front (c1912)	£2.50	–
P	? 224	British Views with Tucketts on front (c1912):		
		A Back 'Karnak Cigarettes'	£2.50	–
		B Back 'T & B' trade mark	£2.50	–
		C Back 'Tuckett's Special Turkish Cigarettes'	£2.50	–
P	80	British Warships (c1915):		
		A Back 'T & B' trade mark	£9.00	–
		B Back 'Tuckett's Special Turkish Cigarettes'	£9.00	–
P	50	Canadian Scenes (c1912)	£2.40	–
	53	Playing Card Premium Certificates (c1930)	£7.50	–
	52	Tucketts Aeroplane Series (1930)	£4.50	–
	52	Tucketts Aviation Series (1929)	£4.50	–
	52	Tucketts Auction Bridge Series (1930)	£6.00	–

UNITED TOBACCO COMPANIES (SOUTH) LTD, South Africa

A WITH FIRM'S NAME

	50	Aeroplanes of Today (1936):		
		A 'Box 78 Capetown'	£1.80	£90.00
		B 'Box 1006 Capetown'	£1.80	£90.00
	50	Animals and Birds Koodoo issue (1923)	£7.00	–
L	24	Arms and Crests of Universities and Schools of South Africa (1930)	£1.40	£35.00
L	52	Boy Scouts, Girl Guide and Voortrekker Badges (1932)	£2.20	–
L	62	British Rugby Tour of South Africa (1938)	£1.80	–
	50	Children of All Nations (1928)	£1.00	–
	50	Cinema Stars 'Flag Cigarettes' (1924)	£2.20	£110.00
	60	Do You Know? (1929)	60p	£36.00
	50	Do You Know 2nd series (1930)	60p	£30.00
	50	Do You Know 3rd series (1931)	60p	£30.00

Size	Number in set		Price per card	Complete set

UNITED TOBACCO COMPANIES (SOUTH) LTD, South Africa *(continued)*

Size	Number in set		Price per card	Complete set
K	28	Dominoes 'Ruger Cigarettes' (1934)	£6.00	—
L	50	Exercises for Men and Women (1932)	£1.00	£50.00
	48	Fairy Tales 1st series Flag issue (1928)	£1.80	—
	48	Fairy Tales 2nd series Flag issue (1928)	£1.80	—
	24	Fairy Tales (1926) (booklets)	£10.00	—
L	120	Farmyards of South Africa (1934)	£1.50	—
M	50	Household Hints (1926)	£2.00	—
	25	Interesting Experiments (1930)	£1.40	£35.00
L	100	Medals and Decorations of the British Commonwealth of Nations (1941)	90p	—
	50	Merchant Ships of the World (1925)	£1.20	£60.00
	50	Motor Cars (1923)	£4.00	—
L	100	Our Land (1938)	25p	£25.00
L	200	Our South Africa Past and Present (1938)	20p	£40.00
L	24	Pastel Plates (1938)	£1.20	£30.00
L	88	Philosophical Sayings (1938)	£1.20	—
	25	Picturesque People of the Empire (1929)	£1.80	£45.00
K	53	Playing Cards 'Flag' Cigarettes	£1.80	—
K	53	Playing Cards 'Lifeboat' Cigarettes (1934)	£2.00	—
M	53	Playing Cards 'Lotus Cigarettes' (1934)	£2.50	—
L	53	Playing Cards 'Loyalist Cigarettes' (1934)	£2.00	—
K	53	Playing Cards 'MP Cigarettes' (1934)	£2.00	—
K	53	Playing Cards 'Rugger Cigarettes' (1934)	£3.00	—
L	50	Racehorses South Africa Set 1 (1929)	£2.00	—
L	52	Racehorses South Africa Set 2 (1930):		
		A Inscribed 'a series of 50'	£2.00	—
		B Inscribed 'a series of 52'	£2.00	—
	50	Regimental Uniforms (1937)	£1.80	£90.00
	50	Riders of the World (1931)	£1.40	£70.00
L	52	S. A. Flora (1935):		
		A With 'CT Ltd'	50p	—
		B Without 'CT Ltd'	40p	£22.00
	25	South African Birds 1st series (1927)	£1.80	—
	25	South African Birds 2nd series (1927)	£1.80	—
L	52	South African Butterflies (1937)	80p	£42.00
L	52	South African Coats of Arms (1931)	50p	£26.00
L	65	South African Rugby Football Clubs (1933)	£2.00	—
L	52	Sports and Pastimes in South Africa (1936)	£1.80	£90.00
L	47	Springbok Rugby and Cricket Teams (1931)	£3.00	—
L	28	1912-13 Springboks (1913)	£75.00	—
	25	Studdy Dogs (1925)	£5.00	—
	? 98	Transfers (c1925)	£6.00	—
L	40	Views of South African Scenery 1st series (1918):		
		A Text back	£4.50	—
		B Anonymous plain back	£4.50	—
L	36	Views of South African Scenery 2nd series (1920)	£4.50	—
	25	Wild Flowers of South Africa 1st series (1925)	£1.60	—
	25	Wild Flowers of South Africa 2nd series (1926)	£1.60	—
	50	The World of Tomorrow (1938)	£1.10	£55.00

B WITHOUT FIRM'S NAME

Size	Number in set		Price per card	Complete set
	50	African Fish (1937)	£1.60	£80.00
	50	British Aeroplanes (1933)	£1.80	—
EL	25	Champion Dogs (1934)	£5.00	—
	30	Do You Know (1933)	80p	£24.00
	50	Eminent Film Personalities (1930)	£2.20	—
	50	English Period Costumes (1932)	£1.00	£50.00
	25	Famous Figures from South African History (1932)	£2.40	—

Size	Number in set		Price per card	Complete set

UNITED TOBACCO COMPANIES (SOUTH) LTD, South Africa *(continued)*

L	100	Famous Works of Art (1939)	30p	£30.00
	25	Flowers of South Africa (1932)	£2.00	—
M	50	Humour in Sport (1929)	£3.50	—
L	100	Our Land (1938)	30p	—
M	150	Our South African Birds (1942)	50p	£75.00
L	150	Our South African Birds (1942)	40p	£60.00
M	100	Our South African Flora (1940)	25p	£25.00
L	100	Our South African Flora (1940)	20p	£17.00
M	100	Our South African National Parks (1941)	25p	£25.00
L	100	Our South African National Parks (1941)	22p	£22.00
L	50	Pictures of South Africa's War Effort (1942)	40p	£20.00
	50	Riders of the World (1931)	£1.40	£70.00
	50	Safety First (1936)	£1.20	£60.00
	40	Ships of All Times (1931)	£1.80	—
	25	South African Birds 2nd series	£2.60	—
L	17	South African Cricket Touring Team (1929):		
		A Fronts with autographs	£20.00	—
		B Fronts without autographs	£20.00	—
M	100	South African Defence (1939)	25p	£25.00
L	50	South African Places of Interest (1934)	40p	£20.00
P	50	Stereoscopic Photographs Assorted Subjects (1928)	£1.20	—
P	50	Stereoscopic Photographs of South Africa (1929)	£1.20	—
	50	The Story of Sand (1934)	£1.00	£50.00
M	50	Tavern of the Seas (1939)	50p	£25.00
	25	Warriors of All Nations (crossed swords at base) (1937)	£2.00	£50.00
	25	What's This (1929)	£1.80	£45.00
	50	Wild Animals of the World (1932)	£1.50	£75.00
M	40	Wonders of the World (1931)	£1.10	—
M	100	World Famous Boxers (c1935)	£6.00	—

C SILK ISSUES

M	20	British Butterflies (c1920)	£10.00	—
M	30	British Roses (c1920)	£10.00	—
M	65	Flags of All Nations (c1920)	£3.00	—
M	25	Old Masters (c1920)	£8.00	—
M	50	Pottery Types (c1920)	£7.00	—
M	50	South African Flowers Nd 1-50 (c1920)	£3.75	—
M	50	South African Flowers Nd 51-100 (c1920)	£3.75	—

UNIVERSAL TOBACCO CO. PTY LTD, South Africa

	835	Flags of All Nations (1935)	£1.20	—

S.W. VENABLE TOBACCO CO., USA

EL	? 56	Actresses, multi-backed (c1890)	£38.00	—

GEO. F. YOUNG & BRO., USA

L	?	Actresses (c1890)	£32.00	—

ANONYMOUS SERIES — Chinese Language

M	10	Chinese Beauties (Ref ZE2-11) (c1930)	—	£20.00
M	10	Chinese Series (Ref ZE9-31) (c1930)	—	£20.00
	10	Chinese Views & Scenes (Ref ZE9-49) (c1930) (San Shing)	—	£20.00
	48	Hints on Association Football (Ref ZE3-2) (c1930)	—	£10.00
	30	Safety First (Ref ZE9-41) (c1930) (Hwa Ching)	—	£45.00

SECTION 3

REPRINT SERIES

During the past twenty years or so, around 350 classic cigarette and trade card series have been reprinted. Many of the originals are extremely rare and do not often turn up in collections, so reprints provide an opportunity to enjoy cards rarely seen. At such low prices, reprints have established a following in their own right, and have also become popular for framing to make an interesting decorative feature. The quality of reproduction is very good, and they are clearly marked as reprints to avoid confusion.

NOTE: C.C.S. = Card Collectors Society

Size	*Print-ing*	*Number in set*		*Complete set*
ADKIN & SONS				
—	C	4	Games by Tom Browne (135 × 83mm) c1900 (reprinted 2001)	£4.00
A.W. ALLEN LTD (Australia)				
D2	U	18	Bradman's Records (Cricketer) 1932 (reprinted 2002)	£7.00
ALLEN & GINTER/GOODWIN/KIMBALL (USA)				
A	C	28	Baseball Greats of 1890 (reprinted 1991)	£6.00
ALLEN & GINTER (USA)				
A	C	50	Celebrated American Indian Chiefs 1888 (reprinted 1989)	£8.50
A	C	50	Fans of The Period 1890 (reprinted 2005)	£8.50
A	C	50	Fruits (Children) 1891 (reprinted 1989)	£8.50
A	C	50	Pirates of the Spanish Main 1888 (reprinted 1996)	—
A	C	50	Prize and Game Chickens c1890 (reprinted 2000)	£10.00
D2	U	9	Women Baseball Players c1888 (reprinted 2001)	£3.00
—	C	50	The World's Champions 2nd Series (82 × 73mm) c1890 (reprinted 2001)	£17.50
AMERICAN TOBACCO CO. (USA)				
B	C	50	Lighthouse Series 1912 (reprinted 2000)	£12.00
A	C	25	Military Uniforms — numbered (green net design back) 1900 (reprinted 2003)	£6.25
ARDATH TOBACCO CO. LTD				
A2	C	35	Hand Shadows c1930 (reprinted 2001)	£7.50
A. BAKER & CO. LTD				
A	C	25	Star Girls c1898 (reprinted 2001)	£6.00
BARBERS TEA LTD				
A	C	24	Cinema & Television Stars 1955 (reprinted 1993)	£6.25

Size	Printing	Number in set		Complete set

BENSDORP COCOA (Holland)

—	C	3	Deep Sea Divers (99 × 70mm) c1900 (reprinted c1995)	£2.50

FELIX BERLYN

A	C	25	Golfing Series Humorous 1910 (reprinted 1989)	£6.00

ALEXANDER BOGUSLAVSKY LTD

—	C	12	Big Events on the Turf (133 × 70mm) 1924 (reprinted 1995)	—
A	C	25	Conan Doyle Characters 1923 (reprinted 1996)	£6.25
A	C	25	Winners on the Turf 1925 (reprinted 1995)	£6.25

BOWMAN GUM INC. (USA)

—	C	108	Jets-Rockets-Spacemen (80 × 54mm) 1951 (reprinted 1985)	£9.00

WM BRADFORD

D2	U	20	Boer War Cartoons c1901 (reprinted 2001)	£5.00

BRIGHAM & CO

B2	BW	16	Down The Thames From Henley to Windsor c1912 (reprinted 2001)	£6.50

BRITISH AMERICAN TOBACCO CO. LTD

A	C	50	Aeroplanes 1926 (reprinted 2001)	£8.50
D	C	25	Beauties — Blossom Girls c1904 (reprinted 2001)	£6.00
A	C	32	Drum Horses 1910 (reprinted 2001)	£6.25
A	C	50	Indian Regiments 1912 (reprinted 2001)	£8.50
A	C	50	Lighthouses 1926 (reprinted 2000)	£8.50
A	C	45	Melbourne Cup Winners 1906 (reprinted 1992)	£8.50
A	C	50	Motorcycles 1927 (reprinted 1991)	£8.50
A	C	33	Regimental Pets 1911 (reprinted 1998)	£6.25

CADBURY BROS. LTD

—	C	6	Sports Series (109 × 35mm) c1905 (reprinted 2001)	£3.00

CARRERAS LTD

A	C	50	Famous Airmen & Airwomen 1936 (reprinted 1996)	£8.50
A	C	75	Footballers 1934 (reprinted 1997)	£13.50

H. CHAPPEL & CO.

A2	C	10	British Celebrities 1905 (reprinted 2001)	£3.00

W.A. & A.C. CHURCHMAN

A	U	50	Boxing Personalities 1938 (reprinted 1990)	£8.50
A	C	50	Cricketers 1936 (C.C.S. reprinted 1999)	£10.00
A	C	52	Frisky 1935 (reprinted 1994)	£8.50
A	C	50	In Town To-Night 1938 (C.C.S. reprinted 1999)	£10.00
A	C	50	Landmarks in Railway Progress 1931 (reprinted 1994)	£8.50
A	C	50	Pioneers 1956 (reprinted 2000)	£9.50
A	C	25	Pipes of The World 1927 (C.C.S. reprinted 2000)	£6.50
A	C	50	Prominent Golfers 1931 (reprinted 1989)	£8.50
B	C	12	Prominent Golfers 1931 (reprinted 1989)	£6.00
A	C	50	Racing Greyhounds 1934 (reprinted 1989)	£8.50

Size	Printing	Number in set		Complete set

W.A. & A.C. CHURCHMAN *(continued)*

—	C	48	The RAF at Work (68 × 53mm) 1938 (reprinted 1995)	£14.00
A	C	50	The Story of Navigation 1936 (C.C.S. reprinted 1999)	£10.00

WM. CLARKE & SON

A	BW	30	Cricketer Series 1901 (reprinted 2001)	£7.50

COHEN WEENEN & CO. LTD

A	C	60	Football Club Captains 1907-8 (reprinted 1998)	£10.00
A	C	40	Home & Colonial Regiments 1901 (reprinted 1998)	£8.50
A	C	50	Star Artistes 1905 (reprinted 1998)	£8.50
A	C	50	V.C. Heroes (of World War I) 1915 (reprinted 1998)	£8.50

CO-OPERATIVE WHOLESALE SOCIETY LTD (C.W.S.)

A	C	25	Parrot Series 1910 (reprinted 1996)	£6.00
A	C	48	Poultry 1927 (reprinted 1996)	£8.50

COPE BROS. & CO. LTD

A	C	50	British Warriors 1912 (reprinted 1996)	£8.50
A	C	50	Cope's Golfers 1900 (reprinted 1983)	£8.50
A	C	50	Dickens Gallery 1900 (reprinted 1989)	—
—	C	7	The Seven Ages of Man (114 × 78mm) c1885 (reprinted 2001)	£6.00
A	C	50	Shakespeare Gallery 1900 (reprinted 1989)	—
A	C	25	Uniforms of Soldiers and Sailors 1898 (reprinted 1996)	£6.25
A	C	25	The World's Police 1935 (reprinted 2005)	£6.00

DAH TUNG NAN (China)

—	C	18	Golf Girl Series (65 × 50mm) c1920 (reprinted 1997)	£6.00

W. DUKE, SONS & CO (USA)

A	C	25	Fishers c1890 (reprinted 2002)	£6.00
A	C	30	Generals of American Civil War (Histories of Generals) 1888 (reprinted 1995)	£6.25

J. DUNCAN & CO. LTD

D1	C	50	Evolution of The Steamship 1925 (reprinted 2002)	£8.50

H. ELLIS & CO. (USA)

A	C	25	Generals of the Late Civil War 1890 (reprinted 1991)	£6.00

EMPIRE TOBACCO CO.

D	C	6	Franco-British Exhibition 1907 (reprinted 2001)	£2.00

W. & F. FAULKNER

C	C	25	Beauties (coloured) c1898 (reprinted 2001)	£6.00
D	C	12	Cricket Terms 1899 (reprinted 1999)	£2.50
D	C	12	Football Terms 1st Series 1900 (reprinted 1999)	£2.50
D	C	12	Football Terms 2nd Series 1900 (reprinted 1999)	£2.50
D	C	12	Golf Terms (with "Faulkners" on front) 1901 (reprinted 1999)	£2.50
D2	C	12	Golf Terms (without "Faulkners" titled Golf Humour) 1901 (reprinted 1998)	£2.50
D	C	12	Grenadier Guards 1899 (reprinted 1999)	£2.50
D	C	12	Military Terms 1st Series 1899 (reprinted 1999)	£2.50
D	C	12	Military Terms 2nd Series 1899 (reprinted 1999)	£2.50

Size	*Print-ing*	*Number in set*		*Complete set*

W. & F. FAULKNER *(continued)*

D	C	12	Nautical Terms 1st Series 1900 (reprinted 1999)	£2.50
D	C	12	Nautical Terms 2nd Series 1900 (reprinted 1999)	£2.50
D	C	12	Policemen of the World 1899 (reprinted 1999)	£2.50
D	C	12	Police Terms (with "Faulkners" on front) 1899 (reprinted 1999)	£2.50
D2	C	12	Police Terms (without "Faulkners" titled Police Humour) 1899 (reprinted 1998)	£2.50
A	C	25	Prominent Racehorses of the Present day 1923 (reprinted 1993)	£6.00
D	C	12	Puzzle Series 1897 (reprinted 1999)	£2.50
D	C	12	Sporting Terms 1900 (reprinted 1999)	£2.50
D	C	12	Street Cries 1902 (reprinted 1999)	£2.50

FRANKLYN, DAVEY & CO.

A	C	25	Boxing 1924 (reprinted 2002)	£6.00

J.S. FRY & SONS LTD

A	C	25	Days of Nelson 1906 (reprinted 2003)	£6.25
A	C	25	Days of Wellington 1906 (reprinted 2003)	£6.25

J. GABRIEL

A	BW	20	Cricketers Series 1901 (reprinted 1992)	£5.00

GALLAHER LTD

A	C	48	Army Badges 1939 (reprinted 2001)	£8.50
A	C	50	The Great War Nos. 1-50 1915 (reprinted 2001)	£8.50
A	C	50	The Great War Nos. 51-100 1915 (reprinted 2003)	£8.50
A	C	25	The Great War Victoria Cross Heroes 1st Series 1915 (reprinted 2001)	£6.25
A	C	25	The Great War Victoria Cross Heroes 2nd Series 1915 (reprinted 2001)	£6.25
A	C	25	The Great War Victoria Cross Heroes 3rd Series 1915 (reprinted 2001)	£6.25
A	C	25	The Great War Victoria Cross Heroes 4th Series 1915 (reprinted 2001)	£6.25
A	C	25	The Great War Victoria Cross Heroes 5th Series 1915 (reprinted 2003)	£6.25
A	C	25	The Great War Victoria Cross Heroes 6th Series 1915 (not issued)	—
A	C	25	The Great War Victoria Cross Heroes 7th Series 1915 (reprinted 2003)	£6.25
A	C	25	The Great War Victoria Cross Heroes 8th Series 1915 (reprinted 2003)	£6.25
A	C	50	Lawn Tennis Celebrities 1928 (reprinted 1997)	£8.50
A	C	25	Motor Cars 1934 (reprinted 1995)	£6.25
A	C	50	Regimental Colours and Standards 1899 (reprinted 1995)	£8.50
A	C	48	Signed Portraits of Famous Stars 1935 (reprinted 1997)	£8.50
A	C	50	South African Series No. 101-150 (Boer War Uniforms) (reprinted 2000)	£8.50
A	C	50	South African Series No. 151-200 (Boer War Uniforms) (reprinted 2000)	£8.50
A	C	50	Types of the British Army No. 1-50 1900 (reprinted 1995)	£8.50
A	C	50	Types of the British Army No. 51-100 1900 (reprinted 1996)	£8.50

GLOBE CIGARETTE CO.

D	BW	25	Actresses — French c1900 (reprinted 2001)	£6.00

GLOBE INSURANCE

—	U	11	Famous Golfers (75 × 60mm) 1929 (reprinted 1996)	£6.00

G.G. GOODE LTD (Australia)

D2	U	17	Prominent Cricketer Series 1924 (reprinted 2001)	£5.00

THOS. H. HALL (USA)

C1	C	8	Presidential Candidates & Actresses 1880 (reprinted 2001)	£2.00

Size	Printing	Number in set		Complete set

HIGNETT BROS. & CO.

A	C	25	Greetings of The World 1907 (C.C.S. reprinted 2000)	£6.50
A	C	50	Prominent Racehorses of 1933 (C.C.S. reprinted 2000)	£10.00

R. & J. HILL LTD

A	C	25	Battleships and Crests 1901 (reprinted 1995)	£6.25
A	C	20	Types of The British Army 1914 (reprinted 2001)	£6.25

HUDDEN & CO. LTD

A	C	25	Famous Boxers 1927 (reprinted 1992)	£6.25

HUNTLEY & PALMER (France)

—	C	12	Aviation (114 × 85mm) c1908 (reprinted 2001)	£7.50

IMPERIAL TOBACCO COMPANY OF CANADA LTD

A	C	45	Hockey Players 1912 (reprinted 1987)	—
A	C	36	Hockey Series 1911 (reprinted 1987)	—

INTERNATIONAL CHEWING GUM (USA)

—	C	24	Don't Let It Happen Over Here (80 × 64mm) 1938 (reprinted 1984)	£10.00

JAMES & CO.

—	C	20	Arms of Countries (70 × 52mm) c1915 (reprinted 2001)	£7.50

JONES BROS., Tottenham

A	BW	18	Spurs Footballers 1912 (reprinted 1986)	£2.50

WM. S. KIMBALL & CO. (USA)

A1	C	50	Champions of Games & Sports c1890 (reprinted 2001)	£10.00

KINNEAR LTD

D1	BW	15	Australian Cricketers 1897 (reprinted 2001)	£4.00

KINNEY BROS. (USA)

A	C	25	Famous English Running Horses 1889 (reprinted 1996)	£6.25
A	C	25	Leaders 1889 (reprinted 1990)	£6.00

J. KNIGHT (HUSTLER SOAP)

A	C	30	Regimental Nicknames 1924 (reprinted 1996)	£6.25

B. KRIEGSFELD & CO.

A	C	50	Phrases and Advertisements c1900 (reprinted 2001)	£10.00

A. KUIT LTD

A	U	25	Principal Streets of British Cities and Towns 1916 (reprinted 2001)	£6.00

LACY'S CHEWING GUM

A	BW	50	Footballers c1925 (reprinted 2001)	£10.00

Size	Printing	Number in set		Complete set

LAMBERT & BUTLER

A	C	25	Aviation 1915 (reprinted 1997)	£6.00
A	C	25	Dance Band Leaders 1936 (reprinted 1992)	£6.00
A	C	50	Empire Air Routes 1936 (C.C.S. reprinted 2000)	£10.00
A	C	25	Hints and Tips for Motorists 1929 (reprinted 1994)	£6.00
A	C	50	Horsemanship 1938 (reprinted 1994)	£8.50
A	C	50	Interesting Sidelights On The Work of The GPO 1939 (C.C.S. reprinted 1999)	£10.00
A	C	20	International Yachts 1902 (reprinted 2001)	£5.00
A	C	25	London Characters 1934 (reprinted 1992)	£6.00
A	C	25	Motor Cars 1st series 1922 (reprinted 1988)	£6.25
A	C	25	Motor Cars 2nd series 1923 (reprinted 1988)	£6.25
A	C	25	Motor Cars 1934 (reprinted 1992)	£6.25
A	C	50	Motor Cycles 1923 (reprinted 1990)	£8.50
A	C	25	Motors 1908 (reprinted 1992)	£6.00
A	C	25	Winter Sports 1914 (reprinted 1998)	£6.00
A	C	50	World's Locomotives 1912 (reprinted 1988)	£8.50

R. J. LEA LTD

A	C	50	Flowers to Grow 1913 (reprinted 1997)	£8.50

LEAF GUM CO. (USA)

—	BW	72	Star Trek (87 × 61mm) 1967 (reprinted 1981)	£12.50

J. LEES

A	C	20	Northampton Town Football Club c1912 (reprinted 2001)	£5.00

LIEBIG (France)

J2	C	6	Famous Explorers (F1088) 1914 (reprinted 2001)	£5.00

LUSBY LTD

D	C	25	Scenes From Circus Life c1900 (reprinted 2001)	£6.00

MARBURG BROS. (USA)

A	C	15	Beauties "PAC" c1890 (reprinted 2001)	£4.00

P.H. MAYO & BROTHER (USA)

C	U	35	Prizefighters c1890 (reprinted 2001)	£7.50

STEPHEN MITCHELL & SON

A	C	25	Angling 1928 (reprinted 1993)	£6.00
A	C	50	Famous Scots 1933 (C.C.S. reprinted 1999)	£10.00
A	C	50	A Gallery of 1935 (C.C.S. reprinted 1999)	£10.00
A	C	50	Humorous Drawings 1924 (C.C.S. reprinted 1999)	£10.00
A	C	25	Money 1913 (C.C.S. reprinted 2000)	£6.50
A	C	25	Regimental Crests, Nicknames and Collar Badges 1900 (reprinted 1993)	£6.50
A	C	50	Scotland's Story (C.C.S. reprinted 2000)	£10.00

MURRAY, SONS & CO. LTD

A	BW	20	Cricketers 1912 (reprinted 1991)	£7.50
A	C	20	War Series K — Uniforms 1915 (reprinted 2000)	£6.25
A	C	15	War Series K — World War I Leaders & Generals 1915 (reprinted 2000)	—

Size	Print-ing	Number in set		Complete set

NATIONAL CIGARETTE CO. (Australia)

A	BW	13	English Cricket Team 1897-8 (reprinted 2001)	£4.00

NATIONAL EXCHANGE BANK, USA

—	C	9	Seven Ages of Golf (85 × 57mm) c1885 (reprinted 1995)	£4.50

OGDENS LTD

A	C	50	A.F.C. Nicknames 1933 (reprinted 1996)	£8.50
A	C	50	Air Raid Precautions 1938 (C.C.S. reprinted 1999)	£10.00
A	C	50	British Birds 1905 (C.C.S. reprinted 2000)	£10.00
A	C	50	By The Roadside 1932 (C.C.S. reprinted 2000)	£10.00
A	C	50	Champions of 1936 (C.C.S. reprinted 2000)	£10.00
D2	U	50	Cricketers and Sportsmen c1898 (reprinted 2001)	£10.00
A	C	50	Flags and Funnels of Leading Steamship Lines 1906 (reprinted 1997)	£8.50
A	C	50	Jockeys 1930 (reprinted 1990)	—
A	C	50	Modern Railways 1936 (reprinted 1996)	£8.50
A	C	50	Motor Races 1931 (reprinted 1993)	£8.50
A	C	25	Poultry 1st Series 1915 (reprinted 1998)	£6.00
A	C	25	Poultry 2nd Series 1916 (reprinted 2000)	£6.00
A	C	50	Shakespeare Series 1903 (C.C.S. reprinted 2000)	£10.00
A	C	50	Smugglers & Smuggling 1931 (C.C.S. reprinted 1999)	£10.00
A	C	50	Soldiers of the King 1909 (reprinted 1993)	£8.50
A	C	50	The Story of the Life Boat 1940 (reprinted 1989)	—
A	C	50	The Story of The Lifeboat 1940 (without "Ogdens") (reprinted 2001)	£8.50
A	C	50	Swimming, Diving and Life-Saving 1931 (C.C.S. reprinted 2000)	£10.00

OLD CALABAR BISCUIT CO. LTD

J2	C	16	Sports and Games c1900 (reprinted 2001)	£7.50

THE ORLANDO CIGARETTE & CIGAR CO.

A	C	40	Home & Colonial Regiments c1901 (reprinted 2001)	£8.50

PALMER MANN & CO (Sifta Sam)

A	C	25	Famous Cricketers (set 24 plus 1 variety) 1950 (reprinted 2001)	£6.00

J.A. PATTREIOUEX, Manchester

A	C	75	Cricketers Series 1926 (reprinted 1997)	£13.50

GODFREY PHILLIPS LTD

A	C	30	Beauties "Nymphs" c1896 (reprinted 2001)	£7.50
A	C	25	Railway Engines 1924 (reprinted 1997)	—
A	C	20	Russo-Japanese War Series 1904 (reprinted 2001)	£5.00
A	C	25	Territorial Series 1908 (reprinted 2001)	£6.25
A	C	25	Types of British Soldiers 1900 (reprinted 1997)	£6.25

JOHN PLAYER & SONS

A	C	50	Aeroplanes (Civil) 1935 (reprinted 1990)	£8.50
A	C	50	Aircraft of The Royal Air Force 1938 (reprinted 1990)	£8.50
A	C	50	Animals of The Countryside 1939 (C.C.S. reprinted 1999)	£10.00
A	C	50	Aviary & Cage Birds 1933 (reprinted 1989)	£8.50
B	C	25	Aviary and Cage Birds 1935 (reprinted 1987)	£8.50
A	C	50	British Empire Series 1904 (C.C.S. reprinted 1999)	£10.00
A	C	50	Butterflies & Moths 1904 (C.C.S. reprinted 2000)	£10.00

Size	*Printing*	*Number in set*		*Complete set*

JOHN PLAYER & SONS *(continued)*

B	C	24	Cats 1936 (reprinted 1986)	£8.50
A	C	25	Characters from Dickens 1912 (reprinted 1990)	£6.00
A	C	25	Characters from Dickens 2nd series 1914 (reprinted 1990)	£6.00
A	C	50	Cities of The World 1900 (C.C.S. reprinted 1999)	£10.00
B	C	25	Country Sports 1930 (reprinted 2000)	£8.50
A	C	50	Cricketers 1930 (reprinted 2000)	£8.50
A	C	50	Cricketers 1934 (reprinted 1990)	£8.50
A	C	50	Cricketers 1938 (C.C.S. reprinted 2000)	£10.00
A	C	50	Cricketers Caricatures by "Rip" 1926 (reprinted 1993)	£8.50
A	C	50	Derby and Grand National Winners 1933 (reprinted 1988)	£8.50
A	C	50	Dogs' Heads (silver-grey backgrounds) 1940 (reprinted 1994)	£8.50
A2	C	25	England's Naval Heroes 1898 descriptive (reprinted 1987)	—
A	C	50	Film Stars 1st Series 1934 (C.C.S. reprinted 2000)	£10.00
A	C	50	Film Stars 3rd series 1938 (reprinted 1989)	£8.50
A	C	50	Fire-Fighting Appliances 1930 (reprinted 1991)	£8.50
A	C	50	Game Birds and Wild Fowl 1927 (C.C.S. reprinted 1999)	£10.00
B	C	25	Game Birds and Wild Fowl 1928 (reprinted 1987)	£8.50
A	C	50	Gilbert & Sullivan 2nd series 1927 (reprinted 1990)	£8.50
B	C	25	Golf 1939 (reprinted 1986)	£8.50
A	C	25	Highland Clans 1908 (reprinted 1997)	£6.00
A	C	50	Kings & Queens 1935 (reprinted 1990)	£8.50
A	C	50	Military Head-Dress 1931 (C.C.S. reprinted 1999)	£10.00
A	C	50	Military Series 1900 (reprinted 1983)	£8.50
A	C	50	Motor Cars 1st series 1936 (reprinted 1990)	£8.50
A	C	50	Motor Cars 2nd series 1937 (C.C.S. reprinted 2000)	£10.00
A	C	25	Napoleon 1916 (reprinted 1989)	£6.00
A	C	50	Nature Series 1908 (C.C.S. reprinted 2000)	£10.00
A	C	50	Old England's Defenders 1898 (reprinted 1987)	—
B	C	25	Old Hunting Prints 1938 (reprinted 1989)	£8.50
B	C	25	Old Naval Prints 1936 (reprinted 1989)	£8.50
B	C	25	Picturesque London 1931 (reprinted 1997)	£8.50
A	C	50	Poultry 1931 (reprinted 1993)	£8.50
A	C	50	Products of The World 1928 (C.C.S. reprinted 1999)	£10.00
B	C	25	Racing Yachts 1938 (reprinted 1987)	£8.50
A	C	50	Regimental Standards & Cap Badges 1930 (reprinted 1993)	£8.50
A	C	50	Regimental Uniforms Nd. 51-100 1914 (reprinted 1995)	£8.50
A	C	50	Speedway Riders 1937 (C.C.S. reprinted 2000)	£10.00
A	C	50	Tennis 1936 (C.C.S. reprinted 1999).	£10.00
B	C	24	Treasures of Britain 1931 (reprinted 1996)	£8.50
B	C	25	Types of Horses 1939 (reprinted 1998)	£8.50
A	C	50	Uniforms of the Territorial Army 1939 (reprinted 1990)	£8.50
B	C	25	Wild Birds 1934 (reprinted 1997)	£8.50

JOHN PLAYER & SONS (OVERSEAS)

A	C	50	Ships, Flags and Cap Badges 1930 (reprinted 1997)	—

REEVES LTD

D	C	25	Cricketers 1912 (reprinted 1993)	£8.00

RICHMOND CAVENDISH CO. LTD

A	C	20	Yachts c1900 (reprinted 2001)	£5.00

E. ROBINSON & SONS LTD

A	C	6	Medals & Decorations of Great Britain c1905 (reprinted 2001)	£2.00
A2	C	25	Regimental Mascots 1916 (reprinted 2001)	£6.00

Size	Print-ing	Number in set		Complete set

S.D.V. TOBACCO CO. LTD

A1	BW	16	British Royal Family c1901 (reprinted 2001)	£4.00

SALMON & GLUCKSTEIN LTD

A	C	15	Billiard Terms 1905 (reprinted 1997)	£5.00
A	C	25	Coronation Series 1911 (C.C.S. reprinted 2000)	£6.50
C2	C	30	Music Hall Celebrities c1902 (reprinted 2001)	£7.50

JOHN SINCLAIR LTD

A	C	50	British Sea Dogs 1926 (reprinted 1997)	£8.50

SINGLETON & COLE LTD

A	BW	35	Famous Boxers 1930 (reprinted 1992)	£6.25
D	BW	50	Footballers c1905 (reprinted 2001)	£10.00

F. & J. SMITH

A	C	25	Advertisement Cards 1899 (reprinted 2001)	£6.00
D	BW	50	Champions of Sport (unnumbered) 1902 (reprinted 2001)	£10.00
A	C	25	Cinema Stars 1920 (reprinted 1987)	£6.50
A	C	50	Fowls, Pigeons and Dogs 1908 (C.C.S. reprinted 2000)	£10.00
A	C	25	Holiday Resorts 1925 (C.C.S. reprinted 2000)	£6.50
A	C	25	Prominent Rugby Players 1924 (reprinted 1992)	£8.00

SPIRO VALLERI & CO.

A1	U	10	Noted Footballers c1905 (reprinted 2001)	£3.00

SPRATTS PATENT LTD

C2	C	12	Prize Dogs c1910 (reprinted 2001)	£3.50

TADDY & CO.

A	C	20	Clowns & Circus Artists 1920 (reprinted 1991)	£6.00
A	BW	238	County Cricketers 1907 (reprinted 1987)	£40.00
			Individual Counties of the above set:	
		15	Derbyshire	£2.50
		15	Essex	£2.50
		16	Gloucestershire	£2.50
		15	Hampshire	£2.50
		15	Kent	£2.50
		15	Lancashire	£2.50
		14	Leicestershire	£2.50
		15	Middlesex	£2.50
		15	Northamptonshire	£2.50
		14	Nottinghamshire	£2.50
		15	Somersetshire	£2.50
		15	Surrey	£2.50
		15	Sussex	£2.50
		15	Warwickshire	£2.50
		14	Worcestershire	£2.50
		15	Yorkshire	£2.50
A	U	5	English Royalty c1898 (reprinted 2001)	£2.00
A	C	25	Famous Jockeys 1910 (reprinted 1996)	£6.25
A	C	25	Natives of the World c1900 (reprinted 1999)	£6.00
A	BW	15	Prominent Footballers Aston Villa 1907 (reprinted 1992)	£2.50
A	BW	15	Prominent Footballers Chelsea 1907 (reprinted 1998)	£2.50

Size	Printing	Number in set		Complete set

TADDY & CO. *(continued)*

A	BW	15	Prominent Footballers Everton 1907 (reprinted 1998)	£2.50
A	BW	15	Prominent Footballers Leeds 1907 (reprinted 1992)	£2.50
A	BW	15	Prominent Footballers Liverpool 1907 (reprinted 1992)	£2.50
A	BW	15	Prominent Footballers Manchester Utd 1907 (reprinted 1992)	£2.50
A	BW	15	Prominent Footballers Middlesbrough 1907 (reprinted 1998)	£2.50
A	BW	15	Prominent Footballers Newcastle Utd 1907 (reprinted 1992)	£2.50
A	BW	15	Prominent Footballers Queens Park Rangers 1907 (reprinted 1992)	—
A	BW	15	Prominent Footballers Sunderland 1907 (reprinted 1998)	£2.50
A	BW	15	Prominent Footballers Tottenham Hotspur 1907 (reprinted 1998)	£2.50
A	BW	15	Prominent Footballers West Ham Utd 1907 (reprinted 1998)	£2.50
A	BW	15	Prominent Footballers Woolwich Arsenal 1907 (reprinted 1992)	£2.50
A2	C	20	Royalty, Actresses, Soldiers c1898 (reprinted 2001)	£5.00
A	C	25	Royalty Series 1908 (reprinted 1998)	£6.25
A	BW	15	South African Cricket Team 1907 (reprinted 1992)	£7.50
A	C	25	Territorial Regiments 1908 (reprinted 1996)	£6.25
A	C	25	Thames Series 1903 (reprinted 1996)	£6.25
A	C	20	Victoria Cross Heroes (Nos 1-20) 1900 (reprinted 1996)	£6.25
A	C	20	Victoria Cross Heroes (Nos 21-40) 1900 (reprinted 1996)	£6.25
A	C	20	VC Heroes — Boer War (Nos 41-60) 1901 (reprinted 1997)	£6.25
A	C	20	VC Heroes — Boer War (Nos 61-80) 1901 (reprinted 1997)	£6.25
A	C	20	VC Heroes — Boer War (Nos 81-100) 1902 (reprinted 1997)	£6.25
A	C	25	Victoria Cross Heroes (Nos 101-125) 1905 (reprinted 1996)	£6.25

TEOFANI & CO. LTD

A	C	24	Past and Present The Army 1938 (reprinted 2001)	£6.25
A	C	24	Past and Present Weapons of War 1938 (reprinted 2001)	£6.25

D. C. THOMSON

A	C	24	Motor Bike Cards 1929 (reprinted 1993)	£6.00
A	C	20	Motor Cycles 1923 (Wizard Series) (reprinted 1993)	£6.00

TOPPS CHEWING GUM INC. (USA)

—	C	56	Mars Attacks (90 × 64mm) 1962 (reprinted 1987)	£12.50
—	C	51	Outer Limits (90 × 64mm) 1964 (reprinted 1995)	£12.50

UNION JACK

—	C	8	Police of All Nations (70 × 45mm) 1922 (reprinted 2005)	£4.00

UNITED TOBACCONISTS' ASSOCIATION LTD

A	C	10	Actresses "MUTA" c1900 (reprinted 2001)	£3.00

HENRY WELFARE & CO.

D	BW	22	Prominent Politicians c1911 (reprinted 2001)	£6.00

W.D. & H.O. WILLS

—	C	4	Advert Postcards of Packings (140 × 90mm) 1902 (reprinted 1988)	£5.00
A	C	50	Allied Army Leaders 1917 (C.C.S reprinted 2000)	£10.00
A	C	50	Arms of Companies 1913 (C.C.S reprinted 1999).	£10.00
A	C	50	Builders of The Empire 1898 (C.C.S. reprinted 1999)	£10.00
B	C	7	Cathedrals 1933 (from set of 25) (reprinted 2000)	£2.50
A	C	50	Cricketers 1896 (reprinted 1982)	£8.50
A	C	50	Cricketers 1901 (reprinted 1983)	—
B	C	25	Dogs 1914 (reprinted 1987)	£8.50

Size	Print-ing	Number in set		Complete set

W.D. & H.O. WILLS *(continued)*

A	C	50	Double Meaning 1898 (C.C.S. reprinted 1999)	£10.00
A	C	50	Engineering Wonders 1927 (C.C.S. reprinted 1999)	£10.00
B	C	25	Famous Golfers 1930 (reprinted 1987)	£8.50
A	C	50	Fish & Bait 1910 (reprinted 1990)	£8.50
A	C	50	Flower Culture In Pots 1925 (C.C.S. reprinted 2000)	£10.00
A	C	50	Household Hints 1st Series 1927 (C.C.S. reprinted 1999)	£10.00
B	C	25	Lawn Tennis 1931 (reprinted 1988)	£8.50
A	C	50	Life in the Hedgerow 1950 (reprinted 1991, Swan Vestas)	£12.50
A	C	50	Life In The Royal Navy 1939 (C.C.S. reprinted 1999)	£10.00
A	C	50	Military Aircraft (unissued c1967) (reprinted 1991)	£8.50
A	C	50	Military Motors 1916 (reprinted 1994)	£8.50
A	C	58	Musical Celebrities 2nd series including 8 substituted cards 1914 (reprinted 1987)	£9.50
A	C	25	National Costumes c1895 (reprinted 1999)	£6.00
A	C	50	Naval Dress & Badges 1909 (reprinted 1997)	£8.50
A	C	25	Naval Dress & Badges 1909 (Nos. 1 to 25 Naval Dress only reprinted) Inscribed Commissioned by Sydney Cigarette Card Company, Australia (reprinted 1993)	£6.25
A	C	50	Old English Garden Flowers 2nd Series 1913 (reprinted 1994)	£8.50
B	C	40	Puppies by Lucy Dawson (unissued) (reprinted 1990)	£12.50
A	C	50	Railway Engines 1924 (reprinted 1995)	£8.50
A	C	50	Railway Engines 1936 (reprinted 1992)	£8.50
A	C	50	Railway Equipment 1939 (reprinted 1993)	£8.50
A	C	50	Railway Locomotives 1930 (reprinted 1993)	£8.50
A	C	12	Recruiting Posters 1915 (reprinted 1987)	£3.00
B	C	25	Rigs of Ships 1929 (reprinted 1987)	£8.50
A	C	50	Roses 1st series 1912 (reprinted 1994)	£8.50
A	C	50	Rugby Internationals 1929 (reprinted 1996)	£8.50
A	C	50	School Arms 1906 (C.C.S. reprinted 2000)	£10.00
A	C	50	Ships Badges 1925 (C.C.S. reprinted 2000)	£10.00
A	C	50	Waterloo 1915 (reprinted 1987)	£10.00
A	C	50	Wild Flowers 1923 (C.C.S. reprinted 1999)	£10.00
A	C	50	Wild Flowers 1st series 1936 (reprinted 1993)	—
A	C	50	Wonders of The Sea 1928 (C.C.S. reprinted 2000)	£10.00
A	C	25	World's Dreadnoughts 1910 (reprinted 1994)	£6.00

W.D. & H.O. WILLS (Australia)

A	C	50	Types of the British Army 1912 (reprinted 1995)	£8.50
A	C	50	War Incidents 2nd Series 1917 (reprinted 1995)	£8.50

W.H. & J. WOODS LTD

A	C	25	Types of Volunteers & Yeomanry 1902 (reprinted 1996)	£8.50

THEMATIC LISTINGS

If you are interested in a particular subject the thematic listings on our website may be of help. Alternatively, lists can be sent on request.

SUBJECTS COVERED

American Football, Baseball etc.
Animals and Wildlife
Aviation, Space Travel and Astronomy
Birds, Butterflies and Moths
Boxing
Brooke Bond Tea Cards
Cricket
Dinosaurs
Dogs and Pets
Fantasy Art
Film and Stage Stars (1920-40 issues)
Fish, Fishing and the Ocean
Flags, Arms and Maps
Flowers and the Garden
Football
Golf
Horses and the Turf
Liebig Card Issues
Military
Motoring
Native North American Indians and Cowboys
Pop Stars and Singers
Railways
Reprints
Royalty
Rugby League and Union
Ships, Shipping and Naval
Speedway
Sports (general)
Star Trek
Star Wars
Tennis
TV, Films and Sci-Fi
Wrestling
Miscellaneous Cigarette Card Issues
Miscellaneous Trade Card Issues
Selection of Cigarette Card Sets £20 and under
Selection of Trade Card Sets under £5

Website
www.londoncigcard.co.uk

Other Catalogues Available

Trade Card Catalogue 2014 Edition

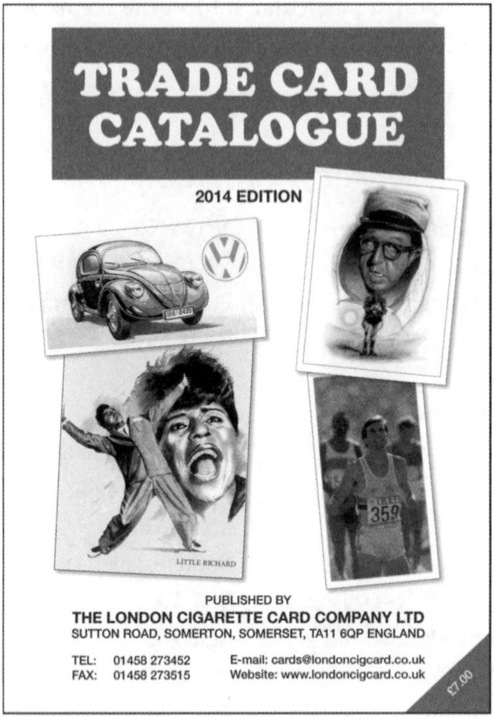

Price £7.00

This is the only major catalogue devoted to trade cards. It gives details of a magnificent selection of over 6000 different series issued by non-tobacco companies, with prices of sets, odd cards and makers' albums. The new 39th edition features the issues of Brooke Bond, Bassett, Topps, Typhoo, Inkworks, Rittenhouse, Comic Images, J F Sporting Collectibles, Philip Neil and hundreds of other firms, with prices from £2.50 a set. It also has a colourful 8-page section of 73 illustrations.

Visit our website or order your catalogue via post or telephone — details on the front cover

Other Catalogues Available

Liebig Card Catalogue 2009 Edition

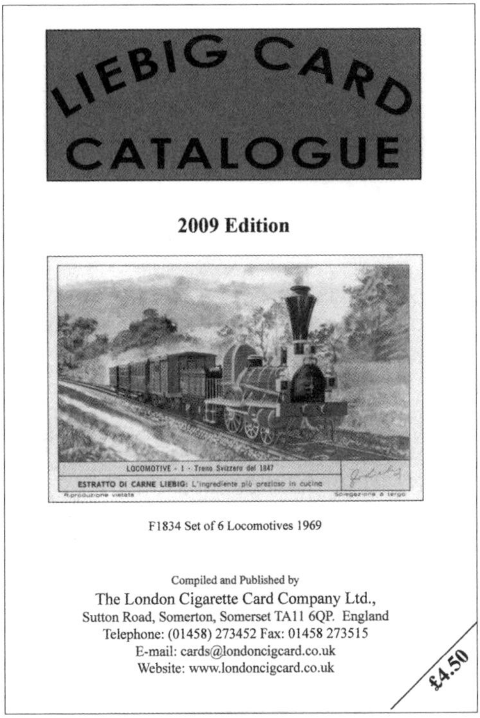

Price £4.50

This price guide lists over 1500 fascinating sets issued in the different European languages (all except the earliest) by this manufacturer. It includes a brief history of the company, an English translation of each set title, together with the 'Fada' reference number, the number in each set and date of issue from 1891 to 1973. The prices in the 2009 catalogue will remain until further notice.

Visit our website or order your catalogue via post or telephone – details on the front cover

Collecting Cigarette & Trade Cards

By Gordon Howsden

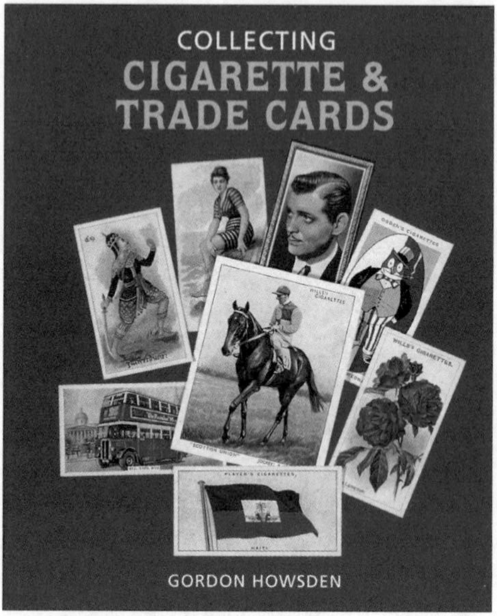

Price £17.50

Collecting Cigarette & Trade Cards by Gordon Howsden traces the history and development of cards from their beginning to the present day and includes the background of the issuing firms, thematic collecting, printing and production, grading, pricing and so on. Authoritatively written in an easy-to-read style and beautifully illustrated in colour, the book approaches the subject from a fresh angle which will appeal to seasoned collectors and newcomers alike. *Cigarette & Trade Cards* is not only an indispensable reference work but also a joy to read or just browse through.
152 large-format pages with 220 colour illustrations
featuring 750 cards and related ephemera.

Visit our website or order the book via post or telephone — details on the front cover.

NOTES

NOTES

NOTES